# Bibliography

## Available books by Henry Miller

*Tropic of Cancer* 1934
*Black Spring* 1936
*Max and the White Phagocytes* 1938
*The Hamlet Correspondence* 1939
*Tropic of Capricorn* 1939
*The Cosmological Eye* 1940
*The Air Conditioned Nightmare* 1941
*The Colossus of Maroussi* 1941
*The World of Sex* 1940
*The Wisdom of the Heart* 1941
*Sunday after the War* 1944
*Remember to Remember* 1947
*The Smile at the Foot of the Ladder* 1948
*Sexus* 1949
*The Books in My Life* 1952
*Rimbaud* 1951 (Republished as *The Time of the Assassins* 1956)
*Big Sur and the Oranges of Hieronymous Bosch* 1957
*Plexus* 1953
*Nights of Love and Laughter* 1955
*Quiet Days in Clichy* 1958
*Nexus* 1959
*The Henry Miller Reader*. Ed Lawrence Durrell 1959
*Art and Outrage* 1959
*To Paint is to Love Again* 1960
*Stand Still Like the Hummingbird* 1962
*Just Wild about Harry* (Play) 1963
*Lawrence Durrell and Henry Miller* (Correspondence) 1963
*Letters to Anaïs Nin* 1965
*The Book of Friends* Vol.1 1976
*Sextet* 1977
*The Book of Friends* Vol.2 1978
*Reflections* 1981

## Books About Henry Miller

Alfred Perles: *My Friend Henry Miller* 1955
William Gordon: *The Mind and Art of Henry Miller* 1967
Kingsley Widmer: *Henry Miller* 1967
E R Hutchison: *Tropic of Cancer on Trial* 1968

*edited by*
John Calder

# A
# Henry Miller
# Reader

**PICADOR**
published by Pan Books

This collection first published 1985 by Pan Books Ltd
Cavaye Place, London SW10 9PG

9 8 7 6 5 4 3 2 1

This collection © Pan Books Ltd 1983

ISBN 0 330 28689 7
Printed and bound in Great Britain by
Cox & Wyman Ltd, Reading

# Contents

*My aim, in writing, is to establish a greater reality. I am not a realist or naturalist; I am for life, which in literature, it seems to me, can only be attained by the use of dream and symbol. I am at bottom a metaphysical writer, and my use of drama and incident is only a device to posit something more profound. I am against pornography and for obscenity – and violence. Above all for imagination, fantasy, for a liberty as yet undreamed of.*

Henry Miller.
*The Cosmological Eye.*

# Introduction

The Bohemian tradition in literature needs little definition. In its own time it is usually difficult to justify as literature because it is seen as a current running against or apart from the mainstream, naïvely non-elitist and therefore unfashionable and easy to denigrate. Bohemian writers tend to be self-educated, are accustomed to poverty, lack the inhibitions of middle-class norms and, by instinct, are in basic opposition to the social, political and artistic establishment.

Henry Miller's literary ancestors include among others: his countryman Walt Whitman; the creators of the American working-class novel; the French *poètes* and *romanciers maudits*; those English writers who fell foul of the censors, especially D. H. Lawrence, Frank Harris and Norman Douglas, while among his contemporaries, there is a strong similarity of outlook with George Orwell.

What Bohemian writers have in common is primarily a feeling of exclusion, of being *declassé* in both the social and the artistic sense, and they write from an inner anger in which contempt, envy and resentment all play a part. George Orwell, child of middle-class but impecunious parents, won a scholarship to Eton where the difference between his own circumstances and those of nearly all the other boys in that most snobbish of schools impressed itself profoundly and painfully on his consciousness and personality; his feelings of inferiority became part of the larger consciousness of oppression that resulted from five years subsequently spent in the Burma Imperial Police and his later observation of the effects of the depression on working-class life, experiences which turned him into a socialist humanist and a rebel against all forms of authority.

Henry Miller has much in common with Orwell, although his Bohemianism was more of a protest against a Germanic, blue-stockinged mother and a natural lack of sympathy with the American work-and-money ethos than in Orwell's case where it developed out of other circumstances and choice. Miller, unlike Orwell, was not a scholar, but neither had much interest in self-advancement through the system by way of work and merit, and Miller was possibly incapable of it. Interestingly, he never mentions Orwell among authors he has read and admired, although Orwell thought well of Miller in *Inside the Whale*, one of the first serious studies of his writing[1], perhaps because of his 'deep and mysterious aversion for everything British'[2]. Another writer with whom one would expect Miller to have something in common is Ernest Hemingway, seven years his junior, but Hemingway is also not mentioned, and indeed the list of his favourite authors and influences, other than childhood reading, is largely confined to the classics of the nineteenth century and the generations immediately before his own time, with the exception of contemporaries like Blaise Cendrars who were also friends.

Henry Miller had a compulsion to share his literary discoveries and his reading with friends. Many great classics which he first read with eagerness and expectation left him utterly cold, Shakespeare and Voltaire for instance. He lists various Elizabethan dramatists among his influences, but specifically excludes Shakespeare. The reason may lie in Shakespeare's determinism: like the Greek dramatists, for whom Miller also expresses no admiration, Shakespeare portrays man as the pawn of history, his destiny outside his own control, his life at the whim of fortune. Such an attitude would be anathema to Henry Miller to whom freedom was the essence of life and who passionately believed in free will.

Born of German parentage (his two German grandfathers both left Germany in the nineteenth century to avoid military service), Henry Miller disliked all things German and loved France in a way that only foreigners can. 'I've ranted and raved against the Germans because from my earliest days I was struggling to set myself free from their punctuality and super-cleanliness,' he is quoted as saying.[3] Americans often dislike the French who mingle little with foreigners and only accept those who have become entirely francofied, but their aloofness is really a form of tolerance. Miller admired their practicality, intelligence and live-and-let-die attitude, so different from the disapproval and conformity that had made his early life in America so unhappy. 'More than anything the French have a profound knowledge of the ways of life. They possess a tolerance and an acceptance of the way things are. Problems are faced with intelligence, patience, and a sense of humanity. I have more respect for them than any other nationality

---

1. In a letter to Anaïs Nin (21 April 1944), Miller refers to Orwell's 'lefthanded attack upon me'.
2. *The Books in My Life*: Chapter 2.
3. *Reflections*: Henry Miller, ed. Twinka Thiebaud.

on the face of the earth.'[3] It was in France that he found himself, and in spite of the poverty of his first years there, he was profoundly happy; more importantly he found his own voice when he wrote his masterpiece *Tropic of Cancer*, a hymn to the city of eroticism and freedom.

It is, of course, for his frankness about sex that Henry Miller is most famous. He was not the first to write with total frankness about his sexual experiences, but his work, smuggled in ever increasing quantities into Britain, the United States and other English-speaking countries, had an enormous influence on other writers. In Britain, Lawrence Durrell deliberately imitated Miller and in the United States he became the father figure for a whole school and generation, even before his most famous works could be bought openly in a bookshop. His frankness and naturalism are unlikely to titillate any but the most prurient today, later writers having taken erotic obsession, sexual description and fantasy into another realm, but on that account it is now possible to read Henry Miller with more enjoyment and understanding, and to evaluate his work in a more objective light.

His best work was written in and about Paris: it has a lightness, a poetry, a self-mocking and humorous quality that is largely lacking in the books that are set in America. It is surprising that he did not decide, once his books were freely published internationally and his finances were secure, to live in France instead of withdrawing to California. The reasons were possibly not of his own choice; when *Tropic of Cancer* became a bestseller and income was flowing in from publishers, he was prevailed on to turn himself into a corporation to reduce his liability to taxation. The result was that lawyers and accountants appeared to derive more benefit than the author from these arrangements, which virtually made him a prisoner of his own success. His last visit to Europe in 1969 was a nostalgic journey to old haunts: one could detect that he felt it was his last trip to France and that he would have liked to stay longer.

There was in Henry Miller, underneath the warmth and simplicity of his outward presence, a quality of mingled sadness and surprise, one based on nostalgia both for the past and for those things he had missed in life, and surprise at his own success and recognition. The success came late and in two stages; first with publication by Jack Kahane, after many delays, of *Tropic of Cancer* in 1934, which brought him fame as a pornographer, although some establishment figures including Ezra Pound, Katherine Anne Porter and, more surprisingly, T S Eliot, greeted the book with respect; and then with American and British publication in the sixties and translation into

European languages. His surprise at achieving the status of a contemporary classic in old age was very touching, and I do not believe he was ever entirely comfortable with it.

Henry Miller was born in Brooklyn on 26 December, 1891. His father was a first generation immigrant from Germany, a reasonably successful tailor, and for a time Henry worked for him, mainly he says because his mother wanted him to report back on his father's drinking habits. His mother, also of German stock, was strict, and punctilious about cleanliness and work; to Henry she represented 'cleanliness and sterility' and in discussion he compared her to a Nazi soldier. His father had no intellectual interests, never read books, and Henry had difficulty in obtaining them to read himself, partly because he lacked money to buy them and partly because as a teenager most of the books he wanted to borrow from the library were restricted.

> 'One of the first things I associate with the reading of books is the struggle I waged to obtain them. Not to own them, mind you, but to lay hands on them. From the moment the passion took hold of me I encountered nothing but obstacles. The books I wanted at the public library were always out. And of course I never had the money to buy them. To get permission from the library in my neighbourhood – I was then 18 or 19 years of age – to borrow such a demoralizing work as *The Confession of a Fool* by Strindberg, was just impossible. In those days the books which young people were prohibited from reading were decorated with stars – according to the degree of immorality attributed to them'[4].

After attending the City College of New York for only two months, Miller worked at a number of odd jobs and finally became employment manager of the Western Union Telegraph Company, which in *Tropic of Capricorn* becomes the Cosmodemonic Telegraph Company. In that book he amusingly relates the period of his career which lasted until 1924 when he stopped working in order to write. That year he divorced his first wife, Beatrice Wilkins, whom he had married in 1917; she had originally been his piano teacher during a period when he thought he might become a musician and he had a daughter with her in 1919. His first marriage is described in *Tropic of Capricorn* and *Sexus*. He remarried immediately after the divorce. His second wife, June Smith, appears at the end of *Tropic of Capricorn* and plays a large role in *Sexus*. He first met her in a dance hall and lived with her for nine turbulent years, mostly in considerable poverty. Apart from his obsession with June, they were years of depression; his writing was

4. *The Books in My Life*: Chapter 1.

not going well and he felt totally out of sympathy with American society without knowing how to escape. Then, suddenly, a windfall in 1929 gave him some temporary freedom and the couple spent a year travelling in Europe, much of it bicycling.

He returned to Europe in March 1930 on his own, intending to go to Spain, but found himself stranded in Paris. There began the experiences which were to become the subject matter of *Tropic of Cancer*.

> It is now the fall of my second year in Paris. I was sent here for a reason I have not yet been able to fathom.
>
> I have no money, no resources, no hopes. I am the happiest man alive. A year ago, six months ago, I thought that I was an artist. I no longer think about it, I *am*. Everything that was literature has fallen from me. There are no more books to be written, thank God. This then? This is not a book. This is libel, slander, defamation of character. This is not a book in the ordinary sense of the word. No, this is a prolonged insult, a gob of spit in the face of Art, a kick in the pants to God, Man, Destiny, Time, Love, Beauty . . . what you will. I am going to sing for you, a little off key perhaps, but I will sing. I will sing while you croak, I will dance over your dirty corpse . . . To sing you must first open your mouth. You must have a pair of lungs, and a little knowledge of music. It is not necessary to have accordions, or a guitar. The essential thing is to *want* to sing. This then is a song. I am singing.[5]

And sing he does. *Tropic of Cancer* is a paean to limitless and guiltless sex; like Whitman's *Song of Myself*, it is exuberant, extravagant and drunk with words and bodily function. He had become in Lawrence Durrell's phrase a 'great vagabond of literature', the most Rabelaisian writer of his time. And it was Paris, with its special ability to turn an undiscovered talent into genius, that did it. In the words of Marcel Pagnol:

> You're a little Jew from the Ukraine with something of a gift for painting. You come to Paris. And you become Chagall. You're quite a clever pianist who tinkles at the keyboard in Poland. You arrive in Paris. And you become Chopin. Careful, though! If you haven't genius Paris can do nothing for you. You can live in Paris for generations and remain a gas-meter reader or a ticket collector. But it's only in Paris that you become Offenbach, Nijinsky, Picasso or Apollinaire.

When Henry Miller arrived in Paris, he had been trying to write for twenty years and was totally unknown. He had written four full-

5. *Tropic of Cancer*.

11

length novels of which *Clipped Wings* was, like *Tropic of Capricorn*, based on the lives of messenger boys in New York; he had turned out dozens of stories, articles and bits of journalism, little of which saw print and none of which made any impression. Some poems he had even had printed on tinted cardboard for June to sell, door to door in Brooklyn. When he arrived in Paris he tried to sell his fourth novel *Crazy Cock*; on the advice of friends he cut it drastically, but found no publisher for it. But gradually he sold short works in Paris and was published in such English language magazines as *Transition*, which Eugene Jolas edited and which featured Joyce, Hart Crane, Edith Sitwell, Hemingway, Beckett and countless expressionists and surrealists, and in Samuel Putnam's *New Review*. He developed a circle of Bohemian friends who became the characters in *Cancer* and in the living-from-day-to-day atmosphere of sharing good and bad fortune he never went entirely hungry or lacked a bed to sleep in. He fell in love not just with Bohemian Paris, with the women who went through his bed and the lifestyle he shared with his friends, but with the people of the street, workmen and prostitutes. He learned reasonable French and began to read French literature. Paris became 'mother, mistress, home and muse. It was in Paris that I found myself, as a man and as an artist.' He decided not to write fiction in the conventional sense, but 'an autobiographical document, a human book'.

Miller earned a little money from teaching English and worked for a while for the now defunct Paris edition of the *Chicago Tribune*. He had formed a close friendship with Anaïs Nin, with whom he was to correspond until her death in 1977, and his letters to her, some of which are quoted here, are a faithful record of his most fruitful years. His other closest friend was Alfred Perles, an Austrian journalist and writer, whom he had first met in 1928. Perles lent him money, found him jobs, let him stay in his room, brought him books, food, cigarettes and women and eventually shared a flat with him for over two years. In the autumn of 1931 June came to Paris but, unable to bear the grimy hotels, lack of money and her husband's eccentric friends, soon left; they were divorced in 1934.

By the middle of 1932, *Tropic of Cancer* was finished and Miller took his manuscript to an American literary agent in Paris, William A. Bradley. Bradley was excited by it and sent it to Jack Kahane, an Englishman from Manchester who had started a publishing company, Obelisk Press, for English language books in Paris, particularly those that in the puritanical climate of British publishing could not appear in his native country, hoping to rival those, like Sylvia Beach and

Eugene Jolas, who were publishing important and daring English and American writers. Kahane instantly saw the merits and saleability of *Cancer*, but was afraid of prosecution, and he dithered for two years before bringing out the book. His initial enthusiasm was genuine. ' "At last!" I murmured to myself. I had read the most terrible, the most sordid, the most magnificent manuscript that had ever fallen into my hands; nothing I had yet received was comparable to it for the splendour of its writing, the fathomless depth of its despair, the savour of its portraiture, the boisterousness of its humour. Walking into the house I was exalted by the triumphant sensation of all explorers who have at last fallen upon the object of their years of search. I had in my hands a work of genius and it had been offered to me for publication.'

Kahane had already published Frank Harris's *My Life and Loves* and a number of books written by himself under the name Cecil Barr, but had turned down *Lady Chatterley's Lover*. The economic situation was uncertain, and although the French were not very interested in English language books, there was still censorship and too much publicity or a request from the British Home Office could lead to a prosecution. The contract was drawn up late in 1932 and Kahane's hesitations were finally overcome when, in May 1934, Anaïs Nin agreed to finance publication herself and wrote a perceptive preface in which she said:

> Here is a book which, if such a thing were possible, might restore our appetite for fundamental realities. The predominant note will seem one of bitterness, and bitterness there is, to the full. But there is also a wild extravagance, a mad gaiety, a verve, a gusto, at times almost a delirium A continual oscillation between extremes, with bare stretches that taste like brass and leave the full flavour of emptiness. It is beyond optimism or pessimism. The author has given us the last *frisson*. Pain has no more secret recesses.
>
> It is no false primitivism which gives rise to this savage lyricism. It is not a retrogressive tendency, but a swing forward into unbeaten areas. To regard a naked book such as this with the same critical eye that is turned upon even such diverse types as Lawrence, Breton, Joyce and Céline is a mistake. Rather let us try to look at it with the eye of the Patagonian for whom all that is sacred and taboo in our world is meaningless. For the adventure which has brought the author to the spiritual ends of the earth is the history of every artist, who, in order to express himself, must traverse the intangible gridirons of his imaginary world.

The jacket of the first edition compared Miller to Céline, quoted from the preface and also carried a warning to booksellers, in French, not to display the book in their windows. Indeed Kahane did nothing very positive to promote the book, but its fame spread rapidly by word of mouth and sales increased, although it took over two years to sell the first thousand copies. Miller himself and his friends did what they could to help sales and Kahane finally admitted that the author was 'the most useful collaborator a book publisher ever had'. Miller even bought copies at author's discount for his friends to sell to the public on the boulevards and sent others to critics and writers at his own expense. Ezra Pound was one of those who replied and in the second of two postcards wrote: 'Great deal more to the book than I thought when I wrote you yesterday after reading about 40 pages.' Praise also came from Katherine Ann Porter, Marcel Duchamp and Blaise Cendrars. Indirectly friends elicited favourable reactions from other eminent writers including Somerset Maugham.

In the meantime, while waiting for *Tropic of Cancer* to appear, Miller wrote *Black Spring* and embarked on a study of D. H. Lawrence which latter was not to appear in the US until 1979 and in Britain in 1985. He intended the Lawrence book to become a massive study of a writer he idolized, but abandoned it, partly on the advice of Anaïs Nin, partly to get on with more fiction. *Black Spring* was designed as a self-portrait employing the new freedom in technique that he had developed in *Cancer*, but going back in memory to earlier years. In essence a collection of episodes, it contained memories of his Brooklyn childhood and events leading up to his move to Paris. He later said that it 'came nearer to being myself, I believe, than any book I have written before or since.'

From 1930 to 1939 Henry Miller lived at a number of addresses, for one long creative period at the Villa Seurat in the 14th arrondissement, which is still an artists' quarter today, an *impasse* full of workshops and studios, where he was first a temporary guest and later a tenant. He lived for a time in Clichy, a suburb outside the city boundary, which inspired another book (*Quiet Days in Clichy*) and on and off in hotels or with friends for different periods depending on how desperate his finances were. Miller paid two short visits in 1935 and 1936 to New York which he found no more congenial than previously; he also visited Britain – one disastrously comic trip when he was turned back at Dover is related in this volume.

But the rise of Hitler could not be ignored. Europe was getting ready for another war and Miller realized that his Paris days were numbered. By the time of the 1938 Munich crisis, he had published, in addition to *Tropic of Cancer*, *Aller Retour* (1935), a record of a visit to New York, *Black Spring* (1936), *Max and the White Phagocytes* (1938) and was waiting for *Tropic of Capricorn* to appear. In July 1939, having dispersed or stored his possessions and papers, he travelled to Marseilles and from there sailed first to Corfu where he stayed with Lawrence Durrell, then for the rest of the year toured Greece, an experience which was to result in *The Colossus of Maroussi* (1941), a book of impressions which, being in no way obscene was, with *The Cosmological Eye*, for some time virtually the only publication of his that could be bought freely in the US.

He returned to America with Europe at war and with strong feelings about the evil of fascism, although his approach to the war was, strangely and illogically, pacifist. Back in his native America, he travelled to rediscover it and wrote about it in various forms, most notably in a collection of non-fictional essays, *The Air Conditioned Nightmare*, and in the three volume set of novels, *The Rosy Crucifixion*, which takes up the narrative after the events of *Tropic of Capricorn*. The second and most creative period of his life had ended. Now he was again stony-broke in his native town where his most famous books could not be published or sold.

But he began to make some money painting and sold a number of watercolours, while friends he had known in Paris lent him a little money. He continued to write, finishing *The World of Sex* and *Quiet Days in Clichy*, neither of which could be published in America, and started on *Sexus*, the first volume of *The Rosy Crucifixion*. *The Air Conditioned Nightmare*, first published in 1945, resulted from a tour he made, partly with Abraham Rattner, across the United States; it contained a jaundiced look at all the things he disliked about America. In 1942, he stopped in Los Angeles. Two years later he moved north and found at Big Sur a congenial place to live, remote enough to feel safe from his critics and from the war. Friends gradually turned up and a little colony gathered around him. He became the first guru for a new school of anti-bourgeois writers, artists and hangers-on, creating a similar ambience to the one at St Germain-des-Pres over which Jean-Paul Sartre presided in the late forties. He married again in 1944, this time a girl thirty years younger than himself (he was now in his early fifties), Janina Lepska, who bore him two children, but divorced him after seven years.

He was only making about $500 a year, with the odd bonanza from the sale of a few watercolours, and had incurred heavy debts estimated at over $24,000. He says: 'I immediately paid out the monies which

15

suddenly poured in from the sale of watercolours – something like $1,400. I had naïvely thought it would continue *ad infinitum* . . . Now I am being absolutely honest when I say that all I got out of this sudden influx of wealth was three pairs of woollen socks, a plaid woollen shirt, and some good watercolour paper . . . I didn't even get a good meal out of it.'[6]

But by 1950 things were getting better. He was the centre of a thriving artists' colony and much of his less controversial work was published, while royalties began to come from Paris where the *Tropics* were reprinted and selling briskly to GIs and tourists. He married for the fourth time and separated not long after. The other banned books all appeared in Paris, this time under the imprint of Olympia Press, founded after the war by Maurice Girodias, son of Jack Kahane, who to this day is still laying claim to the copyrights of his father, which during the war had largely passed into the possession of Hachette.

In 1961, *Tropic of Cancer*, which had been read by everyone with any pretension to a knowledge of modern literature, was finally published in the United States by Grove Press. In no time, it was a *cause célèbre*. Barney Rosset, son of a Chicago banker who had started publishing even before leaving university, gave evidence in justification that it was a work he had read as a student at Swarthmore; indeed he had written a paper on it for a course in American literature. He had published, two years earlier, *Lady Chatterley's Lover* in its first American edition, much avant-garde European and American literature, and was without question the most discussed and admired young publisher in America. He had gone to much effort to persuade Miller to grant him the rights, working largely through Girodias, who advised him how to convince Miller himself, Dr Hoffmann, Miller's post-war Parisian agent, and Hachette, who now had the rights to the *Tropics*. Girodias saw himself reimporting the American edition into France as sales agent for Grove and wrote to Rosset: 'Thus I will be able to distribute for you in France, and symbolically recover my lost property.'

Henry Miller, who did not want to find himself once more in the firing line, had written to Rosset in July 1959, 'The notoriety, the unpleasantness involved, seem hardly worth the price.' In an interview with *The Economist* he was quoted as having said: 'I don't want to take time from my writing to be interviewed on the radio and television or for the newspapers. Besides, the people whose opinion I

6. Private letter.

most care about have read the books and I am not interested in those who want to buy them just to look at what they think are dirty words.' But the combined weight of Girodias, whose advice to Rosset was shrewd enough to convince all parties, and Heinrich Ledig-Rowohlt, who had already published *Tropic of Cancer* in Germany and with whose secretary Miller was in love at the time, was decisive and Henry Miller finally signed a contract with Rosset for American publication.

American publication was complicated because the copyright law as it stood in 1961 did not protect American authors whose books had been printed or published abroad and imported into the United States beyond the permitted level of 1500 copies. Although it had not been imported legally, hundreds of copies had been seized by customs over the years and the assumption was made that many thousands of other copies had slipped through. Grove Press had to deal with a double problem: the rash of local prosecutions all over the country which they had to defend, to the tune of over $250,000, was followed by the appearance of pirate editions, trying to cash in on the anomaly in the copyright law whereby an American author, published abroad, lost his copyright.

After some initial hesitation, the US post office decided that it would not impede the sale of *Cancer*, although there were a number of bannings in Massachusetts, Texas and elsewhere; Grove Press succeeded in making *Tropic of Cancer* a bestseller in its initial hardcover edition. It was then that they heard that a pirate paperback edition had been printed in Chicago and, after much legal correspondence, agreed to buy the whole edition in exchange for a recognition of copyright. But this forced Grove to bring out a mass-market paperback much earlier than they had intended. This, more than any other factor, led to widescale local prosecutions, because now the book could be bought for less than a dollar, not just in bookshops where the owners might be expected to use their judgement in withholding it from minors, but in every conceivable outlet where paperbacks and magazines were sold. A year after first publication, over 100,000 hardcover copies had been sold at $7.50 but then – in spite of the many areas where local prosecutions and bannings made the book difficult to obtain – over two million were quickly sold at 95 cents. The prosecutions only served to publicize the book, its author and publisher, and ultimately they increased sales. Probably the publicity was more important to Grove Press than the little profit that they might have made after paying the massive legal costs.

British publication was a direct result of Henry Miller's visit, at my invitation, to the Edinburgh Festival in 1962 to take part in an *International Writer's Conference* which I organized at the request of Lord Harewood, the festival director. About 100 writers were invited, and although there were many changes among the acceptances up to the last minute, about seventy eventually attended, novelists from all over the world who came to discuss the contemporary novel. They included many of the most distinguished living writers, among them, from Britain, Henry Miller's long-standing friend Lawrence Durrell, as well as Rosamund Lehmann, Muriel Spark, Rebecca West and Angus Wilson, and many East and West Europeans, Latin Americans and writers from the Antipodes. But it was a quartet of Americans who made the success of the conference: Mary McCarthy, Norman Mailer, William Burroughs and Henry Miller. Miller talked little but to the point, and when, on the fourth day, when the subject was censorship, he set out his credo of literary freedom, he received a standing ovation from nearly three thousand people packed into Edinburgh's McEwan Hall. It was obvious that, at least to a younger generation, he had become a legendary literary figure; he had fought battles before the war that were then very much in the public eye in Britain as well as the US (Penguin had successfully defended their publication of *Lady Chatterley's Lover* the year before), and he symbolized the right of the artist to work without interference from the state, as did no one else in the western world at that time; indeed censorship in Eastern Europe and South Africa was also much discussed. The echoes of that conference were to go around the world: it was the first time that serious literary topics had been discussed in public before a large audience in adult terms and with passion – the literary puritans were also well represented and put their arguments forcefully, but failed to convince the majority of those present – and if Mary McCarthy came out as the Voltaireian persuader and Norman Mailer as the orator whose ringing phrases were to be the most quoted, both in defence of literary freedom and in praise of his controversial compatriots, it was Henry Miller and William Burroughs who were to make the greatest impression, both in terms of their presence and the ideas and values they represented. Burroughs symbolized the new American avant-garde, the generation which had built on the foundations created in the early thirties by Henry Miller, and he was carrying the literary presentation of sex and bohemianism many steps forward; the presence of two controversial writers on one platform, Miller with his *Tropics* still unpublished in Britain and Burroughs known only to the very few, was a watershed. *Tropic of*

*Cancer* and *Dead Fingers Talk*, the first Burroughs work to appear in Britain, were both published the following year.

As the organizer of the conference, I felt constrained not to take a personal advantage from it, but Maurice Girodias, who was one of the speakers on the day devoted to censorship, persuaded me otherwise. He turned up at the Frankfurt Book Fair two months after the conference, and having failed to book himself a room shared mine for two nights, during which he persuaded me that by inviting Henry Miller to Edinburgh and making possible his apotheosis, publication in Britain had become feasible and it was unlikely that the Home Office, having failed to convict *Lady Chatterley's Lover* and with the knowledge that *Tropic of Cancer* in its American edition was now freely available almost everywhere except the British Commonwealth, would take action against it. In the event prosecution remained a possibility until ten days before publication when my solicitors, who had offered on my behalf to delay publication if the Director of Public Prosecutions wanted another test case, were told that no such action would be taken. On publication day, every BBC news bulletin announced that the book was now available in Britain for the first time and the line of willing buyers stretched for blocks around some bookshops.

Thereafter the barriers fell in Australia, New Zealand and throughout the Western world. Grove Press quixotically published a Russian language edition which they expected to be smuggled into Eastern Europe, but commercially this was a failure. Miller was soon to be available in translation in Yugoslavia, but he has still to penetrate the other Communist countries.

Henry Miller was to visit Britain once again at my invitation in 1969 when he also visited France for the last time. It was his last nostalgic visit to old haunts. He had moved from Big Sur to Pacific Palisades outside Los Angeles to avoid some of the consequences of his own celebrity, and at eighty wanted peace above all.

> Success, from the worldly standpoint, is like the plague for a writer who still has something to say. Now, when he should be enjoying a little leisure, he finds himself more occupied than ever. Now he is the victim of his fans and well wishers, of all those who desire to exploit his name. Now it is a different kind of struggle that one has to wage. The problem now is how to keep free, how to do only what one wants to do.[7]

At seventy-six he married for the fifth time, a thirty-two-year-old

7. *Sextet*: 'On Turning Eighty'.

Japanese jazz pianist called Hoki Tokuda. In old age he had decided that Oriental women were the most comfortable to be with and although the marriage, like his previous ones, was not to last, he was obsessed with her and grateful to her for the affection she gave him. His constant companion during his last years was his son Tony, who was living with him at Pacific Palisades when he died, the only one of his children who was to be close to him for many years, and whom he had been particularly concerned to keep out of the Vietnam war.

The last section of this *Reader* contains his thoughts 'On Turning Eighty'. He was still writing, but getting possibly more pleasure out of painting, still seeing friends and keeping up with others by correspondence. When I went to visit him in 1976 he was frail with a broken hip which kept him from swimming in his pool, but he read late into the night with evident enjoyment, was in full possession of his intellectual powers and – once again – in love. He did not tell me the object of his affection, but he had a very beautiful secretary, and he made it clear that his love was platonic, so I drew the obvious conclusion.

During his last years he was the victim of his own success, but even more of his own ingenuousness and kindness. Many took advantage of him, but he did not seem to mind. He did his best to please his fans, academics writing theses, and journalists wanting interviews. He entertained with panache and above all enjoyed good company. Much of the essence of the man is caught in Tom Schiller's film *Henry Miller Asleep and Awake* and in Twinka Thiebaud's *Reflections*, which recorded many of his last conversations. He was often mischievous, once telling Jerry Brown, the governor of California, that 'politicians are rather at the lowest rung', philosophical in commenting on past and present manners, especially where relations between the sexes were concerned, and, as far as his health allowed, he remained a *bon viveur* enjoying good conversation, wine and food.

In 1973 he had major surgery for his hip, had to refrain from bicycling, which he had always enjoyed, and thereafter tried to retire as much as possible from the outside world. In words of advice to his children, he said: 'About my death, take it with a smile, don't panic. Just think of it as the end of an act, the curtain falling. I've led a great life, a full life. I welcome my death with open arms, so should you.'

He died on June 7, 1980 at the age of 88. The news came through during the American Booksellers' Association convention in Chicago and a sadness pervaded that gathering of booksellers and publishers. A unique monument of American literary art and, perhaps even more importantly, a twentieth century affirmation of the inability to live without freedom on which the nation had been founded, had left them. But his testament would long continue.

Henry Miller found his real voice, after many unsuccessful attempts 'to become a writer', when he began to write about himself, not projecting a hero for readers to admire, a mould into which he could fit his own aspirations, but instead examining his weaknesses as an ordinary man, a very typical American, different from others mainly because he could not temperamentally share the American obsession with money, success and the Protestant work ethic.

The interest for himself, as he later came to realize, was in eschewing heroics, in not hiding his weaknesses but exposing them fully to the public gaze and in revealing, with total frankness and honesty, the man Henry Miller as a randy, cowardly, hassle-avoiding, self-indulgent, lazy 'bum', living with little forethought or caution, allowing himself to take appalling risks with venereal disease, which he could pass on without compunction, treating his benefactors, especially if they were women, pretty shabbily. He does not emerge as an admirable character, nor as a likeable one, certainly not as trustworthy. Much of the opprobrium that he has attracted from his critics lies not in the reasons given – sloppy writing, immoral situations, the boasting about sexual exploits – but simply because he projected an unlikeable character that his critics believed was true to life, while at the same time disbelieving the extravagances of which he boasted.

It has not occurred to many outside his personal circle of acquaintances that, although he set out, from *Tropic of Cancer* onward, to write honestly about Henry Miller, his actions, thoughts and weaknesses, and was of course writing from his own experience, that he was nevertheless writing fiction and that the Henry Miller he portrayed might not be identical with the man who was writing the novels. Every writer is to some extent a masochist, and the better a writer he is, the more this is true. In laughing at himself, mocking himself, portraying himself as a clown, a fool, a piece of human flotsam, unable to resist a seduction or an opportunity to get a meal, a drink or a loan, he took particular pleasure in wringing every comic opportunity out of an incident and presenting himself to the reader in the worst possible light. He is not the first writer to have done so, and it has been done frequently since, but it was not established practice in the thirties – even Céline pulls his punches on himself – and it did him particular harm at the time, particularly in Britain, where self-revelation and self-mockery were taken at face value. A literary establishment committed to tact, understatement and good taste was not likely to take kindly to the Miller overstatement and exuberance.

The events of the *Tropics*, broadly speaking, are true, the characters real and the motivations, if exaggerated and made worse than reality, not inaccurate. There is no hypocrisy. When Miller did something he felt he should be ashamed about, he worried at the shame like a dog with a flea, exposing it fully and probably giving the whole incident more importance than it had ever had in real life. The novels chronicle his life from young manhood onward, from his first unwanted jobs, from when he married his first wife and left her for a taxi-dancer who supported him during the first period when he stopped work to try, unsuccessfully, to write.

For eleven years from 1909 when he was eighteen, he worked at dull uninspiring jobs, too dull to merit more than a passive mention in his novels. This was followed by four years with Western Union which gave him much rich material for fiction. The arrival of June in his life was both symbolic – she represented poetry as well as sex and became his first genuine muse – and decisive in practical terms: she loved him enough to support him while he struggled to learn the art of writing, she enabled him to leave Western Union. In later years he remembered his passion for her, and his guilt, when, needing her no longer, because in Paris he had emerged from the chrysalis and become what he had always wanted to be, he allowed her to leave when he could so easily have kept her. In old age he recalled his last meeting with her, many years after she left him, when he found her impoverished and lonely, in a depressed district of New York: she was now a physical wreck, 'nothing left of the June I'd been so crazy about, the woman who's inspired me to write volumes'. He went to have dinner with her, lost his courage, and fled in panic after fifteen minutes.

His passion for June, the Mara of *Capricorn*, is well documented in all its intensity in that book. Sex for him at the time was an escape from dull work, poverty and artistic frustration and much as he loved June, he was never faithful to her. There is a discernible pattern in his life: he needed women as a panacea for loneliness and frustration, but as his writing relieved that loneliness his need for emotional stability was replaced by a need to be free and away. The romantic concept of eternal love plays no part in his life. In the words of a Scottish poet he met and liked in Edinburgh, Sydney Goodsir Smith: 'Aathings a flouerin and a deein/ – and sae wi luve.'

> Queen o'luve, the white mune rides
> But syne the dawin briers,

Pale nou the Queen as she doun dwines
And I maun leave my dear;
But as we twyne, juist as we twyne
Anither tryst draws near
And ilka day apairt
But hastes me till my hairt.[8]

One of Miller's most quoted aphorisms, referring to American women in Paris is that they 'were looking for love, but would settle for sex'. The postwar world has been much more realistic about the brevity of love and the sexual needs of women. Certainly Henry Miller is one of the first writers able to show women as flesh and blood creatures, very different from the coy sexless heroines of Victorian fiction who survived as popular prototypes until the last war. By portraying women unromantically, he has contributed more to women's liberation than most will admit; many feminists still attack him for portraying women as sex-objects rather than as people. My contention is that he did the opposite, showed women as they are, appreciated them as women more than as symbols and by making them more human, gave them a natural and unashamed dignity.

Henry Miller was instinctive in his approach to life, but when faced with an intellectual challenge was practical, sensible and able to think out his attitudes better than most other writers because he did not carry around with him a system of learned or preconceived values and prejudices. As a result he was able to cultivate a form of homespun philosophy which was usually spot on target. When Ezra Pound suggested that he might give some thought to the whole subject of money, Henry Miller wrote a perceptive essay, extremely well-researched, that not only gave a history of money as currency but made more telling points about our economic system than most economists.

There can be no understanding of the present deplorable condition of money unless we understand first of all what is meant by a depression, as the history of money in our time is nothing but one series of depressions after another. We find at the very outset that, in order to avoid using such a gloomy word as depression, the economist makes use of the word 'business cycle'. What he means by this is that business has its ups and downs. Sometimes these cyclical fluctuations, as they are called, are rhythmical, sometimes they are only quasi-rhythmical. But in any case the law is that whatever goes up must come down again. This is such a natural phenomenon, so simple to grasp, that it has always been a source of

8. 'Everything flowers and dies and so with love': Sydney Goodsir Smith.

amazement to the writer that men should rack their brains trying to find a way to eliminate these cycles, or to smooth them out. It is almost like expecting the heart to beat without going through the rigmarole of systole and diastole. Money, as we have said before, is as much a part of life as life itself, and it obeys its own laws.

When a country is prosperous it must pay for its prosperity by getting ill. If it is rich enough to afford a good doctor it may recover, but that is not to say that it will remain healthy and prosperous forever. No, one day it must go the way of all flesh and die. Their money may live on, just as the cells of the body live on after death, undergoing mysterious transformations and eventually creating new forms of life. But men of affairs, practical and hardheaded though they may appear to be, are often loath to admit these facts. The wealthier ones display a tendency to run up idle bank balances, as though to prolong their private prosperity by identifying themselves with their wealth. But just as we know that even in sleep time runs on and with time nature takes her course, so we ought to realize that money never rests idle, even though it be locked in a vault. Money is always active, either constructively or destructively. When it is destructively active we have depressions. Usually we have more depressions than prosperity, which is only natural when we reflect that man himself has always been more destructive than constructive. Man would like to shift the burden of his guilt and make money the root of all evil, but as the pope himself has said – *money is not the source of evil*! Money is the evidence of wealth, and wealth is temporal, evanescent and highly fluctuating. That is the most we can say against money.

Indeed Henry Miller treated money rather like books; each was a need that one often had to do without but did not despise on that account; on the other hand he was generous with both books and money when he had them, sharing with friends and not making himself too dependent on either. The American preoccupation with money as an end in itself, and the bourgeois respectability that it buys and so often uses as a weapon against those less fortunate or circumspect, he viewed with contempt. But his writings often describe rich individuals who gave him money for no particularly good reason and random acts of generosity; such things happen in America and replace the organized generosity which is more common in other countries.

Henry Miller was a natural anarchist. Much as he loathed Hitler, Mussolini and the evils of their regimes, he was not in favour of fighting them. At Big Sur, he was an active pacifist and encouraged conscientious objectors against the war, many of whom were interned on the West Coast during the forties. In their defence he wrote the pacifist pamphlet *Murder the Murderers*. When the Allies landed in Normandy on D-Day, his reactions were mixed and he feared that the

Americans would be loathed by the French as barbarians. He did not conceive evil in power terms as a force to be fought, but as a phenomenon which one should walk away from and ignore. He saw the great abstract philosophical ideas as often in diametrical opposition to the practice that their purveyors proposed, and he detected hypocrisy and cant in much political statement.

Justice you ask for! Well every day metes out an inexorable justice. It's not ideal, it may not even be intelligent – from the view point of a Marxian dialectician. But it's justice. The English are particularly noted for shouting about liberty and justice. They make a great point always about 'fair play', even in war. As though war were a game played according to rules. But in crucial matters the English have never indulged in 'fair play'. If they had they would not own the vast empire on which the sun never sets, as they so fatuously boast. No, the English may talk about fair play, but in practice they have always employed the most dastardly tactics.

I know little about history, politics, literature, art, science, philosophy, religion, etc. I know only what I have seized through experience. I put no trust in the men who explain life to us in terms of history, economics, art, etc. They are the fellows who bugger us up, juggling their abstract ideas. I think it a piece of the most cruel deception to urge men to place their hopes of justice in some external order, some form of government, some social order, some system of ideal rights. I read every day somewhere or other about the Marxian dialect, as though to understand this lingo were a blot on the intelligence of man. Well, I must confess, and very willingly, that I have never read a line of Karl Marx. I have never felt compelled to read him. And the more I listen to his disciples the more I realize that I have lost nothing. Karl Marx, they say, explains the structure of our capitalistic society. Fuck your capitalistic society! Fuck your Communistic society and your Fascist Society and all your other societies! Society is made up of individuals. It is the individual who interests me – not the society.[9]

Although interested in surrealism, which in France by the thirties had taken on the aspect of a religion more than a school of artistic creation, Miller was also repelled by the discipline that Breton demanded from his followers and he found the undoctrinaire Dadaists more entertaining. Admitting that 'I was writing Surrealistically in America before I had ever heard the word', he repudiated the movement, if not necessarily its preoccupations and techniques, because it seemed to him to be overly political, too analytical, too concerned with absolutes, with extreme states of the mind, and with death. And yet, much as he loved the old French culture, the American in him

9. *Cosmological Eye*: 'An Open Letter to Surrealists Everywhere'.

also wished to see it die, so that rebirth and renewal would follow one day: therein lay the possible virtue of surrealism.

> But it rather seems to me that Surrealism is merely the reflection of the death process. It is one of the manifestations of a life becoming extinct, a virus which quickens the inevitable end. So it is a movement in the right direction. Europe must die and France with it. Sooner or later a new life must begin, a life from the roots.[10]

It is the anarchist speaking, the man who would rather brave persecution than regimentation, who repeatedly in his life and work refused to conform to any norm, who saw destruction and violence as healthier than any acceptance of discipline. Better a wild hunted animal in the jungle than a domesticated product of civilization. In one of his most extreme statements, he says:

> Ninety-nine percent of what is written – and this goes for all our art products – should be destroyed. I want to be read by less and less people; I have no interest in the life of the masses, nor in the intentions of the existing governments of the world. I hope and believe that the whole civilized world will be wiped out in the next hundred years or so. I believe that man can exist, and in an infinitely better, larger way, without 'civilization'.[11]

The contemporary to whom Henry Miller is most often compared is Céline, born three years later, whose own masterpiece, *Journey to the End of the Night* came out in 1932, the year when *Tropic of Cancer* could and should have appeared. Miller and Céline share a disgust for 'civilization', for the misuse of power by politicians, for the waste and cruelty of war and for mankind as part of a mass, instead of as a series of individuals. He also admired Wyndham Lewis, ten years older than Céline, who shared the French writer's anti-semitism, attraction to fascism and view of art. But Miller was never tempted by the right, nor by any political philosophy, close as he seems to be, as an artist, to Pound, Céline, Lewis and those other advocates of modernism who turned to the right politically because of their disillusionment with corrupt politicians and cynical financiers and the mess they had created during and after the First World War, probably because he never served in it and never experienced at first hand the horrors of that most unnecessary of blood baths. It was the stupidity of the 'old men' and the waste of life and ideals that resulted from the war that so

10. *ibid.*
11. *Cosmological Eye*: 'Autobiographical Note'.

appalled many of Miller's contemporaries and attracted them to new political models that promised efficiency and a world run by technicians and experts. Miller saw through all that, not intellectually but instinctively:

> I am against revolutions because they always involve a return to the status quo. I am against the status quo both before and after revolutions. I don't want to wear a black shirt or a red shirt. I want to wear the shirt that suits my taste. And I don't want to salute like an automaton either. I prefer to shake hands when I meet someone I like. The fact is, to put it simply, I am positively against all this crap which is carried on first in the name of this thing, then in the name of that. I believe only in what is active, immediate and personal. [12]

A more useful comparison might be made with Samuel Beckett, who appears on the surface to have little in common with Miller. Not only are there many similarities between Miller's Paris masterpieces and Beckett's immediate postwar novels in terms of style (they share a lucid prose style that owes much to a knowledge of French), but in their attitudes to art and civilization as well; the bohemianism, while not identical, is certainly related. Both, in different ways, are stoics: to Beckett life has to be endured – we are brought reluctantly into the world through no act or will of our own and must in our ways make the best of the charnel house where we find ourselves, any pleasures that might come our way soured by the inevitability of death; to Miller, life is also an accident, but a happy one, which we may not deserve, but which, having free will, we can turn to some good account if we wish to do so. Beckett is totally engrossed in the tragedy, but Miller, without losing awareness, ignores it. The difference lies in the attitude, not the outlook. And both see the apocalypse coming without too much regret, Beckett as a merciful end to human suffering, Miller as nature's means of regeneration.

Miller's theology consists of an honest agnosticism. He was aware of many different cultures and his instinct was towards pantheism, but he was more interested in enquiry than belief. His reflections on God, the world and afterlife are simply recorded reflections, not attempts to convince. His philosophy is perhaps more revealing about his character and his mind than of interest in itself.

This *Reader* has two purposes. First to resurrect a reputation that has, at least where the British critical establishment is concerned, always lain in the shadows. Many admit his importance, but few will

12. *Cosmological Eye*: 'An Open Letter to Surrealists Everywhere'.

credit his merit. The honesty and folksiness has always stood in the way of the recognition he deserves as a major twentieth-century writer. This is not the case where America and Europe are concerned, where his literary reputation is now well established, but the British preoccupation with good taste and discretion still enables Miller to be misunderstood and undervalued. Secondly, my purpose is to put into a single volume the essence of his fiction and non-fiction, to be enjoyed and savoured and to guide readers to the complete works, major and minor, of a writer who remains provoking, fresh and life-enhancing. We live once again in times not dissimilar to those when Miller achieved his prime, when his humour, gusto and discovery of his own potential, enabled him to be, in spite of poverty and debt, 'the happiest man alive'.

As Henry Miller's work is autobiographical in nature, the five parts of this *Reader* have been arranged, not in the chronological order of writing, but in the order of his life as he lived it, to give a picture, in his own words, of the man as well as the writer. *The Waters Reglitterized* comes near the end because that is where I think it belongs. Watercolours became increasingly important when he was writing less.

John Calder

# Part I

# Youth

# From *Black Spring*

I am a patriot – of the 14th Ward Brooklyn, where I was raised. The rest of the United States doesn't exist for me, except as idea, or history, or literature. At ten years of age I was uprooted from my native soil and removed to a cemetery, a *Lutheran* cemetery, where the tombstones were always in order and the wreaths never faded.

But I was born in the street and raised in the street. 'The post-mechanical open street where the most beautiful and hallucinating iron vegetation,' etc. . . . Born under the sign of Aries which gives a fiery, active, energetic and somewhat restless body. *With Mars in the ninth house!*

To be born in the street means to wander all your life, to be free. It means accident and incident, drama, movement. It means above all dream. A harmony of irrelevant facts which gives to your wandering a metaphysical certitude. In the street you learn what human beings really are; otherwise, or afterwards, you invent them. What is not in the open street is false, derived, that is to say, *literature*. Nothing of what is called 'adventure' ever approaches the flavour of the street. It doesn't matter whether you fly to the Pole, whether you sit on the floor of the ocean with a pad in your hand, whether you pull up nine cities one after the other, or whether, like Kurtz, you sail up the river and go mad. No matter how exciting, how intolerable the situation, there are always exits, always ameliorations, comforts, compensations, newspapers, religions. But once there was none of this. Once you were free, wild, murderous. . . .

The boys you worshipped when you first came down into the street remain with you all your life. They are the only real heroes. Napoleon, Lenin, Capone – all fiction. Napoleon is nothing to me in comparison with Eddie Carney who gave me my first black eye. No man I have ever met seems as princely, as regal, as noble, as Lester Reardon, who, by the mere act of walking down the street, inspired fear and admiration. Jules Verne never led me to the places that Stanley Borowski had up his sleeve when it came dark. Robinson Crusoe lacked imagination in comparison with Johnny Paul. All these boys of the 14th Ward have a flavour about them still. They were not invented or imagined: they were real. Their names ring out like gold coins – Tom Fowler, Jim Buckley, Matt Owen, Rob Ramsay, Harry Martin, Johnny Dunne, to say nothing of Eddie Carney or the great Lester Reardon. Why, even now when I say Johnny Paul the names of the saints leave a bad taste in my mouth. Johnny Paul was the living Odyssey of the 14th Ward; that he later became a truck-driver is an irrelevant fact.

Before the great change no one seemed to notice that the streets were ugly or dirty. If the sewer mains were opened you held your nose. If you blew your nose you found snot in your handkerchief and not your nose. There was more of inward peace and contentment. There was the saloon, the race-track, bicycles, fast women and trot horses. Life was still moving along leisurely. In the 14th Ward, at least. Sunday mornings no one was dressed. If Mrs Gorman came down in her wrapper with dirt in her eyes to bow to the priest – 'Good morning, Father!' 'Good morning, Mrs Gorman!' – the street was purged of all sin. Pat McCarren carried his handkerchief in the tail-flap of his frock coat; it was nice and handy there, like the shamrock in his buttonhole. The foam was on the lager and people stopped to chat with one another.

In my dreams I come back to the 14th Ward as a paranoiac returns to his obsessions. When I think of those steel-grey battleships in the Navy Yard I see them lying there in some astrologic dimension in which I am the gunnersmith, the chemist, the dealer in high explosives, the undertaker, the coroner, the cuckold, the sadist, the lawyer and contender, the scholar, the restless one, the jolt-head and the brazen-faced.

Where others remember of their youth a beautiful garden, a fond mother, a sojourn at the seashore, I remember, with a vividness as if it were etched in acid, the grim, soot-covered walls and chimneys of the tin factory opposite us and the bright circular pieces of tin that were strewn in the street, some bright and gleaming, others rusted, dull, copperish, leaving a stain on the fingers; I remember the iron-works where the red furnace glowed and men walked towards the glowing pit with huge shovels in their hands, while outside were the shallow wooden forms like coffins with rods through them on which you scraped your shins or broke your neck. I remember the black hands of the iron-moulders, the grit that had sunk so deep into the skin that nothing could remove it, not soap, nor elbow grease, nor money, nor love, nor death. Like a black mark on them! Walking into the furnace like devils with black hands – and later, with flowers over them, cool and rigid in their Sunday suits, not even the rain can wash away the

32

grit. All these beautiful gorillas going up to God with swollen muscles and lumbago and black hands . . . .

For me the whole world was embraced in the confines of the 14th Ward. If anything happened outside it either didn't happen or it was unimportant. If my father went outside that world to fish it was of no interest to me. I remember only his boozy breath when he came home in the evening and opening the big green basket spilled the squirming, goggle-eyed monsters on the floor. If a man went off to the war I remember only that he came back of a Sunday afternoon and standing in front of the minister's house puked up his guts and then wiped it up with his vest. Such was Rob Ramsay, the minister's son. I remember that everybody liked Rob Ramsay — he was the black sheep of the family. They liked him because he was a good for nothing and he made no bones about it. Sundays or Wednesdays made no difference to him: you could see him coming down the street under the drooping awnings with his coat over his arm and the sweat rolling down his face; his legs wobbly, with that long, steady roll of a sailor coming ashore after a long cruise; the tobacco juice dribbling from his lips, together with warm, silent curses and some loud and foul ones too. The utter indolence, the insouciance of the man, the obscenities, the sacrilege. Not a man of God, like his father. No, a man who inspired love! His frailties were human frailties and he wore them jauntily, tauntingly, flauntingly, like banderillas. He would come down the warm open street with the gas mains bursting and the air full of sun and shit and oaths and maybe his fly would be open and his suspenders undone, or maybe his vest bright with vomit. Sometimes he came charging down the street, like a bull skidding on all fours, and then the street cleared magically, as if the manholes had opened up and swallowed their offal. Crazy Willy Maine would be standing on the shed over the paint shop, with his pants down, jerking away for dear life. There they stood in the dry electrical crackle of the open street with the gas mains bursting. A tandem that broke the minister's heart.

That was how he was then, Rob Ramsay. A man on a perpetual spree. He came back from the war with medals, and with fire in his guts. He puked up in front of his own door and he wiped up his puke with his own vest. He could clear the street quicker than a machine gun. *Faugh a balla!* That was his way. And a little later, in his warm-heartedness, in that fine, careless way he had, he walked off the end of a pier and drowned himself.

I remember him so well and the house he lived in. Because it was on the door-step of Rob Ramsay's house that we used to congregate in the warm summer evenings and watch the goings-on over the saloon

33

across the street. A coming and going all night long and nobody bothered to pull down the shades. Just a stone's throw away from the little burlesque house called 'The Bum'. All around 'The Bum' were the saloons, and Saturday nights there was a long line outside, milling and pushing and squirming to get at the ticket window. Saturday nights, when the Girl in Blue was in her glory, some wild tar from the Navy Yard would be sure to jump out of his seat and grab off one of Millie de Leon's garters. And a little later that night they'd be sure to come strolling down the street and turn in at the family entrance. And soon they'd be standing in the bedroom over the saloon, pulling off their tight pants and the women yanking off their corsets and scratching themselves like monkeys, while down below they were scuttling the suds and biting each other's ears off, and such a wild, shrill laughter all bottled up inside there, like dynamite evaporating. All this from Rob Ramsay's door-step, the old man upstairs saying his prayers over a kerosene lamp, praying like an obscene nanny-goat for an end to come, or when he got tired of praying coming down in his nightshirt, like an old leprechaun, and belaying us with a broomstick.

From Saturday afternoon on until Monday morning it was a period without end, one thing melting into another. Saturday morning already – how it happened God only knows – you could *feel* the war vessels lying at anchor in the big basin. Saturday mornings my heart was in my mouth. I could see the decks being scrubbed down and the guns polished and the weight of those big sea-monsters resting on the dirty glass lake of the basin was a luxurious weight on me. I was already dreaming of running away, of going to far places. But I got only as far as the other side of the river, about as far north as Second Avenue and 28th Street, via the Belt Line. There I played the Orange Blossom Waltz and in the entr'actes I washed my eyes at the iron sink. The piano stood in the rear of the saloon. The keys were very yellow and my feet wouldn't reach to the pedals. I wore a velvet suit because velvet was the order of the day.

Everything that passed on the other side of the river was sheer lunacy: the sanded floor, the Argand lamps, the mica pictures in which the snow never melted, the crazy Dutchmen with stains in their hands, the iron sink that had grown such a mossy coat of slime, the woman from Hamburg whose ass always hung over the back of the chair, the courtyard choked with sauerkraut. . . . Everything in three-quarter time that goes on forever. I walk between my parents, with one hand in my mother's muff and the other in my father's sleeve. My eyes are tight shut, tight as clams which draw back their lids only to weep.

# The Tailor Shop

The day used to start like this: 'ask so-and-so for a little something on account, *but don't insult him!*' They were ticklish bastards, all these old farts we catered to. It was enough to drive any man to drink. There we were, just opposite the Olcott, Fifth Avenue tailors even though we weren't on the Avenue. A joint corporation of father and son, with mother holding the boodle.

Mornings, eight am or thereabouts, a brisk intellectual walk from Delancey Street and the Bowery to just below the Waldorf. No matter how fast I walked old man Berger was sure to be there ahead of me, raising hell with the cutter because neither of the bosses was on the job. How was it we could never get there ahead of that old buzzard Berger? He had nothing to do, Berger, but run from the tailor to the shirt-maker and from the shirt-maker to the jeweller's; his rings were either too loose or too tight, his watch was either twenty-five seconds slow or thirty-three seconds fast. He raised hell with everybody, including the family doctor, because the latter couldn't keep his kidneys clear of gravel. If we made him a sack coat in August by October it was too large for him, or too small. When he could find nothing to complain about he would dress on the right side so as to have the pleasure of bawling the pants maker out because he was strangling his, H. W. Berger's, balls. A difficult guy. Touchy, whimsical, mean, crotchety, miserly, capricious, malevolent. When I look back on it all now, see the old man sitting down to table with his boozy breath and saying *shit why don't someone smile, why do you all look so glum,* I feel sorry for him and for all merchant tailors who have to kiss rich people's asses. If it hadn't been for the Olcott bar across the way and the sots he picked up there God knows what would have become of the old man. He certainly got no sympathy at home. My mother hadn't the least idea what it meant to be kissing rich people's backsides. All she knew how to do was to groan and lament all day, and with her groaning and lamenting she brought on the boozy breath and the potato dumplings grown cold. She got us so damned jumpy with her anxiety that we would choke on our own spittle, my brother and I.

My brother was a half-wit and he got on the old man's nerves even more than H. W. Berger with his 'Pastor So-and-so's going to Europe. . . Pastor So-and-so's going to open a bowling alley', etc. 'Pastor So-and-so's an ass,' the old man would say, 'and why aren't the dumplings hot?'

There were three Bergers – H. W., the grumpy one, A. F., whom the old man referred to in the ledger as Albert, and R. N., who never visited the shop because his legs were cut off, a circumstance, however, which did not prevent him from wearing out his trousers in due season. R. N. I never saw in the flesh. He was an item in the ledger which Bunchek the cutter spoke of glowingly because there was always a little schnapps about when it came time to try on the new trousers. The three brothers were eternal enemies; they never referred to one another in our presence. If Albert, who was a little cracked and had a penchant for dotted vests, happened to see a cutaway hanging on the rack with the words H. W. Berger written in green ink on the try-on notice, he would give a feeble little grunt and say – 'feels like spring today, eh?' There was not supposed to be a man by the name of H. W. Berger in existence, though it was obvious to all and sundry that we were not making clothes for ghosts.

Of the three brothers I liked Albert the best. He had arrived at that ripe age when the bones become as brittle as glass. His spine had the natural curvature of old age, as though he were preparing to fold up and return to the womb. You could always tell when Albert was arriving because of the commotion in the elevator – a great cussing and whining followed by a handsome tip which accompanied the process of bringing the floor of the elevator to a dead level with the floor of our tailor shop. If it could not be brought to within a quarter of an inch exactitude there was no tip and Albert with his brittle bones and his bent spine would have a devil of a time choosing the right buttons to go with his dotted vest, his *latest* dotted vest. (When Albert died I inherited all his vests – they lasted me right through the war.) If it happened, as was sometimes the case, that the old man was across the street taking a little nip when Albert arrived, then somehow the whole day became disorganized. I remember periods when Albert grew so vexed with the old man that sometimes we did not see him for three days; meanwhile the vest buttons were lying around on little cards and there was talk of nothing but vest buttons, vest buttons, as if the vest itself didn't matter, only the buttons. Later, when Albert had grown accustomed to the old man's careless ways – they had been growing accustomed to each other for twenty-seven years – he would give us a ring to notify us that he was on the way. And just before hanging up he would add: 'I suppose it's all right my coming in at eleven o'clock . . . it won't inconvenience you?' The purport of this little query was twofold. It meant – 'I suppose you'll have the decency to be on hand when I arrive and not make me fiddle around for a half hour while you swill it down with your cronies across the street.' *And*, it also meant – 'At eleven o'clock I suppose there is little danger of bumping into a certain individual bearing the initials H. W.?' In the twenty-seven years during which we made perhaps 1,578 garments for the three Berger brothers it so happened that they never met, not in our presence at least. When Albert died R. N. and H. W. both had mourning bands put on their sleeves, on all the left sleeves of their sack coats and overcoats – that is, those which were not black coats – but nothing was said of the deceased, nor even *who* he was. R. N., of course, had a good excuse for not going to the funeral – his legs were gone. H. W. was too mean and too proud to even bother offering an excuse.

About ten o'clock was the time the old man usually chose to go down for his first nip. I used to stand at the window facing the hotel and watch George Sandusky hoisting the big trunks on to the taxis. When there were no trunks to be hoisted George used to stand there with his hands clasped behind his back and bow and scrape to the clients as they swung in and out of the revolving doors. George Sandusky had been scraping and bowing and hoisting and opening doors for about twelve years when I first came to the tailor shop and took up my post at the front window. He was a charming, soft-spoken man with beautiful white hair, and strong as an ox. He had raised this ass-kissing business to an art. I was amazed one day when he came up the elevator and ordered a suit from us. In his off hours he was a gentleman, George Sandusky. He had quiet tastes – always a blue serge or an Oxford grey. A man who knew how to conduct himself at a funeral or a wedding.

After we got to know each other he gave me to understand that he had found Jesus. With the smooth tongue he had, and the brawn, and the active help of said Jesus he had managed to lay aside a nest-egg, a little something to ward off the horrors of old age. He was the only man I ever met in that period who had not taken out life insurance. He maintained that God would look after those who were left behind just as He had looked after him, George Sandusky. He had no fear of the world collapsing upon his decease. God had taken care of everybody and everything up to date – no reason to suppose He would fall down on the job after George Sandusky's death. When one day George retired it was difficult to find a man to replace him. There was no one oily or unctuous enough to fill the bill. No one who could bow and scrape like George. The old man always had a great affection for George. He used to try to persuade him to take a drink now and then, but George always refused with that habitual and stubborn politeness which had endeared him to the Olcott guests.

The old man often had moods when he would ask anybody to take a drink with him, even such as George Sandusky. Usually late in the afternoon on a day when things were going wrong, when nothing but bills were coming in. Sometimes a week would pass without a customer showing up, or if one did show up it was only to complain, to ask for an alteration, to bawl the piss out of the coat maker, or to demand a reduction in the price. Things like this would make the old man so blue that all he could do was to put on his hat and go for a drink. Instead of going across the street as usual he would wander off base a bit, duck into the Breslin or the Broztell, sometimes getting as far off the path as the Ansonia where his idol, Julian Legree, kept a suite of rooms.

Julian, who was then a matinée idol, wore nothing but grey suits, every shade of grey imaginable, but only greys. He had the depressingly cheerful demeanour of the beefy-faced English actor who lounges about here and there swapping stories with swollen salesmen, liquor dealers and others of no account. His accent alone was enough to make men swarm about him; it was English in the traditional stage sense, warm, soapy, glutinous English which gives to even the most insignificant thought an appearance of importance. Julian never said anything that was worth recording but that voice of his worked magic on his admirers. Now and then, when he and the old man were doing the rounds, they would pick up a derelict such as Corse Payton who belonged across the river in the ten-twenty-thirties. Corse Payton was the idol of Brooklyn! Corse Payton was to art what Pat McCarren was to politics.

What the old man had to say during these discussions was always a source of mystery to me. The old man had never read a book in his life, nor had he ever been to a play since the days when the Bowery gave way to Broadway. I can see him standing there at the free lunch counter – Julian was very fond of the caviar and the sturgeon that was served at the Olcott – sponging it up like a thirsty dog. The two matinée idols discussing Shakespeare – whether *Hamlet* or *Lear* was the greatest play ever written. Or else arguing the merits of Boz Ingersoll.

Behind the bar at that time were three doughty Irishmen, three low-down micks such as made the bars of that day the congenial haunts they were. They were so highly thought of, these three, that it was considered a privilege to have such as Patsy O'Dowd, for example, call you a god-damned degenerate cock-sucking son of a bitch who hadn't sense enough to button up his fly. And if, in return for the compliment, you asked him if he wouldn't have a little something himself said Patsy O'Dowd would coldly and sneeringly reply that only such as yourself were fit to pour such rot-gut down your throat, and so saying he would scornfully lift your glass by the stem and wipe the mahogany because that was part of his job and he was paid to do it but be damned to you if you thought you could entice such as him to poison his intestines with the vile stuff. The more vicious his insults the more he was esteemed; financiers who were accustomed to having their asses wiped with silk handkerchiefs would drive all the way uptown, after the ticker closed down, in order to have this foul-mouthed bastard of an Irish mick call them god-damned degenerate cock-sucking sons of bitches. It was the end of a perfect day for them.

The boss of this jaunty emporium was a portly little man with aristocratic shanks and the head of a lion. He always marched with his stomach thrown forward, a little wine cask hidden under his vest. He usually gave a stiff, supercilious nod to the sots at the bar, unless they happened to be guests of the hotel, in which case he would pause a moment, extend three fat little fingers with blue veins and then, with a swirl of his moustache and a gingerly, creaky pirouette, he would whisk away. He was the only enemy the old man had. The old man simply couldn't stomach him. He had a feeling that Tom Moffatt looked down upon him. And so when Tom Moffatt came round to order his clothes the old man would tack on ten or fifteen per cent to cover the rents in his pride. But Tom Moffatt was a genuine aristocrat: he never questioned the price and he never paid his bills. If we dunned him he would get his accountant to find a discrepancy in our statements. And when it came time to order another pair of flannel trousers, or a cutaway, or a dinner jacket, he would sail in with his usual portly dignity, his stomach well forward, his moustache waxed, his shoes brightly polished and squeaky as always, and with an air of weary indifference, of aloof disdain, he would greet the old man as follows: 'Well, have you straightened out that error yet?' Upon which the old man would fly into a rage and palm off a remnant or a piece of American goods on his enemy Tom Moffatt. A long correspondence ensued over the 'little error' in our statements. The old man was beside himself. He hired an expert accountant who drew up statements three feet long – but to no avail. Finally the old man hit upon an idea.

Towards noon one day, after he had had his usual portion, after he had stood treat to all the woollen salesmen and the trimmings salesmen who were gathered at the bar, he quietly picked up the bar stubs and taking a little silver pencil which was attached to his watch chain he signed his name to the checks and sliding them across to Patsy O'Dowd he said: 'Tell Moffatt to charge them up to my account.' Then he quietly moved off and, inviting a few of his select cronies, he took a table in the dining room and commanded a spread. And when Adrian the frog presented the bill he calmly said: 'Give me a pencil. There . . . them's my demi-quivers. Charge it up to my account.' Since it was more pleasant to eat in the company of others he would always invite his cronies to lunch with him, saying to all and sundry – 'if that bastard Moffatt won't pay for his clothes then we'll eat them.' And so saying he would commandeer a juicy squab, or a lobster à la Newburg, and wash it down with a fine Moselle or any other vintage that Adrian the frog might happen to recommend.

To all this Moffatt, surprisingly enough, pretended to pay no heed. He continued to order his usual allotment of clothes for winter, spring, fall and summer, and he also continued to squabble about the bill which had become easier to do now since it was complicated with bar checks, telephone calls, squabs, lobsters, champagne, fresh strawberries, Benedictines, etc., etc. In fact, the old man was eating into that bill so fast that spindle-shanks Moffatt couldn't wear his clothes out quickly enough. If he came in to order a pair of flannel trousers the old man had already eaten it the next day.

Finally Moffatt evinced an earnest desire to have the account straightened out. The correspondence ceased. Patting me on the back one day as I happened to be standing in the lobby he put on his most cordial manner and invited me upstairs to his private office. He said he had always regarded me as a very sensible young man and that we could probably straighten the matter out between ourselves, without bothering the old man. I looked over the accounts and I saw that the old man had eaten way into the minus side. I had probably eaten up a few raglans and shooting jackets myself. There was only one thing to do if we were to keep Tom Moffatt's despised patronage and that was to find an error in the account. I took a bundle of bills under my arm and promised the old geezer that I would look into the matter thoroughly.

The old man was delighted when he saw how things stood. We kept looking into the matter for years. Whenever Tom Moffatt came round to order a suit the old man would greet him cheerily and say: 'Have you straightened out that little error yet? Now here's a fine Barathea weave that I laid aside for you . . .' And Moffatt would frown and grimace and strut back and forth like a turkey cock, his comb bristling, his thin little legs blue with malice. A half hour later the old man would be standing at the bar swilling it down. 'Just sold Moffatt another dinner jacket,' he would say. 'By the way, Julian, what would you like to order for lunch today?'

It was towards noon, as I say, that the old man usually went down for an appetizer; lunch lasted anywhere from noon till four or five in the afternoon. It was marvellous the companionship the old man enjoyed in those days. After lunch the troupe would stagger out of the elevator, spitting and guffawing, their cheeks aflame, and lodge themselves in the big leather chairs beside the cuspidors. There was Ferd Pattee who sold silk linings and trimmings such as skeins of thread, buttons, chest padding, canvas, etc. A great hulk of a man, like a liner that's been battered by a typhoon, and always walking about in a somnambulistic state; so tired he was that he could scarcely move his lips, yet that slight movement of the lips kept everybody about him in stitches. Always muttering to himself – about cheeses particularly. He was passionate about cheese, about schmierkäse and limburger especially – the mouldier the better. In between the cheeses he told stories about Heine and Schubert, or he would ask for a match just as he was about to break wind and hold it under his seat so that we could tell him the colour of the flame. He never said goodbye or see you tomorrow; he commenced talking where he had left off the day before, as though there had been no interruption of time. No matter whether it was nine in the morning or six in the evening he walked with the same exasperating slow shambling gait, muttering in his vici-kids, his head down, his linings and trimmings under his arm, his breath foul, his nose purple and translucent. Into the thickest traffic he would walk with head down, schmierkäse in one pocket and limburger in the other. Stepping out of the elevator he would say in that weary monotonous voice of his that he had some new linings and the cheese was fine last night were you thinking of returning the book he had loaned you and better pay up soon if you want more goods or like to see some dirty pictures please scratch my back there a little higher that's it excuse me I'm going to fart now have you the time I can't waste all day here better tell the old man to put on his hat it's time to go for a drink. Still mumbling and grumbling he turns on his big scows and presses the elevator button while the old man with a straw hat on the back of his head is making a slide for the home plate from the back of the store, his face lit up with love and gratitude and saying: 'Well, Ferd, how are you this morning? It's good to see you.' And Ferd's big heavy mask of a face relaxes for a moment into a broad amiable grin. Just a second he holds it and then, lifting his voice he bellows at the top of his lungs – so that even Tom Moffatt across the way can hear it – 'BETTER PAY UP SOON WHAT THE HELL DO YOU THINK I'M SELLING THESE THINGS FOR?'

And as soon as the elevator has started down out comes little Rubin from the bushelling room and with a wild look in his eye he says to me: 'Would you like me to sing for you?' He knows damned well that I would. So, going back to the bench, he picks up the coat that he's stitching and with a wild Cossack shout he lets loose.

If you were to pass him in the street, little Rubin, you would say 'dirty little kike', and perhaps he was a dirty little kike but he knew how to sing and when you were broke he knew how to put his hand in his pocket and when you were sad he was sadder still and if you tried to step on him he spat on your shoe and if you were repentant he wiped it off and he brushed you down and put a crease in your trousers like Jesus H. Christ himself couldn't do.

They were all midgets in the bushelling room – Rubin, Rapp and Chaimowitz. At noon they brought out big round loaves of Jewish bread which they smeared with sweet butter and slivers of lax. While the old man was ordering squabs and Rhine wine Bunchek the cutter and the three little bushelmen sat on the big bench among the goose irons and the legs and sleeves and talked earnestly and solemnly about things like the rent or the ulcers that Mrs Chaimowitz had in her womb. Bunchek was an ardent member of the Zionist party. He believed that the Jews had a happy future ahead of them. But despite it all he could never properly pronounce a word like 'screw'. He always said: 'He *scruled* her.' Besides his passion for Zionism Bunchek had another obsession and that was to make a coat one day that would hug the neck. Nearly all the customers were round-shouldered and pot-bellied, especially the old bastards who had nothing to do all day but run from the shirt-maker to the tailor and from the tailor to the jeweller's and from the jeweller's to the dentist and from the dentist to the druggist. There were so many alterations to be made that by the time the clothes were ready to be worn the season had passed and they had to be put away until next year, and by next year the old bastards had either gained twenty pounds or lost twenty pounds and what with sugar in their urine and water in the blood it was hell to please them even when the clothes did fit.

Then there was Paul Dexter, a $10,000 a year man but always out of work. Once he almost had a job, but it was at $9,000 a year and his pride wouldn't permit him to accept it. And since it was important to be well groomed, in the pursuit of this mythical job, Paul felt it incumbent upon him to patronize a good tailor such as the old man. Once he landed the job everything would be settled in full. There was never any question about that in Paul's mind. He was thoroughly honest. But he was a dreamer. He came from Indiana. And like all dreamers from Indiana he had such a lovable disposition, such a smooth, mellow, honeyed way that if he had committed incest the world would have forgiven him. When he had on the right tie, when he had chosen the proper cane and gloves, when the lapels were softly rolled and the shoes didn't squeak, when he had a quart of rye under his belt and the weather wasn't too damp or dismal then there flowed from his personality such a warm current of love and understanding that even the trimmings salesmen, hardened as they were to soft language, melted in their boots. Paul, when all circumstances were favourably conjoined, could walk up to a man, any man on God's green earth and, taking him by the lapel of his coat, drown him in love. Never did I see a man with such powers of persuasion, such magnetism. When the flood began to rise in him he was invincible.

Paul used to say: 'Start with Marcus Aurelius, or Epictetus, and the rest will follow.' He didn't recommend studying Chinese or learning Provençal: he began with the fall of the Roman Empire. It was my great ambition in those days to win Paul's approbation, but Paul was difficult to please. He frowned when I showed him *Thus Spake Zarathustra*. He frowned when he saw me sitting on the bench with the midgets trying to expound the meaning of *Creative Evolution*. Above all, he loathed the Jews. When Bunchek the cutter appeared, with a piece of chalk and a tape measure slung around his neck, Paul became excessively polite and condescending. He knew that Bunchek despised him, but because Bunchek was the old man's right hand man he rubbed him down with oil, he larded him with compliments. So that eventually even Bunchek had to admit that there was something

43

to Paul, some strange mark of personality which, despite his short-comings, endeared him to every one.

Outwardly Paul was all cheerfulness. But at bottom he was morose. Every now and then Cora, his wife, would sail in with eyes brimming with tears and implore the old man to take Paul in hand. They used to stand at the round table near the window conversing in a low voice. She was a beautiful woman, his wife, tall, statuesque, with a deep contralto voice that seemed to quiver with anguish whenever she mentioned Paul's name. I could see the old man putting his hand on her shoulder, soothing her, and promising her all sorts of things no doubt. She liked the old man, I could see that. She used to stand very close to him and look into his eyes in a way that was irresistible. Sometimes the old man would put his hat on and the two of them would go down the elevator together, arm in arm, as if they were going to a funeral. Off looking for Paul again. Nobody knew where to find him when he had a drinking fever on. For days on end he would disappear from sight. And then one day he would turn up, crestfallen, repentant, humiliated, and beg everybody's forgiveness. At the same time he would hand in his suit to be dry cleaned, to have the vomit stains removed, and a bit of expert repairing done at the knees.

It was after a bout that Paul talked most eloquently. He used to sit back in one of the deep leather chairs, the gloves in one hand, the cane between his legs, and discourse about Marcus Aurelius. He talked even better when he came back from the hospital, after he had had the fistula repaired. The way he lowered himself into the big leather chair made me think then that he came expressly to the tailor shop because nowhere else could he find such a comfortable seat. It was a painful operation either to sit down or to get up. But once accomplished Paul seemed to be in bliss and the words rolled off his tongue like liquid velvet. The old man could listen to Paul all day long. He used to say that Paul had the gift of gab, but that was only his inarticulate way of saying that Paul was the most lovable creature on God's earth and that he had a fire in his bowels. And when Paul was too conscience-stricken to order another suit the old man would coax him into it, saying to Paul all the while, 'nothing's too good for you, Paul . . . nothing!'

Paul must have recognized something of a kindred nature in the old man too. Never have I seen two men look at each other with such a warm glow of admiration. Sometimes they would stand there looking into each other's eyes adoringly until the tears came. In fact, neither of them was ashamed of showing his tears, something which seems to have gone out of the world now. I can see Paul's homely freckled face and his rather thick, blubbery lips twitching as the old man told him for the thousandth time what a great guy he was. Paul never spoke to the old man about things he wouldn't understand. But into the simple, everyday things which he discoursed about so earnestly he put such a wealth of tenderness that the old man's soul seemed to leave his body and when Paul was gone he was like a man bereaved. He would go then into the little cubby-hole of an office and he would sit there quietly all by himself staring ecstatically at the row of pigeon coops which were filled with letters unanswered and bills unpaid. It used to affect me so, to see him in one of these moods, that I would sneak quietly down the stairs and start to walk home, down the Avenue to the Bowery and along the Bowery to the Brooklyn Bridge, and then over the bridge past the string of cheap flops that extended from City Hall to Fulton Ferry. And if it were a summer's evening, and the entrance ways crowded with loungers, I would look among these wasted figures searchingly, wondering how many Pauls there were among them and what it is about life that makes these obvious failures so endearing to men. The others, the successful ones, I had seen with their pants off; I had seen their crooked spines, their brittle bones, their varicose veins, their tumours, their sunken chests, their big bread-baskets which had grown shapeless with years of swilling it. Yes, all the silk-lined duffers I knew well – we had the best families in America on our roster. And what a pus and filth when they opened their dirty traps! It seemed as though when they had undressed before their tailor they felt compelled to unload the garbage which had accumulated in the plugged- up sinks which they had made of their minds. All the beautiful diseases of boredom and riches. Talked about themselves *ad nauseam*. Always 'I', 'I'. I and my kidneys. I and my gout. I and my liverworts. When I think of Paul's dreadful hemorrhoids, of the marvellous fistula they repaired, of all the love and learning that issued from his grievous wounds, then I think that Paul was not of this age at all but sib brother to Moses Maimonides, he who under the Moors gave us those astounding learned treatises on 'hemorrhoids, warts, carbuncles', etc.

In the case of all these men whom the old man so cherished death came quickly and unexpectedly. In Paul's case it happened while he was at the seashore. He was drowned in a foot of water. Heart failure, they said. And so, one fine day Cora came up the elevator, clad in her beautiful mourning garb, and wept all over the place. Never had she looked more beautiful to me, more svelte, more statuesque. Her ass particularly – I remember how caressingly the velvet clung to her figure. Again they stood near the round table at the front window, and this time she wept copiously. And again the old man put on his hat and down the elevator they went, arm in arm.

A short time later the old man, moved by some strange whim, urged me to call on Paul's wife and offer my condolences. When I rang the bell at her apartment I was trembling. I almost expected her to come out stark naked, with perhaps a mourning band around her breasts. I was infatuated with her beauty, with her years, with that somnolent, plant-like quality she had brought from Indiana and the perfume which she bathed in. She greeted me in a low-cut mourning gown, a beautiful clinging gown of black velvet. It was the first time I had ever had a tête-à-tête with a woman bereft, a woman whose breasts seemed to sob out loud. I didn't know what to say to her, especially about Paul. I stammered and blushed, and when she asked me to sit beside her on the couch I almost fell over in my embarrassment.

Sitting there on the low sofa, the place flooded with soft lights, her big, heaving loins rubbing against me, the Malaga pounding my temples and all this crazy talk about Paul and how good he was, I finally bent over and without saying a word I raised her dress and slipped it into her. And as I got it into her and began to work it around she took to moaning like, a sort of delirious sorrowful guilt punctuated with gasps and little shrieks of joy and anguish, saying over and over again – 'I never thought you would do this . . . I never thought you would do this!' And when it was all over she ripped off the velvet dress, the beautiful low-cut mourning gown, and she put my head down on her and she told me . . . . . . . and with her two strong arms she squeezed me almost in half and moaned and sobbed. And then she got up and she walked around the room naked for a while. And then finally she got down on her knees beside the sofa where I was stretched out and she said in a low tearful voice – 'You promise me you'll love me always, won't you? You promise me?' And I said Yes with one hand working around in her crotch. Yes I said and I thought to myself what a sap you've been to wait so long. She was so wet and juicy down there, and so child-like, so trustful, why anybody could have come along and had what's what. She was a push-over.

*Always merry and bright!* Regularly, every season, there were a few deaths. Sometimes it was a good egg like Paul, or Julian Legree, sometimes a bartender who had picked his nose with a rusty nail – hale and hearty one day, dead the next – but regularly, like the movements

46

of the seasons themselves, the old buzzards dropped off, one by one. *Alors*, nothing to do but draw a red line slantwise down the right-hand side of the ledger and mark 'dead'. Each death brought a little business – a new black suit or else mourning bands on the left sleeve of every coat. Those who ordered mourning bands were cheapskates, according to the old man. And so they were.

As the old 'uns died off they were replaced by young blood. *Young blood!* That was the war-cry all along the Avenue, wherever there were silk-lined suits for sale. A fine bloody crew they were, the young bloods. Gamblers, race-track touts, stock-brokers, ham actors, prize fighters, etc. Rich one day, poor the next. No honour, no loyalty, no sense of responsibility. A fine bunch of gangrened syphilitics they were, most of 'em. Came back from Paris or Monte Carlo with dirty postcards and a string of big blue rocks in their groin. Some of them with balls as big as a lamb's fry.

One of them was the Baron Carola von Eschenbach. He had earned a little money in Hollywood posing as the Crown Prince. It was the period when it was considered riotously funny to see the Crown Prince plastered with rotten eggs. It must be said for the Baron that he was a good double for the Crown Prince. A death's head with arrogant nose, a waspish stride, a corseted waist, lean and ravished as Martin Luther, dour, glum, fanatical, with that brassy, fatuous glare of the Junker class. Before going to Hollywood he was just a nobody, the son of a German brewer in Frankfort. He wasn't even a baron. But afterwards, when he had been knocked about like a medicine ball, when his front teeth had been pushed down his throat and the neck of a broken bottle had traced a deep scar down his left cheek, afterwards when he had been taught to flaunt a red necktie, twirl a cane, clip his moustache short, like Chaplin, then he became somebody. Then he stuck a monocle in his eye and named himself Baron Carola von Eschenbach. And all might have gone beautifully for him had he not fallen for a red-haired walk-on who was rotting away with syphilis. That finished him.

Up the elevator he came one day in a cutaway and spats, a bright red rose in his buttonhole and the monocle stuck in his eye. Blithe and dapper he looked, and the card he took out of his wallet was handsomely engraved. It bore a coat of arms which had been in the family, so he said, for nine hundred years. 'The family skeleton,' he called it. The old man was highly pleased to have a baron among his clients, especially if he paid cash, as this one promised to do. And then too it was exhilarating to see the baron come sailing in with a pair of soubrettes on his arm – each time a different pair. Even more exhilarating when he invited them into the dressing room and asked them to help him off with his trousers. It was a European custom, he explained.

Gradually he got acquainted with all the old cronies who hung out in the front of the shop. He showed them how the Crown Prince walked, how he sat down, how he smiled. One day he brought a flute with him and he played the Lorelei on it. Another day he came in with a finger of his pig-skin glove sticking out of his fly. Each day he had a new trick up his sleeve. He was gay, witty, amusing. He knew a thousand jokes, some that had never been told before. He was a riot.

And then one day he took me aside and asked me if I could lend him a dime – for carfare. He said he couldn't pay for the clothes he had ordered but he expected a job soon in a little movie house on Ninth Avenue, playing the piano. And then, before I knew it, he began to weep. We were standing in the dressing room and the curtains were drawn fortunately. I had to lend him a handkerchief to wipe his eyes. He said he was tired of playing the clown, that he dropped in to our place every day because it was warm there and because we had comfortable seats. He asked me if I couldn't take him to lunch – he had had nothing but coffee and buns for the last three days.

I took him to a little German restaurant on Third Avenue, a bakery and restaurant combined. The atmosphere of the place broke him down completely. He could talk of nothing but the old days, the old days, the days before the war. He had intended to be a painter, and then the war came. I listened attentively and when he got through, I proposed that he come to my home for dinner that evening – perhaps I could put him up with us. He was overwhelmed with gratitude. Sure, he would come – at seven o'clock *punkt*. Fine!

At the dinner table my wife was amused by his stories. I hadn't said anything about his being broke. Just that he was a baron – the Baron von Eschenbach, a friend of Charlie Chaplin's. My wife – one of my first ones – was highly flattered to sit at the same table with a baron. And Puritanical bastard that she was, she never so much as blushed when he told a few of his risqué stories. She thought they were delightful – *so European*. Finally, however, it came time to spill the beans. I tried to break the news gently, but how can you be gentle about a subject like syphilis? I didn't call it syphilis at first – I said 'venereal disease'. *Maladie intime, quoi!* But just that little word 'venereal' sent a shudder through my wife. She looked at the cup he was holding to his lips and then she looked at me imploringly, as though to say – 'how could you ask a man like that to sit at the same table with us?' I saw that it was necessary to bring the matter to a head at once. 'The baron here is going to stay with us for a while,' I said quietly. 'He's broke and he needs a place to flop.' My word, I never saw a woman's expression change so quickly. '*You!*' she said, '*you* ask *me* to do that? And what about the baby? You want us all to have syphilis, is that it? It's not enough that *he* has it – you want the baby to have it too!'

The baron of course was frightfully embarrassed by this outburst. He wanted to leave at once. But I told him to keep his shirt on. I was used to these scenes. Anyway, he got so wrought up that he began to choke over his coffee. I thumped him on the back until he was blue in the face. The rose fell out of his buttonhole on to the plate. It looked strange there, as though he had coughed it up out of his own blood. It made me feel so god-damned ashamed of my wife that I could have strangled her on the spot. He was still choking and sputtering as I led him to the bathroom. I told him to wash his face in cold water. My wife followed us in and watched in murderous silence as he performed his ablutions. When he had wiped his face she snatched the towel from his hands and, flinging the bathroom window open, flung it out. That made me furious. I told her to get the hell out of the bathroom and mind her own business. But the baron stepped between us and flung himself at my wife supplicatingly. 'You'll see, my good woman, and you, Henry, you won't have to worry about a thing. I'll bring all my syringes and ointments and I'll put them in a little valise – there, under the sink. You mustn't turn me away, I have nowhere to go. I'm a desperate man. I'm alone in the world. You were so good to me before – why must you be cruel now? Is it my fault that I have the syph? Anybody can get the syph. It's human. You'll see, I'll pay you back a thousand times. I'll do anything for you. I'll make the beds, I'll wash the dishes . . . I'll cook for you . . .' He went on and on like that, never stopping to take a breath for fear that she would say No. And after he had gotten all through with his promises, after he had begged her forgiveness a hundred times, after he had knelt down and tried to kiss her hand which she drew away abruptly, he sat down on the toilet seat, in his cutaway and spats, and he began to sob, to sob like a child. It was ghastly, the sterile, white-enamelled bathroom and the splintering light as if a thousand mirrors had been shattered under a magnifying glass, and then this wreck of a baron in his cutaway and spats, his spine filled with mercury, his sobs coming like the short puffs of a locomotive getting under way. I didn't know what the hell to do. A man sitting on the toilet like that and sobbing – it got under my skin. Later I became inured to it. I got hard-boiled. I feel quite certain now that had it not been for the 250 bed patients whom he was obliged to visit twice a day at the hospital in Lyons Rabelais would never have been so boisterously gay. I'm sure of it.

Anyhow, apropos the sobs . . . A little later, when another kid was on the way and no means of getting rid of it, though still hoping, still hoping that something would happen, a miracle perhaps, and her stomach blown up like a ripe watermelon, about the sixth or seventh month, as I say, she used to succumb to fits of melancholy and, lying on the bed with that watermelon staring her in the eye, she would commence to sob fit to break your heart. Maybe I'd be in the other room, stretched out on the couch, with a big, fat book in my hands, and those sobs of hers would make me think of the Baron Carola von Eschenbach, of his grey spats and the cutaway with braided lapels, and the deep red rose in his buttonhole. Her sobs were like music to my ears. Sobbing away for a little sympathy she was, and not a drop of sympathy in the house. It was pathetic. The more hysterical she grew the more deaf I became. It was like listening to the boom and sizzle of surf along the beach on a summer's night: the buzz of a mosquito can drown out the ocean's roar. Anyway, after she had worked herself up to a state of collapse, when the neighbours couldn't stand it any longer and there were knocks on the door, then her aged mother would come crawling out of the bed-room and with tears in her eyes would beg me to go in there and quiet her a bit. 'Oh, leave her be,' I'd say, 'she'll get over it.' Whereupon, ceasing her sobs for a moment, the wife would spring out of bed, wild, blind with rage, her hair all down and tangled up, her eyes swollen and bleary, and still hiccoughing and sobbing she would commence to pound me with her fists, to lambast me until I became hysterical with laughter. And when she saw me rocking to and fro like a crazy man, when her arms were tired and her fists sore, she would yell like a drunken whore – 'Fiend! Demon!' – and then slink off like a weary dog. Afterwards, when I had quieted her down a bit, when I realized that she really needed a kind word or two, I would tumble her on the bed again and throw a good fuck into her. Blast me if she wasn't the finest piece of tail imaginable after those scenes of grief and anguish! I never heard a woman moan and gibber like she could. 'Do *anything* to me!' she used to say. 'Do what you want!' I could stand her on her head and blow into it, I could back-scuttle her, I could drag her past the parson's house, as they say, any god-damn thing at all – she was simply delirious with joy. Uterine hysteria, that's what it was! *And I hope God take me*, as the good master used to say, *if I am lying in a single word I say*.

(God, mentioned above, being defined by St Augustine, as follows: 'An infinite sphere, the centre of which is everywhere, the circumference nowhere.')

However, *always merry and bright!* If it was before the war and the thermometer down to zero or below, if it happened to be Thanksgiving Day, or New Year's, or a birthday, or just any old excuse to get together, then off we'd trot, the whole family, to join the other freaks who made up the living family tree. It always seemed astounding to me how jolly they were in our family despite the calamities that were always threatening. Jolly in spite of everything. There was cancer, dropsy, cirrhosis of the liver, insanity, thievery, mendacity, buggery, incest, paralysis, tape-worms, abortions, triplets, idiots, drunkards, ne'er-do-wells, fanatics, sailors, tailors, watch-makers, scarlet fever, whooping cough, meningitis, running ears, chorea, stutterers, gaol birds, dreamers, story-tellers, bartenders – and finally there was Uncle George and Tante Melia. The morgue and the insane asylum. A merry crew and the table loaded with good things; – with red cabbage and green spinach, with roast pork and turkey and sauerkraut, with kartoffeln-klösze and sour black gravy, with radishes and celery, with stuffed goose and peas and carrots, with beautiful white cauliflower, with apple sauce and figs from Smyrna, with bananas big as a blackjack, with cinnamon cake and Streussel Kuchen, with chocolate layer cake and nuts, all kinds of nuts, walnuts, butternuts, almonds, pecans, hickory nuts, with lager beer and bottled beer, with white wines and red, with champagne, kümmel, malaga, port, with schnapps, with fiery cheeses, with dull, innocent store cheese, with flat Holland cheeses, with limburger and schmierkäse, with home made wines, elderberry wine, with cider, hard and sweet, with rice pudding and tapioca, with roast chestnuts, mandarines, olives, pickles, with red caviar and black, with smoked sturgeon, with lemon meringue pie, with lady fingers and chocolate eclairs, with macaroons and cream puffs, with black cigars and long thin stogies, with Bull Durham and Long Tom and meerschaums, with corn-cobs and tooth-picks, wooden tooth-picks which gave you gum-boils the day after, and napkins a yard wide with your initials stitched in the corner, and a blazing coal fire and the windows steaming, everything in the world before your eyes except a fingerbowl.

Zero weather and crazy George, with one arm bitten off by a horse, dressed in dead men's remnants. Zero weather and Tante Melia

51

looking for the birds she left in her hat. Zero, zero, and the tugs snorting below in the harbour, the ice floes bobbing up and down, and long thin streams of smoke curling fore and aft. The wind blowing down at seventy miles an hour; tons and tons of snow all chopped up into tiny flakes and each one carrying a dagger. The icicles hanging like cork-screws outside the window, the wind roaring, the panes rattling. Uncle Henry is singing 'Hurrah for the German Fifth!' His vest is open, his suspenders are down, the veins stand out on his temples. *Hurrah for the German Fifth!*

Up in the loft the creaking table is spread; down below is the warm stable, the horses whinnying in the stalls, whinnying and champing and pawing and stomping, and the fine aromatic smell of manure and horse piss, of hay and oats, of steaming blankets and dry cruds, the smell of malt and old wood, of leather harness and tan-bark floats up and rests like incense over our heads.

The table is standing on horses and the horses are standing in warm piss and every now and then they get frisky and whisk their tails and they fart and whinny. The stove is glowing like a ruby, the air is blue with smoke. The bottles are under the table, on the dresser, in the sink. Crazy George is trying to scratch his neck with an empty sleeve. Ned Martini, the ne'er-do-well, is fiddling with the phonograph; his wife Carrie is guzzling it from the tin growler. The brats are downstairs in the stable, playing stink-finger in the dark. In the street, where the shanties begin, the kids are making a sliding-pond. It's blue everywhere, with cold and smoke and snow. Tante Melia is sitting in a corner fingering a rosary. Uncle Ned is repairing a harness. The three grandfathers and the two great-grandfathers are huddled near the stove talking about the Franco-Prussian war. Crazy George is lapping up the dregs. The women are getting closer together, their voices low, their tongues clacking. Everything fits together like a jig-saw puzzle – faces, voices, gestures, bodies. Each one gravitates within his own orbit. The phonograph is working again, the voices get louder and shriller. The phonograph stops suddenly. I oughtn't to have been there when they blurted it out, but I was there and I heard it. I heard that big Maggie, the one who kept a saloon out in Flushing, well that Maggie had slept with her own brother and that's why George was crazy. She slept with everybody – except her own husband. And then I heard that she used to beat George with a leather belt, used to beat him until he foamed at the mouth. That's what brought on the fits. And then Mele sitting there in the corner – she was another case. She was queer even as a child. So was the mother, for that matter. It was too bad that Paul had died. Paul was Mele's husband. Yes, everything would have been all right if that woman from Hamburg hadn't shown up and corrupted Paul. What could Mele do against a clever woman like that – against a shrewd strumpet! Something would have to be done about Mele. It was getting dangerous to have her around. Just the other day they caught her sitting on the stove. Fortunately the fire was low. But supposing she took it into her head to set fire to the house – when they were all asleep? It was a pity that she couldn't hold a job any more. The last place they had found for her was such a nice berth, such a kind woman. Mele was getting lazy. She had had it too easy with Paul.

The air was clear and frosty when we stepped outdoors. The stars were crisp and sparkly and everywhere, lying over the bannisters and steps and window-ledges and gratings, was the pure white snow, the driven snow, the white mantle that covers the dirty, sinful earth. Clear and frosty the air, pure, like deep draughts of ammonia, and the skin smooth as chamois. Blue stars, beds and beds of them, drifting with the antelopes. Such a beautiful, deep, silent night, as if under the snow there lay hearts of gold, as if this warm German blood was running away in the gutter to stop the mouths of hungry babes, to wash the crime and ugliness of the world away. Deep night and the river choked with ice, the stars dancing, swirling, spinning like tops. Along the broken street we straggled, the whole family. Walking along the pure white crust of the earth, leaving tracks, foot-stains. The old German family sweeping the snow with a Christmas tree. The whole family there, uncles, cousins, brothers, sisters, fathers, grand-fathers. The whole family is warm and winey and no one thinks of the other, of the sun that will come in the morning, of the errands to run, of the doctor's verdict, of all the cruel, ghastly duties that foul the day and make this night holy, this holy night of blue stars and deep drifts, of arnica blossoms and ammonia, of asphodels and carborundum.

No one knew that Tante Melia was going completely off her nut, that when we reached the corner she would leap forward like a reindeer and bite a piece out of the moon. At the corner she leapt forward like a reindeer and she shrieked. 'The moon, the moon!' she cried, and with that her soul broke loose, jumped clean out of her body. Eighty-six million miles a minute it travelled. Out, out, to the moon, and nobody could think quick enough to stop it. Just like that it happened. In the twinkle of a star.

And now I'm going to tell you what those bastards said to me . . .

They said – *Henry, you take her to the asylum tomorrow. And don't tell them that we can afford to pay for her.*

Fine! *Always merry and bright!* The next morning we boarded the trolley together and we rode out into the country. If Mele asked where we were going I was to say – 'to visit Aunt Monica'. But Mele didn't ask any questions. She sat quietly beside me and pointed to the cows now and then. She saw blue cows and green ones. She knew their names. She asked what happened to the moon in the day-time. And did I have a piece of liverwurst by any chance?

During the journey I wept – I couldn't help it. When people are too good in this world they have to be put under lock and key. There's something wrong with people who are too good. It's true Mele was lazy. She was born lazy. It's true that Mele was a poor housekeeper. It's true Mele didn't know how to hold on to a husband when they found her one. When Paul ran off with the woman from Hamburg Mele sat in a corner and wept. The others wanted her to do something – put a bullet in him, raise a rumpus, sue for alimony. Mele sat quiet. Mele wept. Mele hung her head. What little intelligence she had deserted her. She was like a pair of torn socks that are kicked around here, there, everywhere. Always turning up at the wrong moment.

Then one day Paul took a rope and hanged himself. Mele must have understood what had happened because now she went completely crazy. The day before they found her eating her own dung. The day before that they found her sitting on the stove.

And now she's very tranquil and she calls the cows by their first name. The moon fascinates her. She has no fear because I'm with her and she always trusted me. I was her favourite. Even though she was a half-wit she was good to me. The others were more intelligent, but their hearts were bad.

When brother Adolphe used to take her for a carriage ride the others used to say – 'Mele's got her eye on him!' But I think that Mele must have talked just as innocently then as she's talking to me now. I think that Mele, when she was performing her marriage duties, must have been dreaming innocently of the beautiful gifts she would give to everybody. I don't think that Mele had any knowledge of sin or of guilt or remorse. I think that Mele was born a half-witted angel. I think Mele was a saint.

Sometimes when she was fired from a job they used to send me to fetch her. Mele never knew her way home. And I remember how happy she was whenever she saw me coming. She would say innocently that she wanted to stay with us. Why couldn't she stay with us?

I used to ask myself that over and over. Why couldn't they make a place for her by the fire, let her sit there and dream, if that's what she wanted to do? Why must everybody *work* – even the saints and the angels? Why must half-wits set a good example?

I'm thinking now that after all it may be good for Mele where I'm taking her. No more work. Just the same, I'd rather they had made a corner for her somewhere.

Walking down the gravel path towards the big gates Mele becomes uneasy. Even a puppy knows when it is being carried to a pond to be drowned. Mele is trembling now. At the gate they are waiting for us. The gate yawns. Mele is on the inside, I am on the outside. They are trying to coax her along. They are gentle with her now. They speak to her so gently. But Mele is terror-stricken. She turns and runs towards the gate. I am still standing there. She puts her arms through the bars and clutches my neck. I kiss her tenderly on the forehead. Gently I unlock her arms. The others are going to take her again. I can't bear seeing that. I must go. I must run. For a full minute, however, I stand and look at her. Her eyes seem to have grown enormous. Two great round eyes, full and black as the night, staring at me uncomprehendingly. No maniac can look that way. No idiot can look that way. Only an angel or a saint.

Mele wasn't a good housekeeper I said, but she knew how to make fricadellas. Here is the recipe, while I think of it: a distemper composed of a humus of wet bread (from a nice urinal) plus horse meat (the fetlocks only) chopped very fine and mixed with a little sausage meat. Roll in palm of hands. The saloon that she ran with Paul, before the Hamburg woman came along, was just near the bend in the Second Avenue L, not far from the Chinese pagoda used by the Salvation Army.

When I ran away from the gate I stopped beside a high wall and burying my head in my arms, my arms against the wall, I sobbed as I had never sobbed since I was a child. Meanwhile they were giving Mele a bath and putting her into regulation dress; they parted her hair in the middle, brushed it down flat and tied it into a knot at the nape of the neck. Thus no one looks exceptional. All have the same crazy look, whether they are half crazy or three-quarters crazy, or just slightly cracked. When you say 'may I have pen and ink to write a letter' they say 'yes' and they hand you a broom to sweep the floor. If you pee on the floor absent-mindedly you have to wipe it up. You can sob all you like but you mustn't violate the rules of the house. A bug-house has to be run in orderly fashion just as any other house.

Once a week Mele would be allowed to receive. For thirty years the sisters had been visiting the bug-house. They were fed up with it. When they were tiny tots they used to visit their mother on Blackwell's Island. The mother always said to be careful of Mele, to watch over her. When Mele stood at the gate with eyes so round and bright her mind must have travelled back like an express train. Everything must have leaped to her mind at once. Her eyes were so big and bright, as if they saw more than they could comprehend. Bright with terror, and beneath the terror a limitless confusion. That's what made them so beautifully bright. You have to be crazy to see things so lucidly, so all at once. If you're great you can stay that way and people will believe in you, swear by you, turn the world upside down for you. But if you're only partly great, or just a nobody, then what happens to you is lost.

Mornings a brisk intellectual walk under the screaming elevated line, walking north from Delancey Street towards the Waldorf where the evening before the old man had been lounging around in Peacock Alley with Julian Legree. Each morning I write a new book, walking from the Delancey Street station north towards the Waldorf. On the fly-leaf of each book is written in vitriol: *The Island of Incest*. Every morning it starts with the drunken vomit of the night before; it makes a huge gardenia which I wear in the buttonhole of my lapel, the lapel of my double-breasted suit which is lined with silk throughout. I arrive at the tailor shop with the black breath of melancholy, perhaps to find Tom Jordan in the bushelling room waiting to have the spots removed from his fly. After having written 369 pages on the trot the futility of saying Good Morning prevents me from being ordinarily polite. I have just this morning finished the 23rd volume of the ancestral book, of which not even a comma is visible since it was all written extemporaneously without even a fountain pen. I, the tailor's son, am now about to say Good Morning to Endicott Mumford's crack woollen salesman who stands before the mirror in his underwear examining the pouches under his eyes. Every limb and leaf of the family tree dangles before my eyes: out of the crazy black fog of the Elbe there floats this changing island of incest which produces the marvellous gardenia that I wear in my buttonhole each morning. I am just about to say Good Morning to Tom Jordan. It trembles there on my lips. I see a huge tree rising out of the black fog and in the hollow of the trunk there sits the woman from Hamburg, her ass squeezed tightly through the back of the chair. The door is on the latch and through the chink I see her green face, the lips set tight, the nostrils distended. Crazy George is going from door to door with picture post-cards, the arm that was bitten off by a horse lost and buried, the empty sleeve flapping in the wind. When all the pages have been torn from the calendar except the last six Crazy George will ring the doorbell and, with icicles in his moustache, he will stand on the threshold, cap in hand, and shout – 'Merry Christmas!' This is the craziest tree that ever rose out of the Elbe, with every limb blasted and every leaf withered. This is the tree that shouts regularly once a year – 'Merry Christmas!' Despite the calamities, despite the flow of cancer, dropsy, thievery, mendacity, buggery, paralysis, tape-worms, running ears, chorea, meningitis, epilepsy, liverworts, et cetera.

I am just about to say Good Morning. It trembles there on my lips. The 23 volumes of the Domesday Book are written with incestuous fidelity, the covers bound in finest morocco and a lock and key for each volume. Tom Jordan's blood-shot eyes are pasted on the mirror; they shudder like a horse shaking off a fly. Tom Jordan is always either taking off his pants or putting on his pants. Always buttoning or unbuttoning his fly. Always having the stains removed and a fresh crease put in. Tante Melia is sitting in the cooler, under the shade of the family tree. Mother is washing the vomit stains out of last week's dirty wash. The old man is stropping his razor. The Jews are moving up from under the shadow of the bridge, the days are getting shorter, the tugs are snorting or croaking like bull-frogs, the harbour is jammed with ice cakes. Every chapter of the book which is written in the air thickens the blood; the music of it deafens the wild anxiety of the outer air. Night drops like a boom of thunder, deposits me on the floor of the pedestrian highway leading nowhere eventually, but brightly ringed with gleaming spokes along which there is no turning back nor standing still.

From the shadow of the bridges the mob moves up, closer and closer, like a ring-worm, leaving a huge festering sore that runs from river to river along 14th Street. This line of pus, which runs invisibly from ocean to ocean, and age to age, neatly divides the Gentile world that I knew from the ledger from the Jewish world that I am about to know from life. Between these two worlds, in the middle of the pus line that runs from river to river, stands a little flower pot filled with gardenias. This is as far as the mastodons roam, where the buffaloes can graze no more; here the cunning, abstract world rises like a cliff in the midst of which are buried the fires of the revolution. Each morning I cross the line, with a gardenia in my buttonhole and a fresh volume written in the air. Each morning I wade through a trench filled with vomit to reach the beautiful island of incest; each day the cliff rises up more toweringly, the window-lines straight as a railroad track and the gleam of them even more dazzling than the gleam of polished skulls. Each morning the trench yawns more menacingly.

I should be saying Good Morning now to Tom Jordan, but it hangs there on my lips tremblingly. What morning is this that I should waste in salutation? Is it *good*, this morning of mornings? I am losing the power to distinguish morning from morning. In the ledger is the world of the fast disappearing buffalo; next door the riveters are sewing up the ribs of the coming skyscrapers. Cunning Oriental men with leaden shoes and glass craniums are plotting the paper world of tomorrow, a world made entirely of merchandise which rises box on box like a paper box factory, f. o. b. Canarsie. Today there is still time to attend the funeral of the recent dead; tomorrow there will be no time, for the dead will be left on the spot and woe to him who sheds a tear. This is a good morning for a revolution if only there were machine guns instead of firecrackers. This morning would be a splendid morning if yesterday's morning had not been an utter fiasco. The past is galloping away, the trench widens. Tomorrow is further off than it was yesterday because yesterday's horse has run wild and the men with leaden shoes cannot catch up with him. Between the good of the morning and the morning itself there is a line of pus which blows a stench over yesterday and poisons the morrow. This is a morning so confused that if it were only an old umbrella the slightest sneeze would blow it inside out.

My whole life is stretching out in an unbroken morning. I write from scratch each day. Each day a new world is created, separate and complete, and there I am among the constellations, a god so crazy about himself that he does nothing but sing and fashion new worlds. Meanwhile the old universe is going to pieces. The old universe resembles a bushelling room in which pants are pressed and stains removed and buttons sewn on. The old universe smells like a wet seam receiving the kiss of a red hot iron. Endless alterations and repairs, a sleeve lengthened, a collar lowered, a button moved closer, a new seat put in. But never a new suit of clothes, never a creation. There is the morning world, which starts from scratch each day, and the bushelling room in which things are endlessly altered and repaired. And thus it is with my life through which there runs the sewer of night. All through the night I hear the goose irons hissing as they kiss the wet seams; the rinds of the old universe fall on the floor and the stench of them is sour as vinegar.

The men my father loved were weak and lovable. They went out, each and every one of them, like brilliant stars before the sun. They went out quietly and catastrophically. No shred of them remained – nothing but the memory of their blaze and glory. They flow now inside me like a vast river choked with falling stars. They form the black flowing river which keeps the axis of my world in constant revolution. Out of this black, endless, ever-expanding girdle of night springs the continuous morning which is wasted in creation. Each morning the river overflows its banks, leaving the sleeves and button-holes and all the rinds of a dead universe strewn along the beach where I stand contemplating the ocean of the morning of creation.

Standing there on the ocean's shore I see crazy George leaning against the wall of the undertaker's shop. He has on a funny little cap, a celluloid collar and no tie; he sits on the bench beside the coffin, neither sad nor smiling. He sits there quietly, like an angel that has stepped outside of a Jewish painting. The man in the coffin, whose body is still fresh, is decked out in a modest pepper and salt suit just George's size. He has a collar and tie on and a watch in his vest pocket. George takes him out, undresses him and, while he changes his clothes, lays him on the ice. Not wishing to steal the watch he lays the watch on the ice beside the body. The man is lying on the ice with a celluloid collar around his neck. It is getting dark as George steps out of the undertaker's shop. He has a tie now and a good suit of clothes. At the corner drug store he stops off to buy a joke book which he saw in the window; he memorizes a few jokes standing in the subway. They are Joe Miller's jokes.

At precisely the same hour Tante Melia is sending a Valentine greeting to the relatives. She has a grey uniform on and her hair is parted in the middle. She writes that she is very happy with her new-found friends and that the food is good. She would like them to remember however that she asked for some *Fastnacht Kuchen* the last time – could they send some by mail, by parcel post? She says that there are some lovely petunias growing up around the garbage can outside the big kitchen. She says that she took a long walk on Sunday last and saw lots of reindeer and rabbits and ostriches. She says that her spelling is very poor, but that she was never a good hand at writing anyway. Everybody is very kind and there is lots of work to do. She would like some *Fastnacht Kuchen* as soon as possible, by air-mail if possible. She asked the director to make her some for her birthday but they forgot. She says to send some newspapers because she likes to look at the advertisements. There was a hat she saw once, from Bloomingdale's, she thought, and it was marked down. Maybe they could send the hat along with the *Fastnacht Kuchen*? She thanks them all for the lovely cards they sent her last Christmas – she still remembers them, especially the one with the silver stars on it. Everybody thought it was lovely. She says that she will soon be going to bed and that she will pray for all of them because they were always so good to her.

It's growing slowly, always about the same hour, and I'm standing there gazing at the ocean's mirror. Ice-cold time, neither fast nor slow, but a stiff lying on the ice with a celluloid collar – and if only he had an erection it would be marvellous . . . too marvellous! In the dark hall-way below Tom Jordan is waiting for the old man to descend. He has two blowsers with him and one of them is fixing her garter; Tom Jordan is helping her to fix her garter. Same hour, toward dusk, as I say, Mrs Lawson is walking through the cemetery to look once again at her darling son's grave. Her dear boy Jack, she says, though he was thirty-two when he kicked off seven years ago. They said it was rheumatism of the heart, but the fact is the darling boy had knocked up so many venereal virgins that when they drained the pus from his body he stank like a shit-pump. Mrs Lawson doesn't seem to remember that at all. It's her darling boy Jack and the grave is always tidy; she carries a little piece of chamois in her hand-bag in order to polish the tomb-stone every evening.

Same dusky time, the stiff lying there on the ice, and the old man is standing in a telephone booth with the receiver in one hand and something warm and wet with hair on it in the other. He's calling up to say not to hold the dinner, that he's got to take a customer out and he'll be home late, not to worry. Crazy George is turning the leaves of Joe Miller's Joke Book. Down further, towards Mobile, they're practising the St Louis Blues without a note in front of 'em and people are getting ready to go crazy when they hear it yesterday, today, tomorrow. Everybody's getting ready to get raped, drugged, violated, soused with the new music that seeps out of the sweat of the asphalt. Soon it'll be the same hour everywhere, just by turning a dial or hanging suspended over the earth in a balloon. It's the hour of the kaffee-klatchers sitting around the family table, each one operated on for a different thing, the one with the whiskers and the heavy rings on her fingers having had a harder time than any one else because she could afford it.

It's staggeringly beautiful at this hour when everyone seems to be going his own private way. Love and murder, they're still a few hours apart. Love and murder, I feel it coming with the dusk: new babies coming out of the womb, soft, pink flesh to get tangled up in barbed wire and scream all night long like dead bone a thousand miles from nowhere. Crazy virgins with ice-cold jazz in their veins egging men on to erect new buildings and men with dog collars around their necks wading through the muck up to the eyes so that the czar of electricity will rule the waves. What's in the seed scares the living piss out of me: a brand new world is coming out of the egg and no matter how fast I write the old world doesn't die fast enough. I hear the new machine guns and the millions of bones splintered at once; I see dogs running mad and pigeons dropping with letters tied to their ankles.

*Always merry and bright*, whether north from Delancey Street or south towards the pus line! My two soft hands in the body of the world, ploughing up the warm entrails, arranging and disarranging, cutting them up, sewing them together again. The warm body feeling which the surgeon knows, together with oysters, warts, ulcers, hernias, cancer sprouts, the young kohlrabies, the clips and the forceps, the scissors and tropical growths, the poisons and gases all locked up inside and carefully covered with skin. Out of the leaking mains love gushing like sewer gas: furious love with black gloves and bright bits of garter, love that champs and snorts, love hidden in a barrel and blowing the bung-hole night after night. The men who passed through my father's shop reeked with love: they were warm and winey, weak and indolent, fast yachts trimmed with sex, and when they sailed by me in the night they fumigated my dreams. Standing in the centre of New York I could hear the tinkle of the cow-bells, or, by a turn of the head, I could hear the sweet sweet music of the death-rattle, a red line down the page and on every sleeve a mourning band. By twisting my neck just a little I could stand high above the tallest skyscraper and look down on the ruts left by the huge wheels of modern progress. Nothing was too difficult for me if only it had a little grief and anguish in it. *Chez nous* there were all the organic diseases – and a few of the inorganic. Like rock crystal we spread, from one crime to another. A merry whirl, and in the centre of it my twenty-first year already covered with verdigris.

And when I can remember no more I shall always remember the night I was getting a dose of clap and the old man so stinking drunk he took his friend Tom Jordan to bed with him. Beautiful and touching this – to be out getting a dose of clap when the family honour was at

61

stake, when it was *at par*, you might say. Not to be there for the shindig, with mother and father wrestling on the floor and the broomstick flying. Not to be there in the cold morning light when Tom Jordan is on his knees and begging to be forgiven but not being forgiven even on his knees because the inflexible heart of a Lutheran doesn't know the meaning of forgiveness. Touching and beautiful to read in the paper next morning that about the same hour the night before the pastor who had put in the bowling alley was caught in a dark room with a naked boy on his lap! But what makes it excruciatingly touching and beautiful is this, that not knowing these things, I came home next day to ask permission to marry a woman old enough to be my mother. And when I said 'get married' the old lady picks up the bread knife and goes for me. I remember, as I left the house, that I stopped by the book-case to grab a book. And the name of the book was – *The Birth of Tragedy*. Droll that, what with the broomstick the night before, the bread knife, the dose of clap, the pastor caught red-handed, the dumplings growing cold, the cancer sprouts, et cetera . . . I used to think then that all the tragic events of life were written down in books and that what went on outside was just diluted crap. I thought that a beautiful book was a diseased portion of the brain. I never realized that a whole world could be diseased!

Walking up and down with a package under my arm. A fine bright morning, let's say, and the spittoons all washed and polished. Mumbling to myself, as I step into the Woolworth Building – 'Good morning, Mr Thorndike, fine morning this morning, Mr Thorndike. Are you interested in clothes, Mr Thorndike?' Mr Thorndike is not interested in clothes this morning; he thanks me for calling and throws the card in the waste basket. Nothing daunted I try the American Express Building. 'Good morning, Mr Hathaway, fine morning this morning!' Mr Hathaway doesn't need a good tailor – he's had one for thirty-five years now. Mr Hathaway is a little peeved and damned right he is thinks I to myself stumbling down the stairs. A fine, bright morning, no denying that, and so to take the bad taste out of my mouth and also have a view of the harbour I take the trolley over the bridge and call on a cheapskate by the name of Dyker. Dyker is a busy man. The sort of man who has his lunch sent up and his shoes polished while he eats. Dyker is suffering from a nervous complaint brought on by dry fucking. He says we can make him a pepper and salt suit if we stop dunning him every month. The girl was only sixteen and he didn't want to knock her up. Yes, patch pockets, please!

Besides, he has a wife and three children. Besides, he will be running for judge soon – judge of the Surrogate Court.

Getting towards matinee time. Hop back to New York and drop off at the Burlesk where the usher knows me. The first three rows always filled with judges and politicians. The house is dark and Margie Pennetti is standing on the runway in a pair of dirty white tights. She has the most wonderful ass of any woman on the stage and everybody knows it, herself included. After the show I walk around aimlessly, looking at the movie houses and the Jewish delicatessen stores. Stand awhile in a penny arcade listening to the siren voices coming through the megaphone. Life is just a continuous honeymoon filled with chocolate layer cake and cranberry pie. Put a penny in the slot and see a woman undressing on the grass. Put a penny in the slot and win a set of false teeth. The world is made of new parts every afternoon: the soiled parts are sent to the dry cleaner, the used parts are scrapped and sold for junk.

Walk uptown past the pus line and stroll through the lobbies of the big hotels. If I like I can sit down and watch other people walking through the lobby. Everybody's on the watch. Things are happening all about. The strain of waiting for something to happen is delirious. The elevated rushing by, the taxis honking, the ambulance clanging, the riveters riveting. Bell hops dressed in gorgeous livery looking for people who don't answer to their names. In the golden toilet below men standing in line waiting to take a leak; everything made of plush and marble, the odours refined and pleasant, the flush flushing beautifully. On the sidewalk a stack of newspapers, the headlines still wet with murder, rape, arson, strikes, forgeries, revolution. People stepping over one another to crash the subway. Over in Brooklyn a woman's waiting for me. Old enough to be my mother and she's waiting for me to marry her. The son's got T. B. so bad he can't crawl out of bed any more. Tough titty going up there to her garret to make love while the son's in the next room coughing his lungs out. Besides, she's just getting over an abortion and I don't want to knock her up again – not right away anyhow.

The rush hour! and the subway a free for all Paradise. Pressed up against a woman so tight I can feel the hair on her twat. So tightly glued together my knuckles are making a dent in her groin. She's looking straight ahead, at a microscopic spot just under my right eye. By Canal Street I manage to get my penis where my knuckles were before. The thing's jumping like mad and no matter which way the train jerks she's always in the same position vis-à-vis my dickie. Even when the crowd thins out she stands there with her pelvis thrust forward and her eyes fixed on the miscroscopic spot just under my right eye. At Borough Hall she gets out, without once giving me the eye. I follow her up to the street thinking she might turn round and say hello at least, or let me buy her a frosted chocolate, assuming I could buy one. But no, she's off like an arrow, without turning her head the eighth of an inch. How they do it I don't know. Millions and millions of them every day standing up without underwear and getting a dry fuck. What's the conclusion – a shower? a rub down? Ten to one they fling themselves on the bed and finish the job with their fingers.

Anyway, it's going on towards evening and me walking up and down with an erection fit to burst my fly. The crowd gets thicker and thicker. Everybody's got a newspaper now. The sky's choked with illuminated merchandise every single article of which is guaranteed to be pleasant, healthful, durable, tasty, noiseless, rainproof, imperishable, the *ne plus ultra* without which life would be unbearable were it not for the fact that life is already unbearable because there is no life. Just about the hour when old Henschke is quitting the tailor shop to go to the card club uptown. An agreeable little job on the side which keeps him occupied until two in the morning. Nothing much to do – just take the gentlemen's hats and coats, serve drinks on a little tray, empty the ash trays and keep the match boxes filled. Really a very pleasant job, everything considered. Towards midnight prepare a little snack for the gentlemen, should they so desire it. There are the spittoons, of course, and the toilet bowl. All such gentlemen, however, that there's really nothing to it. And then there's always a little cheese and crackers to nibble on, and sometimes a thimbleful of Port. Now and then a cold veal sandwich for the morrow. Real gentlemen! No gainsaying it. Smoke the best cigars. Even the butts taste good. Really, a very, very pleasant job!

Getting towards dinner time. Most of the tailors have closed shop for the day. A few of them, those who have nothing but brittle old geezers on the books, are waiting to make a try-on. They walk up and down with their hands behind their backs. Everybody has gone except the boss tailor himself, and perhaps the cutter or the bushelman. The boss tailor is wondering if he has to put new chalk marks on again and if the cheque will arrive in time to meet the rent. The cutter is saying to himself – 'why yes, Mr So-and-So, why to be sure . . . yes, I think it should be just a little higher there . . . yes, you're quite right . . . it *is* a little off on the left side . . . yes, we'll have that ready for you in a few days . . . yes, Mr So-and-So . . . yes, yes, yes, yes, yes . . . ' The finished clothes and the unfinished clothes are hanging on the rack; the bolts are neatly stacked on the tables; only the light in the bushelling room is on. Suddenly the telephone rings. Mr So-and-So is on the wire and he can't make it this evening but he would like his tuxedo sent up right away, the one with the new buttons which he selected last week, and he hopes to Christ it doesn't jump off his neck any more. The cutter puts on his hat and coat and runs quickly down the stairs to attend a Zionist meeting in the Bronx. The boss tailor is left to close the shop and switch out all the lights if any were left on by mistake. The boy that he's sending up with the tuxedo right away is himself and it doesn't matter much because he will duck round by the trade entrance and nobody will be the wiser. Nobody looks more like a millionaire than a boss tailor delivering a tuxedo to Mr So-and-So. Spry and spruce, shoes shined, hat cleaned, gloves washed, moustache waxed. They start to look worried only when they sit down for the evening meal. No appetite. No orders today. No cheques. They get so despondent that they fall asleep at ten o'clock and when it's time to go to bed they can't sleep any more.

Walking over the Brooklyn Bridge . . . Is this the world, this walking up and down, these buildings that are lit up, the men and women passing me? I watch their lips moving, the lips of the men and women passing me. What are they talking about – some of them so earnestly? I hate seeing people so deadly serious when I myself am suffering worse than any of them. One life! and there are millions and millions of lives to be lived. So far I haven't had a thing to say about my own life. Not a thing. Must be I haven't got the guts. Ought to go back to the subway, grab a Jane and rape her in the street. Ought to go back to Mr Thorndike in the morning and spit in his face. Ought to stand on Times Square with my pecker in my hand and piss in the gutter. Ought to grab a revolver and fire point-blank into the crowd. The old man's leading the life of Reilly. He and his bosom pals. And I'm walking up and down, turning green with hate and envy. And when I turn in the old woman'll be sobbing fit to break her heart. Can't sleep nights listening to her. I hate her too for sobbing that way. The one robs me, the other punishes me. How can I go into her and comfort her when what I most want to do is to break her heart?

Walking along the Bowery . . . and a beautiful snot-green pasture it is at this hour. Pimps, crooks, cokies, panhandlers, beggars, touts, gunmen, chinks, wops, drunken micks. All gaga for a bit of food and a place to flop. *Walking and walking and walking.* Twenty-one I am, white, born and bred in New York, muscular physique, sound intelligence, good breeder, no bad habits, etc., etc. Chalk it up on the board. Selling out at par. Committed no crime, except to be born here.

In the past every member of our family did something with his hands. I'm the first idle son of a bitch with a glib tongue and a bad heart.

Swimming in the crowd, a digit with the rest. Tailored and retailored. The lights are twinkling – on and off, on and off. Sometimes it's a rubber tyre, sometimes it's a piece of chewing gum. The tragedy of it is that nobody sees the look of desperation on my face. Thousands and thousands of us, and we're passing one another without a look of recognition. The lights jigging like electric needles. The atoms going crazy with light and heat. Conflagration going on behind the glass and nothing burns away. Men breaking their backs, men bursting their brains, to invent a machine which a child will manipulate. If I could only find the hypothetical child who's to run this machine I'd put a hammer in its hands and say: Smash it! Smash it!

*Smash it! Smash it!* That's all I can say. The old man's riding around in an open barouche. I envy the bastard his peace of mind. A bosom pal by his side and a quart of rye under his belt. My toes are blistering with malice. Twenty years ahead of me and this thing growing worse by the hour. It's throttling me. In twenty years there won't be any soft, loveable men waiting to greet me. Every bosom pal that goes now is a buffalo lost and gone for ever. Steel and concrete hedging me in. The pavement getting harder and harder. The new world eating into me, expropriating me. Soon I won't even need a name.

Once I thought there were marvellous things in store for me. Thought I could build a world in the air, a castle of pure white spit that would raise me above the tallest building, between the tangible and the intangible, put me in a space like music where everything collapses and perishes but where I would be immune, great, god-like, holiest of the holies. It was *I* imagined this, *I* the tailor's son! I who was born from a little acorn on an immense and stalwart tree. In the hollow of the acorn even the faintest tremor of the earth reached me: I was part of the great tree, part of the past, with crest and lineage, with pride, *pride*. And when I fell to earth and was buried there I remembered *who* I was, *where* I came from. Now I am lost, *lost*, do you hear? You don't hear? I'm yowling and screaming – don't you hear me? Switch the lights off! Smash the bulbs! Can you hear me now? *Louder!*

you say. *Louder!* Christ, are you making sport of me? Are you deaf, dumb and blind? Must I yank my clothes off? Must I dance on my head?

All right, then! I'm going to dance for you! A merry whirl, brothers, and let her whirl and whirl and whirl! Throw in an extra pair of flannel trousers while you're at it. And don't forget, boys, I dress on the right side. You hear me? Let 'er go! *Always merry and bright!*

# *First Love*

In my mind's eye I can see her today just as vividly as when I first met her, which was in one of the corridors of Eastern District High School (Brooklyn) as she was going from one classroom to another. She was just a little shorter than I, well built, that is to say rather buxom, radiant, bursting with health, head high, glance at once imperious and saucy, concealing a shyness which was disconcerting. She had a warm, generous mouth filled with rather large, dazzling white teeth. But it was her hair and eyes which drew one first. Light golden hair it was, combed up stiff in the form of a conch. A natural blonde such as one seldom sees except in an opera. Her eyes, which were extremely limpid, were full and round. They were a China blue, and they matched her golden hair and her apple-blossom complexion. She was only sixteen, of course, and not very sure of herself, though she seemed to give the impression that she was. She stood out from all the other girls in the school, like someone with blue blood in her veins. Blue blood and icy, I am tempted to say.

That first glance she gave me swept me off my feet. I was not only impressed by her beauty but intimidated as well. How I ever managed to approach her and mumble a few meaningless words I can no longer recall. I know it took weeks after the first encounter to do such a brave thing. I recall vividly how she blushed each time we came within striking distance of one another. Naturally, what conversation we exchanged must have been of a telegraphic nature. She never dropped a word or a phrase that took root in my memory. As I say, these encounters always took place in the corridors, going from one class-room to another. She must have been a class or two behind me, though of the same age. For me, of course, these little nothings were filled with pregnant significance.

It was only after we had graduated from high school that we exchanged a few letters. During the summer holidays she remained at Asbury Park, New Jersey, while I continued my daily drudgery as a clerk in the offices of the Atlas Portland Cement Company. Every evening, on returning from work, I rushed to the mantelpiece over the fireplace, where the mail was always deposited, to see if there was a letter from her. If I received one or two throughout the long vacation season I was lucky. My whole impression of this strange courtship is one of utter frustration. Now and then, rarely, I met her at a dance. Twice, I think, I took her to the theatre. I didn't even possess a photograph of her that I might carry in my wallet and look at secretly.

But I had no need for photographs. Her image was constantly in my mind; her absence was a perpetual torment which served to keep her image alive. I carried her inside me, as it were. Alone, I would often speak to her, either silently or aloud. Often, walking home at night, after having made a tour of her house, I would yell her name aloud, imploringly, as if to beg her to grant me the favour of an audience from on high. She was always up there somewhere, high above me, like some goddess whom I had discovered and regarded as my very own. It was I, idiot that I was, who prevented her from descending to the level of other mortals. This, to be sure, had been determined from the instant I met her; I had no choice.

The strange thing is that she never gave me any indication of being hostile or indifferent. Who knows – perhaps she for her part was pleading silently with me to show her a more human attention, to woo her like a man, to take her, forcibly if need be.

Perhaps two or three times a year we would come together at a party, one of those teenage affairs which last until dawn with singing and dancing and silly games such as 'Kiss the Pillow', or 'Post Office', the game which permits one to call for the creature of one's choice and embrace her furtively in a dark room. Even then, when we might have kissed and embraced unrestrainedly, our shyness prevented us from sharing anything but the most innocent pleasure. If I danced with her I trembled from head to foot and usually stumbled over my own feet, much to her embarrassment.

All I could do was to play the piano – play and jealously watch her dance with my friends. She never came behind me to put her arms around me and whisper some silly nothing. After such evenings I would lie abed and gnash my teeth, or weep like a fool, or pray to a God I no longer believed in, beg Him to have me find favour in her eyes.

And all throughout these five or six years she remained what she had been from the first – a flaming image. I knew nothing of her mind, her hopes or dreams, her aspirations. She was a complete blank on which I fatuously inscribed what I wished. No doubt I was the same to her.

Finally there came the day I said goodbye to her. The day I was leaving for the Wild West, to become a cowboy, so I thought. I went to her home and timidly rang the bell. (It was but the second or third time I had ventured to ring her doorbell.) She came to the door looking thinner, older, more careworn than ever I had seen her.

We were twenty-one now, and I had been going with 'the widow' for two or three years. That was why I was running off to the Far West – to cure myself of a fatal infatuation. Instead of inviting me in, she stepped outdoors and escorted me to the gate which opened onto the sidewalk, and there we stood for perhaps fifteen or twenty minutes exchanging pointless remarks. I had, of course, warned her of my coming and related briefly my plans for the future. What I omitted to say was that I would one day send for her – and all that nonsense. Whatever I may have secretly hoped, by now I knew that the situation was irremediable. She knew that I loved her – everyone knew it – but the affair with 'the widow' had put me definitely out of her pale. It was something she could not understand, much less forgive.

What a sorry figure I must have cut! Even then, had I been courageous and resolute enough, I might have won her. At least, so it seemed to me, reading the pained, lost expression in her eyes. (Yet rambling on fatuously, blindly, about the glorious Golden West.) Even though I felt it might be the last time I would see her I lacked the courage to fling my arms around her and give her a last, passionate kiss. Instead, we shook hands politely, mumbled some awkward words of adieu, and off I walked.

Though I never once turned my head, I had the firm conviction that she was still standing at the gate, following me with her eyes. Did she wait until I had rounded the corner before rushing to her room, flinging herself on the bed, and sobbing fit to break her heart? I will never know, neither in this world nor the next.

About a year later, when I had returned from the West, sadder and wiser, to return to the arms of 'the widow' from whom I had run away, we met again by chance. The last meeting. It was on a streetcar, and fortunately I was with an old chum who knew her well, else I would have bolted. After a few words my friend jokingly suggested that she invite us up to her flat. She was married now and, incredible as it may seem, was living just back of the house in which the widow lived. We tripped up the high stoop and entered her apartment. She took us from one room to another, finishing with the bedroom. Then, in her embarrassment, she let slip an idiotic phrase which went through me like a knife. 'This,' she said, pointing to the big double bed, 'is where we sleep.' With those words it was as if an iron curtain fell between us.

It was the end for me. And yet not an end. In all the years which have since elapsed she remains the woman I loved and lost, the unattainable one. In her China-blue eyes, so cold and inviting, so round and mirror-like, I see myself for ever and ever as the ridiculous man, the lonely soul, the wanderer, the restless frustrated artist, the man in love with love, always in search of the absolute, always seeking the unattainable. Behind the iron curtain her image remains fresh and vivid as of yore, and nothing, it seems, can tarnish it or cause it to fade away.

# From *The Books in My Life*

One of the first things I associate with the reading of books is the struggle I waged to obtain them. Not to own them, mind you, but to lay hands on them. From the moment the passion took hold of me I encountered nothing but obstacles. The books I wanted, at the public library, were always out. And of course I never had the money to buy them. To get permission from the library in my neighbourhood – I was then eighteen or nineteen years of age – to borrow such a 'demoralizing' work as *The Confession of a Fool*, by Strindberg, was just impossible. In those days the books which young people were prohibited from reading were decorated with stars – one, two or three – according to the degree of immorality attributed to them. I suspect this procedure still obtains. I hope so, for I know of nothing better calculated to whet one's appetite than this stupid sort of classification and prohibition.

In books for children, which influence us the most – I mean fairy tales, legends, myths, allegories – humour is, of course, woefully absent. Horror and tragedy, lust and cruelty, seem to be the cardinal ingredients. But it is through the reading of these books that the imaginative faculty is nourished. As we grow older, fantasy and imagination become increasingly rare to find. One is carried along on a treadmill which grows increasingly monotonous. The mind becomes so dulled that it takes a truly extraordinary book to rout one out of a state of indifference or apathy.

With childhood reading there is a factor of significance which we are prone to forget – the physical ambiance of the occasion. How distinctly, in after years, one remembers the feel of a favourite book, the typography, the binding, the illustrations, and so on. How easily one can localize the time and place of a first reading. Some books are associated with illness, some with bad weather, some with punishment, some with reward. In the remembrance of these events the inner and outer worlds fuse. These readings are distinctly 'events' in one's life.

There is one thing, moreover, which differentiates the reading done in childhood from later reading, and that is the absence of choice. The books one reads as a child are thrust upon one. Lucky the child who has wise parents! So powerful, however, is the dominion of certain books that even the ignorant parent can hardly avoid them. What child has not read *Sinbad the Sailor*, *Jason and the Golden Fleece*, *Ali Baba and the Forty Thieves*, the *Fairy Tales* of Grimm and Andersen, *Robinson Crusoe*, *Gulliver's Travels* and such like.

Who also, I ask, has not enjoyed the uncanny thrill which comes later in life on rereading his early favourites? Only recently, after the lapse of almost fifty years, I reread Henty's *Lion of the North*. What an experience! As a boy, Henty was my favourite author. Every Christmas my parents would give me eight or ten of his books. I must have read every blessed one before I was fourteen. Today, and I regard this as phenomenal, I can pick up any book of his and get the same fascinating pleasure I got as a boy. He does not seem to be 'talking down' to his reader. He seems, rather, to be on intimate terms with him. Everyone knows, I presume, that Henty's books are historical romances. To the lads of my day they were vitally important, because they gave us our first perspective of world history. *The Lion of the North*, for instance, is about Gustavus Adolphus and the Thirty Years' War. In it appears that strange, enigmatic figure – Wallenstein. When, just the other day, I came upon the pages dealing with Wallenstein, it was as though I had read them only a few months ago. As I remarked in a letter to a friend, after closing the book, it was in these pages about Wallenstein that I first encountered the words 'destiny' and 'astrology'. Pregnant words, for a boy, at any rate.

I find more and more that the books I long to read again are the ones I read in childhood and early youth. I mentioned Henty, bless his name! There are others – like Rider Haggard, Marie Corelli, Bulwer-Lytton, Eugene Sue, James Fenimore Cooper, Sienkiewicz, Ouida (*Under Two Flags*), Mark Twain (*Huckleberry Finn* and *Tom Sawyer* particularly). Imagine not having read any of these men since boyhood! It seems incredible. As for Poe, Jack London, Hugo, Conan Doyle, Kipling, it matters little if I never look at their works again.

I should also like very much to reread those books which I used to read aloud to my grandfather as he sat on his tailor's bench in our old home in the Fourteenth Ward in Brooklyn. One of these, I recall, was about our great 'hero' (for a day) – Admiral Dewey. Another was about Admiral Farragut – probably about the battle of Mobile Bay, if there ever was such an engagement. Regarding this book I recall now that, in writing the chapter called 'My Dream of Mobile' in *The Air Conditioned Nightmare*, I was actively aware of this tale of Farragut's heroic exploits. Without a doubt, my whole conception of Mobile was coloured by this book I had read fifty years ago. But it was through the book on Admiral Dewey that I became acquainted with my first live hero, who was not Dewey but our sworn enemy, Aguinaldo, the Filipino rebel. My mother had hung Dewey's portrait, floating above the battleship Maine, over my bed. Aguinaldo, whose likeness is now dim in my mind, links up physically with that strange photograph of Rimbaud taken in Abyssinia, the one wherein he stands in prison-like garb on the banks of a stream. Little did my parents realize, in handing me our precious hero, Admiral Dewey, that they were nurturing in me the seeds of a rebel. Beside Dewey and Teddy Roosevelt, Aguinaldo stands out like a colossus. He was the first Enemy Number One to cross my horizon. I still revere his name, just as I still revere the names of Robert E. Lee and Toussaint L'Ouverture, the great Negro liberator who fought Napoleon's picked men and worsted them.

In this vein how can I forbear mentioning Carlyle's *Heroes and Hero Worship?* Or Emerson's *Representative Men?* And why not make room for another early idol, John Paul Jones? In Paris, thanks to Blaise Cendrars, I learned what is not given in history books or biographies concerning John Paul Jones. The spectacular story of this man's life is one of those projected books which Cendrars has not yet written and probably never will. The reason is simple. Following the trail of this adventurous American, Cendrars amassed such a wealth of material that he was swamped by it. In the course of his travels, searching for rare documents and buying up rare books relating to John Paul Jones' myriad adventures, Cendrars confessed that he had spent more than tenfold the amount given him by the publishers in advance royalties. Following John Paul Jones' traces, Cendrars had made a veritable Odyssean voyage. He confessed finally that he would one day either write a huge tome on the subject or a very thin book, something which I understand perfectly.

The first person to whom I ventured to read aloud was my grandfather. Not that he encouraged it! I can still hear him saying to my mother that she would regret putting all those books in my hands. He was right. My mother did regret it bitterly, later. It was my own mother, incidentally, whom I can scarcely recall ever seeing with a book in her hand, who told me one day when I was reading *The Fifteen*

*Decisive Battles of the World* that she had read that book years ago herself – in the toilet. I was flabbergasted. Not that she had admitted to reading in the toilet, but that it should have been that book, of all books, which she had read there.

Reading aloud to my boyhood friends, particularly to Joey and Tony, my earliest friends, was an eye-opener for me. I discovered early in life what some discover only much later, to their disgust and chagrin, namely, that reading aloud to people can put them to sleep. Either my voice was monotonous, either I read poorly, or the books I chose were the wrong sort. Inevitably my audience went to sleep on me. Which did not discourage me, incidentally, from continuing the practice. Nor did these experiences alter the opinion I had of my little friends. No, I came quietly to the conclusion that books were not for everyone. I still hold to that view. The last thing on earth I would counsel is to make everyone learn to read. If I had *my* way, I would first see to it that a boy learned to be a carpenter, a builder, a gardener, a hunter, a fisherman. The practical things first, by all means, then the luxuries. And books *are* luxuries. Of course I expect the normal youngster to dance and sing from infancy. And to play games. I would abet these tendencies with might and main. But the reading of books can wait.

To play games . . . Ah, there is a chapter of life in a category all by itself. I mean, primarily, out-of-door games – the games which poor children play in the streets of the big city. I pass up the temptation to expand on this subject lest I write another, very different, kind of book!

However, boyhood is a subject I never tire of. Neither the remembrance of the wild and glorious games we played by day and night in the streets, nor the characters with whom I hobnobbed and whom I sometimes deified, as boys are prone to do. All my experiences I shared with my comrades, including the experience of reading. Time and again, in my writings, I have made mention of the amazing acumen we displayed in discussing the fundamental problems of life. Subjects such as sin, evil, reincarnation, good government, ethics and morality, the nature of the deity, Utopia, life on other planets – these were food and drink to us. My real education was begun in the street, in empty lots on cold November days, or on street corners at night, frequently with our skates on. Naturally, one of the things we were forever discussing was books, the books we were then reading and which we were not even supposed to know about. It sounds extravagant to say so, I know, but it does seem to me that only the great interpreters of literature can rival the boy in the street when it comes to extracting the flavour and essence of a book. In my humble opinion, the boy is much nearer to understanding Jesus than the priest, much closer to Plato, in his views on government, than the political figures of this world.

During this golden period of boyhood there was suddenly injected into my world of books a whole library, housed in a beautiful walnut bookcase with glass doors and movable shelves, of boys' books. They were from the collection of an Englishman, Isaac Walker, my father's predecessor, who had the distinction of being one of the first merchant tailors of New York. As I review them now in my mind, these books were all handsomely bound, the titles embossed usually in gold, as were the cover designs. The paper was thick and glossy, the type bold and clear. In short, these books were de luxe in every respect. Indeed, so elegantly forbidding was their appearance, that it took some time before I dared tackle them.

What I am about to relate is a curious thing. It has to do with my deep and mysterious aversion for everything English. I believe I am telling the truth when I say that the cause of this antipathy is deeply connected with the reading of Isaac Walker's little library. How profound was my disgust, on becoming acquainted with the contents of these books, may be judged by the fact that I have completely forgotten the titles. Just one lingers in my memory, and even this one I am not positive is correct: *A Country Squire*. The rest is a blank. The nature of my reaction I can put in a few words. For the first time in my life I sensed the meaning of melancholy and morbidity. All these elegant books seemed wrapped in a veil of thick fog. England became for me a land shrouded in murky obscurity, in evil, cruelty and boredom. Not one ray of light issued from these musty tomes. It was the primordial slime, on all levels. Senseless and irrational though it be, this picture of England and the English lasted well into middle life, until, to be honest, I visited England and had the opportunity of meeting Englishmen on their own native heath. (My first impression of London, I must however admit, corresponded closely to my boyhood picture of it; it is an impression which has never been wholly dissipated.)

When I came to Dickens, these first impressions were, of course, corroborated and strengthened. I have very few *pleasant* recollections connected with the reading of Dickens. His books were sombre, terrifying in parts, and usually boring. Of them all, *David Copperfield* stands out as the most enjoyable, the most nearly human, according to my conception (then) of the word. Fortunately, there was one book which had been given me by a good aunt, which served as a corrective to this morose view of England and the English people. The title of this book, if I remember rightly, was *A Boy's History of England*, by Ellis. I remember distinctly the pleasure this book gave me. There were, to be sure, the Henty books, which I was also reading, or had read just a little earlier, and from which I gained a wholly different notion of the English world. But the Henty books were concerned with historical exploits, whereas the books from Isaac Walker's collection dealt with the immediate past. Years later, when I came upon Thomas Hardy's works, I relived these boyish reactions – the bad ones, I mean. Sombre, tragic, full of mishaps and accidental or coincidental misfortunes, Hardy's books caused me once again to adjust my 'human' picture of the world. In the end I was obliged to pass judgment on Hardy. For all the air of realism which permeated his books, I had to admit to myself that they were not 'true to life'. I wanted my pessimism 'straight'.

And now, for no reason, unless it be the afterglow of boyhood reminiscences, there leaps to mind the name of Rider Haggard. *There* was a writer who had me in his thrall! The contents of his books are vague and fuzzy. At best I can recall only a few titles: *She, Ayesha, King Solomon's Mines, Allan Quatermain*. Yet when I think of them I get the same shivers as I do when I relive the meeting between Stanley and Livingstone in darkest Africa. I am certain that when I reread him, as I expect to do shortly, I shall find, as I did with Henty, that my memory will become amazingly alive and fecund.

# From *The World of Sex*

And there was sex. But what *was* sex? Like the deity, it was omnipresent. It pervaded everything. Perhaps the whole universe of the past, to give an image for it, was none other than a mythological monster from which the world, my world, had been whelped, but which failed to disappear with the act of creation, remaining below, supporting the world (and its own self) upon its back.

And now I must break off, since all this has served only as a reminder, to speak of the first little cunt I ever examined.

I was about five or six at the time, and the incident took place in a cellar. The after-image, which solidified at the appropriate time in the form of an incongruity, I labelled 'the man in the iron mask'. Just a few years ago, in riffling the pages of a book containing reproductions of primitive masks, I stumbled upon a womb-like mask which, when one lifted the flap, revealed the head of a full-grown man. Perhaps the shock of seeing this fullblown head peering from the womb was the first genuine response I had had to the question which voiced itself that instant long ago when I had my first serious look at a vagina. (In the *Tropic of Cancer*, it may be remembered, I portrayed a companion who had never recovered from this obsession. He is still, I believe, prying open one cunt after another in order, as he puts it to himself, to get at the mystery it holds.)

It was a hairless world I gazed upon. The very absence of hair, so I now think, served to stimulate the imagination, helped populate the arid region which surrounded the place of mystery. We were concerned less with what lay within than with the future vegetal décor which we imagined would one day beautify this strange waste land. Depending on the time of the year, the age of the players, the place, as well as other more complicated factors, the genitals of certain little creatures seemed as variegated, when I think of it now, as the strange entities which people the imaginative minds of occultists. What presented itself to our impressionable minds was a nameless phantasmagoria swarming with images which were real, tangible, thinkable, yet nameless, for they were unconnected with the world of experience wherein everything has a name, a place and a date. Thus it was that certain little girls were referred to as possessing (hidden beneath their skirts) such queer effects as magnolias, cologne bottles, velvet buttons, rubber mice . . . God only knows what. That every little girl had a crack was of course common knowledge. Now and then rumour had it that such and such a one had no crack at all; of another it might be said that she was a 'morphodite'. Morphodite was a strange and frightening term which no one could clearly define. Sometimes it implied the notion of double sex, sometimes other things, to wit, that where the crack ought to be there was a cloven hoof or a row of warts. *Better not ask to see it!* – that was the dominant thought.

A curious thing about this period was the conviction which obtained among us that some of our little playmates were definitely bad, i.e. incipient whores or sluts. Some girls already possessed a vile vocabulary pertaining to this mysterious realm. Some would do forbidden things, if given a little gift or a few coppers. There were others, I must add, who were looked upon as angels, nothing less. They were that angelic, in fact, that none of us ever thought of them as owning a crack. These angelic creatures didn't even pee.

I make mention of these early attempts at characterization because later in life, having witnessed the development of some of the 'loose ones', I was impressed by the accuracy of our observations. Occasionally one of the angels also fell into the gutter, and remained there. Usually, however, they met a different fate. Some led an unhappy life either through marrying the wrong man or not marrying at all, some were stricken with mysterious illnesses, others were crucified by their parents. Many whom we had dubbed sluts turned out to be excellent human beings, jolly, flexible, generous, human to the core, though often a bit the worse for wear.

With adolescence another kind of curiosity developed, namely, the desire to find out how 'the thing' functioned. Girls of ten or twelve were often induced to adopt the most grotesque poses, in order to demonstrate how they made pipi. The skilled ones were reputed to be able to lie on the floor and piss up to the ceiling. Some were already being accused of using candles – or broomsticks. The conversation, when it got round to this topic, became rather thick and complicated; it was tinged with a flavour strangely reminiscent of the atmosphere which invested the early Greek schools of philosophy. Logic, I mean, played a greater role than empiricism. The desire to explore with the naked eye was subordinated to a greater urge, one which I now realize was none other than the need to talk it out, to discuss the subject *ad nauseam*. The intellect, alas, had already begun to exact its tribute. How 'the thing' functioned was smothered by the deeper query – why? With the birth of the questioning faculty sorrow set in. Our world, hitherto so natural, so marvellous, slipped its moorings. Henceforth nothing was absolutely so any more: everything could be proved – and disproved. The hair which now began to sprout on the sacred Mons Venus was repellent. Even the little angels were breaking out in pimples. And there were some who were bleeding between the legs.

Masturbation was far more interesting. In bed, or in the warm bath, one could imagine himself lying with the Queen of Sheba, or with a burlesque queen whose tantalizing body, featured everywhere, infected one's every thought. One wondered what these women pictured with skirts whirling above their heads did when they appeared before the footlights. Some said that they brazenly removed every stitch of their gorgeous costumes and stood holding their boobies invitingly – until the sailors made a stampede for the stage. Often, so it was said, the curtain had to be rung down and the police summoned.

Something was wrong with the girls we used to play with. They weren't the same any more. In fact, everything was changing, and for the worse. As for the boys, they were being farmed out one after another. Schooling was a luxury reserved for the children of the rich. Out there, 'in the world', from all reports, it was nothing but a slave market. Yes, the world *was* crumbling about us. *Our* world.

And then there were places known as penitentiaries, reformatories, homes for wayward girls, insane asylums, and so on.

Before things were to go utterly to smash, however, a wonderful event might occur. A party, no less. Where someone very precious, someone hardly more than a name, was certain to make an appearance.

To me these 'events' now seem like those fabulous balls which precede a revolution. One looked forward to being violently happy, happier than one had ever been before, yet one also had the presentiment that some untoward thing would happen, something which would affect one's whole life. A deal of sly whispering always surrounded the coming event. It went on among parents, older brothers and sisters, and among the neighbours. Every one seemed to know more about one's sacred emotional life than was warranted. The whole neighbourhood suddenly seemed abnormally interested in one's slightest doings. One was watched, spied upon, talked about behind one's back. Such great emphasis was put on age. The way people said, 'He's fifteen now!' entrained the most embarrassing implications. It all seemed like a sinister puppet show which the elders were staging, a spectacle in which we would be the ridiculous performers there to be laughed at, mocked, goaded to say and do unaccountable things.

After weeks of anxiety the day would finally arrive. The girl too, at the last moment. Just when everything augured well, when all it needed – for what? – was a word, a look, a gesture, one discovered to his dismay that he had grown dumb, that his feet were rooted to the spot on which they had been planted ever since entering the place. Maybe once during the whole long evening did the precious one offer the slightest token of recognition. To move close to her, to brush her skirt, inhale the fragrance of her breath, what a difficult, what a monumental feat! The others appeared to move at will, freely. All that he and she seemed capable of was to slowly gravitate about such uninteresting objects as the piano, the umbrella stand, the bookcase. Only by accident did they seem destined now and then to converge upon one another. Even so, even when all the mysterious, supercharged forces in the room seemed to be pushing them toward each other, something always intervened to make them drift apart. To make it worse, the parents behaved in the most unfeeling fashion, pushing and jostling couples about, gesticulating like goats, making rude remarks, asking pointed questions. In short, acting like idiots.

The evening would come to an end with a great handshaking all around. Some kissed each other goodbye. The bold ones! Those who lacked the courage to behave with such abandon, those who cared, who felt deeply, in other words, were lost in the shuffle. No one noticed their discomfiture. They were non-existent.

Time to go. The streets were empty. He starts walking homeward. Not the slightest trace of fatigue. Elated, though nothing had really happened. Indeed, it had been an utter fiasco, the party. But she had come! And he had feasted his eyes on her the whole evening long. Once he had almost touched her hand. Yes, think of that! *Almost!* Weeks may pass, months perhaps, before their paths cross again. (What if her parents took it into their heads to move to another city? Such things happen.) He tries to fix it in his memory – the way she cast her eyes, the way she talked (to others), the way she threw her head back in laughter, the way her dress clung to her slender figure. He goes through it all piece by piece, moment by moment, from the time she entered and nodded to someone behind him, not seeing him, or not recognizing him perhaps. (Or had she been too shy to respond to his eager glance?) The sort of girl who never revealed her true feelings. A mysterious and elusive creature. How little she knew, how little anyone knew, the oceanic depths of emotion which engulfed him!

To be in love. To be utterly alone . . .

Thus it begins . . . the sweetest and the bitterest sorrow that one can know. The hunger, the loneliness that precedes initiation.

In the loveliest red apple there is hidden a worm. Slowly, relentlessly, the worm eats the apple away. Until there is nothing left but the worm.

And the core, that too? No, the core of the apple lingers, even if only as idea. That every apple has a core, is this not sufficient to counterbalance all uncertainty, all doubt and misgiving? What matter the world, what matter the suffering and death of untold millions, what matter if everything goes to pot – so long as *she*, the heart and core, remains! Even if he is never to see her again he is free to think about her, speak to her in dream, love her, love her from afar, love her for ever and ever. No one can deny him that. No, no one.

# Part II

# The New York Years

# From *Tropic of Capricorn*

It is customary to blame everything on the war. I say the war had nothing to do with me, with my life. At a time when others were getting themselves comfortable berths I was taking one miserable job after another, and never enough in it to keep body and soul together. Almost as quickly as I was hired I was fired. I had plenty of intelligence but I inspired distrust. Wherever I went I fomented discord – not because I was idealistic but because I was like a searchlight exposing the stupidity and futility of everything. Besides, I wasn't a good ass-licker. That marked me, no doubt. People could tell at once when I asked for a job that I really didn't give a damn whether I got it or not. And of course I generally didn't get it. But after a time the mere looking for a job became an activity, a pastime, so to speak. I would go in and ask for most anything. It was a way of killing time – no worse, as far as I could see, than work itself. I was my own boss and I had my own hours, but unlike other bosses I entrained only my own ruin, my own bankruptcy. I was not a corporation or a trust or a state or a federation or a polity of nations – I was more like God, if anything.

This went on from about the middle of the war until . . . well, until one day I was trapped. Finally the day came when I did desperately want a job. I needed it. Not having another minute to lose, I decided that I would take the last job on earth, that of messenger boy. I walked into the employment bureau of the telegraph company – the Cosmodemonic Telegraph Company of North America – towards the close of the day, prepared to go through with it. I had just come from the public library and I had under my arm some fat books on economics and metaphysics. To my great amazement I was refused the job.

The guy who turned me down was a little runt who ran the switchboard. He seemed to take me for a college student, though it was clear enough from my application that I had long left school. I had even honoured myself on the application with a PhD degree from Columbia University. Apparently that passed unnoticed, or else was suspiciously regarded by this runt who had turned me down. I was furious, the more so because for once in my life I was in earnest. Not only that, but I had swallowed my pride, which in certain peculiar ways is rather large. My wife of course gave me the usual leer and sneer. I had done it as a gesture, she said. I went to bed thinking about it, still smarting, getting angrier and angrier as the night wore on. The fact that I had a wife and child to support didn't bother me so much; people didn't offer you jobs because you had a family to support, that much I understood only too well. No, what rankled was that they had rejected *me*, Henry V. Miller, a competent, superior individual who had asked for the lowest job in the world. That burned me up. I couldn't get over it. In the morning I was up bright and early, shaved, put on my best clothes and hot-footed it to the subway. I went immediately to the main offices of the telegraph company . . . up to the 25th floor or wherever it was that the president and the vice-presidents had their cubicles. I asked to see the president. Of course the president was either out of town or too busy to see me, but wouldn't I care to see the vice-president, or his secretary rather. I saw the vice-president's secretary, an intelligent, considerate sort of chap, and I gave him an earful. I did it adroitly, without too much heat, but letting him understand all the while that I wasn't to be put out of the way so easily.

When he picked up the telephone and demanded the general manager I thought it was just a gag, that they were going to pass me around like that from one to the other until I'd get fed up. But the moment I heard him talk I changed my opinion. When I got to the general manager's office, which was in another building uptown, they were waiting for me. I sat down in a comfortable leather chair and accepted one of the big cigars that were thrust forward. This individual seemed at once to be vitally concerned about the matter. He wanted me to tell him all about it, down to the last detail, his big hairy ears cocked to catch the least crumb of information which would justify something or other which was formulating itself inside his dome. I realized that by some accident I had really been instrumental in doing him a service. I let him wheedle it out of me to suit his fancy, observing all the time which way the wind was blowing. And as the talk progressed I noticed that he was warming up to me more and more. At last some one was showing a little confidence in me! That was all I required to get started on one of my favourite lines. For, after years of job hunting I had naturally become quite adept; I knew not only what *not* to say, but I knew also what to imply, what to insinuate. Soon the assistant general manager was called in and asked to listen to my story. By this time I knew what the story was. I understood that

Hymie – 'that little kike', as the general manager called him – had no business pretending that he was the employment manager. Hymie had usurped his prerogative, that much was clear. It was also clear that Hymie was a Jew and that Jews were not in good odour with the general manager, nor with Mr Twilliger, the vice-president, who was a thorn in the general manager's side.

Perhaps it was Hymie, 'the dirty little kike', who was responsible for the high percentage of Jews on the messenger force. Perhaps Hymie was really the one who was doing the hiring at the employment office – at Sunset Place, they called it. It was an excellent opportunity, I gathered, for Mr Clancy, the general manager, to take down a certain Mr Burns who, he informed me, had been the employment manager for some thirty years now and who was evidently getting lazy on the job.

The conference lasted several hours. Before it was terminated Mr Clancy took me aside and informed me that he was going to make *me* the boss of the Works. Before putting me into office, however, he was going to ask me as a special favour, and also as a sort of apprenticeship which would stand me in good stead, to work as a special messenger. I would receive the salary of employment manager, but it would be paid me out of a separate account. In short I was to float from office to office and observe the way affairs were conducted by all and sundry. I was to make a little report from time to time as to how things were going. And once in a while, so he suggested, I was to visit him at his home on the qt and have a little chat about the conditions in the hundred and one branches of the Cosmodemonic Telegraph Company in New York City. In other words I was to be a spy for a few months and after that I was to have the run of the joint. Maybe they'd make me a general manager too one day, or a vice-president. It was a tempting offer, even if it was wrapped up in a lot of horse shit. I said Yes.

In a few months I was sitting at Sunset Place hiring and firing like a demon. It was a slaughter-house, so help me God. The thing was senseless from the bottom up. A waste of men, material and effort. A hideous farce against a backdrop of sweat and misery. But just as I had accepted the spying so I accepted the hiring and firing and all that went with it. I said Yes to everything. If the vice-president decreed that no cripples were to be hired I hired no cripples. If the vice-president said that all messengers over forty-five were to be fired without notice I fired them without notice. I did everything they instructed me to do, but in such a way that they had to pay for it.

When there was a strike I folded my arms and waited for it to blow over. But I first saw to it that it cost them a good penny. The whole system was so rotten, so inhuman, so lousy, so hopelessly corrupt and complicated, that it would have taken a genius to put any sense or order into it, to say nothing of human kindness or consideration. I was up against the whole rotten system of American labour, which is rotten at both ends. I was the fifth wheel on the wagon and neither side had any use for me, except to exploit me. In fact, everybody was being exploited – the president and his gang by the unseen powers, the employees by the officials, and so on and around, in and out and through the whole works. From my little perch at 'Sunset Place' I had a bird's eye view of the whole American society. It was like a page out of the telephone book. Alphabetically, numerically, statistically, it made sense. But when you looked at it up close, when you examined the pages separately, or the parts separately, when you examined one lone individual and what constituted him, examined the air he breathed, the life he led, the chances he risked, you saw something so foul and degrading, so low, so miserable, so utterly hopeless and senseless, that it was worse than looking into a volcano. You could see the whole American life – economically, politically, morally, spiritually, artistically, statistically, pathologically. It looked like a grand chancre on a worn-out cock. It looked worse than that, really, because you couldn't even see anything resembling a cock any more. Maybe in the past this thing had life, did produce something, did at least give a moment's pleasure, a moment's thrill. But looking at it from where I sat it looked rottener than the wormiest cheese. The wonder was that the stench of it didn't carry 'em off . . . I'm using the past tense all the time, but of course it's the same now, maybe even a bit worse. At least now we're getting it full stink.

By the time Valeska arrived on the scene I had hired several army corps of messengers. My office at Sunset Place was like an open sewer, and it stank like one. I had dug myself into the first line trench and I was getting it from all directions at once. To begin with, the man I had ousted died of a broken heart a few weeks after my arrival. He held out just long enough to break me in and then he croaked. Things happened so fast that I didn't have a chance to feel guilty. From the moment I arrived at the office it was one long uninterrupted pandemonium. An hour before my arrival – I was always late – the place was already jammed with applicants. I had to elbow my way up the stairs and literally force my way in to get there. Hymie was worse off than I because he was tied to the barricade. Before I could take my hat off I had to answer a dozen telephone calls. There were three telephones on my desk and they all rang at once. They were bawling the piss out of me before I had even sat down to work. There wasn't even time to take a crap – until five or six in the afternoon. Hymie was worse off than I because he was tied to the switchboard. He sat there from eight in the morning, until six, moving waybills around. A waybill was a messenger loaned by one office to another office for the day or a part of the day. None of the hundred and one offices ever had a full staff; Hymie had to play chess with the waybills while I worked like a madman to plug up the gaps. If by a miracle I succeeded in a day of filling all the vacancies, the next morning would find the situation exactly the same – or worse. Perhaps twenty per cent of the force were steady; the rest was driftwood. The steady ones drove the new ones away. The steady ones earned forty to fifty dollars a week, sometimes sixty or seventy-five, sometimes as much as a hundred dollars a week, which is to say that they earned far more than the clerks and often more than their own managers. As for the new ones, they found it difficult to earn ten dollars a week. Some of them worked an hour and quit, often throwing a batch of telegrams in the garbage can or down the sewer. And whenever they quit they wanted their pay immediately, which was impossible, because in the complicated bookkeeping which ruled no one could say what a messenger had earned until at least ten days later. In the beginning I invited the applicant to sit down beside me and I explained everything to him in detail. I did that until I lost my voice. Soon I learned to save my strength for the grilling that was necessary. In the first place, every other boy was a born liar, if not a crook to boot. Many of them had already been hired and fired a number of times. Some found it an excellent way to find another job, because their duty brought them to hundreds of offices which normally they would never have set foot in. Fortunately McGovern, the old trusty who guarded the door and handed out the application blanks, had a camera eye. And then there were the big ledgers behind me, in which there was a record of every applicant who had ever passed through the mill. The ledgers were very much like a police record; they were full of red ink marks, signifying this or that delinquency. To judge from the evidence I was in a tough spot. Every other name involved a theft, a fraud, a brawl, or dementia or perversion or idiocy. 'Be careful – so-and-so is an epileptic!' 'Don't hire this man – he's a nigger!' 'Watch out – X has been in Dannemora – or else in Sing Sing.'

If I had been a stickler for etiquette nobody would ever have been hired. I had to learn quickly, and not from the records or from those about me, but from experience. There were a thousand and one details by which to judge an applicant: I had to take them all in at once, and quickly, because in one short day, even if you are as fast as Jack Robinson, you can only hire so many and no more. And no matter how many I hired it was never enough. The next day it would begin all over again. Some I knew would last only a day, but I had to hire them just the same. The system was wrong from start to finish, but it was not my place to criticize the system. It was mine to hire and fire. I was in the centre of a revolving disk which was whirling so fast that nothing could stay put. What was needed was a mechanic, but according to the logic of the higher-ups there was nothing wrong with the mechanism, everything was fine and dandy except that things were temporarily out of order. And things being temporarily out of order brought on epilepsy, theft, vandalism, perversion, niggers, Jews, whores and whatnot – sometimes strikes and lockouts. Whereupon, according to this logic, you took a big broom and you swept the stable clean, or you took clubs and guns and you beat sense into the poor idiots who were suffering from the illusion that things were fundamentally wrong. It was good now and then to talk of God, or to have a little community sing – maybe even a bonus was justifiable now and then, that is when things were getting too terribly bad for words. But on the whole, the important thing was to keep hiring and firing; as long as there were men and ammunition we were to advance, to keep mopping up the trenches. Meanwhile Hymie kept taking cathartic pills – enough to blow out his rear end if he had had a rear end, but he hadn't one any more, he only imagined he was taking a crap, he only imagined he was shitting on his can. Actually the poor bugger was in a trance. There were a hundred and one offices to look after and each one had a staff of messengers which was mythical, if not hypothetical, and whether the messengers were real or unreal, tangible or intangible, Hymie had to shuffle them about from morning to night while I plugged up the holes, which was also imaginary because who could say when a recruit had been dispatched to an office whether he would arrive there today or tomorrow or never. Some of them got lost in the subway or in the labyrinths under the skyscrapers; some rode around on the elevated line all day because with a uniform it was a free ride and perhaps they had never enjoyed riding around all day on the elevated lines. Some of them started for Staten Island and ended up in Canarsie, or else were brought back in a coma by a cop. Some forgot where they lived and disappeared completely. Some whom we hired for New York turned up in Philadelphia a month later as though it were normal and according to Hoyle. Some would start for their destination and on the way decide that it was easier to sell newspapers and they would sell them in the uniform we had given them, until they were picked up. Some went straight to the observation ward, moved by some strange preservative instinct.

When he arrived in the morning Hymie first sharpened his pencils; he did this religiously no matter how many calls were coming in, because, as he explained to me later, if he didn't sharpen his pencils first thing off the bat they would never get sharpened. The next thing was to take a glance out the window and see what the weather was like. Then, with a freshly sharpened pencil he made a little box at the head of the slate which he kept beside him and in it he gave the weather report. This, he also informed me, often turned out to be a useful alibi. If the snow were a foot thick or the ground covered with sleet, even the devil himself might be excused for not shuffling the waybills around more speedily, and the employment manager might also be excused for not filling up the holes on such days, no? But why he didn't take a crap first instead of plugging in on the switchboard soon as his pencils were sharpened was a mystery to me. That too he explained to me later. Anyway, the day always broke with confusion, complaints, constipation and vacancies. It also began with loud smelly farts, with bad breaths, with ragged nerves, with epilepsy, with meningitis, with low wages, with back pay that was overdue, with worn-out shoes, with corns and bunions, with flat feet and broken arches, with pocket books missing and fountain pens lost or stolen, with telegrams floating in the sewer, with threats from the vice-president and advice from the managers, with wrangles and disputes, with cloudbursts and broken telegraph wires, with new methods of efficiency and old ones that had been discarded, with hope for better times and a prayer for the bonus which never came. The new messengers were going over the top and getting machine-gunned; the old ones were digging in deeper and deeper, like rats in a cheese. Nobody was satisfied, especially not the public. It took ten minutes to reach San Francisco over the wire, but it might take a year to get the message to the man whom it was intended for – or it might never reach him.

I even accomplished the miracle of stopping the crazy turnover, something that nobody had dared to hope for. Instead of supporting my efforts they undermined me. According to the logic of the higher-ups the turnover had ceased because the wages were too high. So they cut the wages. It was like kicking the bottom out of a bucket. The whole edifice tumbled, collapsed on my hands. And, just as though nothing had happened they insisted that the gaps be plugged up immediately. To soften the blow a bit they intimated that I might even increase the percentage of Jews, I might take on a cripple now and then, if he were capable, I might do this and that, all of which they had informed me previously was against the code. I was so furious that I took on anything and everything; I would have taken on broncos and gorillas if I could have imbued them with the modicum of intelligence which was necessary to deliver messages. A few days previously there had been only five or six vacancies at closing time. Now there were three hundred, four hundred, five hundred – they were running out like sand. It was marvellous. I sat there and without asking a question I took them on in carload lots – niggers, Jews, paralytics, cripples, ex-convicts, whores, maniacs, perverts, idiots, any fucking bastard who could stand on two legs and hold a telegram in his hand. The managers of the hundred and one offices were frightened to death. I laughed. I laughed all day long thinking what a fine stinking mess I was making of it. Complaints were pouring in from all parts of the city. The service was crippled, constipated, strangulated. A mule could have gotten there faster than some of the idiots I put into harness.

The best thing about the new day was the introduction of female messengers. It changed the whole atmosphere of the joint. For Hymie especially it was a godsend. He moved his switchboard around so that he could watch me while juggling the waybills back and forth. Despite the added work he had a permanent erection. He came to work with a smile and he smiled all day long. He was in heaven. At the end of the day I always had a list of five or six who were worth trying out. The game was to keep them on the string, to promise them a job but to get a free fuck first. Usually it was only necessary to throw a feed into them in order to bring them back to the office at night and lay them out on the zinc-covered table in the dressing room. If they had a cosy apartment, as they sometimes did, we took them home and finished it in bed. If they liked to drink Hymie would bring a bottle along. If they were any good and really needed some dough Hymie would flash his roll and peel off a five spot or a ten spot as the case might be. It makes my mouth water when I think of that roll he carried about with him. Where he got it from I never knew, because he was the lowest paid man in the joint. But it was always there, and no matter what I asked for I got. And once it happened that we did get a bonus and I paid

Hymie back to the last penny – which so amazed him that he took me out that night to Delmonico's and spent a fortune on me. Not only that, but the next day he insisted on buying me hat and shirts and gloves. He even insinuated that I might come home and fuck his wife, if I liked, though he warned me that she was having a little trouble at present with her ovaries.

In addition to Hymie and McGovern I had as assistants a pair of beautiful blondes who often accompanied us to dinner in the evening. And there was O'Mara, an old friend of mine who had just returned from the Philippines and whom I made my chief assistant. There was also Steve Romero, a prize bull whom I kept around in case of trouble. And O'Rourke, the company detective, who reported to me at the close of day when he began his work. Finally I added another man to the staff – Kronski, a young medical student, who was diabolically interested in the pathological cases of which we had plenty. We were a merry crew, united in our desire to fuck the company at all costs. And while fucking the company we fucked everything in sight that we could get hold of, O'Rourke excepted, as he had a certain dignity to maintain, and besides he had trouble with his prostate and had lost all interest in fucking. But O'Rourke was a prince of a man, and generous beyond words. It was O'Rourke who often invited us to dinner in the evening and it was O'Rourke we went to when we were in trouble.

That was how it stood at Sunset Place after a couple of years had rolled by. I was saturated with humanity, with experiences of one kind and another. In my sober moments I made notes which I intended to make use of later if ever I should have a chance to record my experiences. I was waiting for a breathing spell. And then by chance one day, when I had been put on the carpet for some wanton piece of negligence, the vice-president let drop a phrase which stuck in my crop. He had said that he would like to see some one write a sort of Horatio Alger book about the messengers; he hinted that perhaps I might be the one to do such a job. I was furious to think what a ninny he was and delighted at the same time because secretly I was itching to get the thing off my chest. I thought to myself – you poor old futzer, you, just wait until I get it off my chest . . . I'll give you an Horatio Alger book . . . just you wait! My head was in a whirl leaving his office. I saw the army of men, women and children that had passed through my hands, saw them weeping, begging, beseeching, imploring, cursing, spitting, fuming, threatening. I saw the tracks they left on the highways, the freight trains lying on the floor, the parents in rags, the coal box empty, the sink running over, the walls sweating and between the cold beads of sweat the cockroaches running like mad; I saw them hobbling along like twisted gnomes or falling backwards in the epileptic frenzy, the mouth twitching, the saliva pouring from the lips, the limbs writhing; I saw the walls giving way and the pest pouring out like a winged fluid, and the men higher up with their ironclad logic, waiting for it to blow over, waiting for everything to be patched up, waiting, waiting contentedly, smugly, with big cigars in their mouths and their feet on the desk, saying things were temporarily out of order. I saw the Horatio Alger hero, the dream of a sick American, mounting higher and higher, first messenger, then operator, then manager, then chief, then superintendent, then vice-president, then president, then trust magnate, then beer baron, then Lord of all the Americas, the money god, the god of gods, the clay of clay, nullity on high, zero with ninety-seven thousand decimals fore and aft. You shits, I said to myself, I will give you the picture of twelve little men, zeros without decimals, ciphers, digits, the twelve uncrushable worms who are hollowing out the base of your rotten edifice. I will give you Horatio Alger as he looks the day after the Apocalypse, when all the stink has cleared away.

I've been so busy I haven't had a chance to go to the toilet. All the telegraph operators, all the managers, suffer from hemorrhoids, so O'Rourke tells me. He's been having electrical massages for the last two years, but nothing works. Lunch time and there are six of us at the table. Some one will have to pay for me, as usual. We gulp it down and rush back. More calls to make, more applicants to interview. The vice-president is raising hell because we can't keep the force up to normal. Every paper in New York and for twenty miles outside New York carries long ads demanding help. All the schools have been canvassed for part time messengers. All the charity bureaux and relief societies have been invoked. They drop out like flies. Some of them don't even last an hour. It's a human flour mill. And the saddest thing about it is that it's totally unnecessary. But that's not my concern. Mine is to do or die, as Kipling says. I plug on, through one victim after another, the telephone ringing like mad, the place smelling more and more vile, the holes getting bigger and bigger. Each one is a human being asking for a crust of bread; I have his height, weight, colour, religion, education, experience, etc. All the data will go into a ledger to be filed alphabetically and then chronologically. Names and dates. Fingerprints too, if we had the time for it. So that what? So that the American people may enjoy the fastest form of communication known to man, so that they may sell their wares more quickly, so that the moment you drop dead in the street your next of kin may be apprised immediately, that is to say, within an hour, unless the messenger to whom the telegram is entrusted decides to throw up the job and throw the whole batch of telegrams in the garbage can. Twenty million Christmas blanks, all wishing you a Merry Christmas and a Happy New Year, from the directors and president and vice-president of the Cosmodemonic Telegraph Company, and maybe the telegram reads 'Mother dying, come at once', but the clerk is too busy to notice the message and if you sue for damages, spiritual damages, there is a legal department trained expressly to meet such emergencies and so you can be sure that your mother will die and you will have a Merry Christmas and Happy New Year just the same. The clerk, of course, will be fired and after a month or so he will come back for a messenger's job and he will be taken on and put on the night shift near the docks where nobody will recognize him, and his wife will come with the brats to thank the general manager, or perhaps the vice-president himself, for the kindness and consideration shown. And then one day everybody will be heartily surprised that said messenger robbed the till and O'Rourke will be asked to take the night train for Cleveland or Detroit and to track him down if it cost ten thousand dollars. And then the vice-president will issue an order that no more Jews are to be hired, but after three or four days he will let up a bit because there are nothing but Jews coming for the job. And because it's getting so very tough and the timber so damned scarce I'm on the point of hiring a midget from the circus and I probably would have hired him if he hadn't broken down and confessed that he was a she. And to make it worse Valeska takes 'it' under her wing, takes 'it' home that night and under pretence of sympathy gives 'it' a thorough examination, including a vaginal exploration with the index finger of the right hand. And the midget becomes very amorous and finally very jealous. It's a trying day and on the way home I bump into the sister of one of my friends and she insists on taking me to dinner. After dinner we go to a movie and in the dark we begin to play with each other and finally it gets to such a point that we leave the movie and go back to the office where I lay her out on the zinc-covered table in the dressing room. And when I get home, a little after midnight, there's a telephone call from Valeska and she wants me to hop into the subway immediately and come to her house, it's very urgent. It's an hour's ride and I'm dead weary, but she said it was urgent and so I'm on the way. And when I get there I meet her cousin, a rather attractive young woman who, according to her own story, had just had an affair with a strange man because she was tired of being a virgin. And what was all the fuss about? Why this, that in her eagerness she had forgotten to take the usual precautions, and maybe now she was pregnant and then what? They wanted to know what I thought should be done and I said: '*Nothing*.' And then Valeska takes me aside and she asks me if I wouldn't care to sleep with her cousin, to break her in, so that there wouldn't be a repetition of that sort of thing.

The whole thing was cock-eyed and we were all laughing hysterically and then we began to drink – the only thing they had in the house was Kümmel and it didn't take much to put us under. And then it got more cock-eyed because the two of them began to paw me and neither one would let the other do anything. The result was I undressed them both and put them to bed and they fell asleep in each other's arms. And when I walked out, towards five a.m., I discovered I didn't have a cent in my pocket and I tried to bum a nickel from a taxi driver but nothing doing so finally I took off my fur-lined overcoat and I gave it to him – for a nickel. When I got home my wife was awake and sore as hell because I had stayed out so long. We had a hot discussion and finally I lost my temper and I clouted her and she fell on the floor and began to weep and sob and then the kid woke up and hearing the wife bawling she got frightened and began to scream at the top of her lungs. The girl upstairs came running down to see what was the matter. She was in her kimono and her hair was hanging down her back. In the excitement she got close to me and things happened without either of us intending anything to happen. We put the wife to bed with a wet towel around her forehead and while the girl upstairs was bending over her I stood behind her and lifting her kimono, I got it into her and she stood there a long time talking a lot of foolish soothing nonsense. Finally I climbed into bed with the wife and to my utter amazement she began to cuddle up to me and without saying a word we locked horns and we stayed that way until dawn. I should have been worn out, but instead I was wide awake, and I lay there beside her planning to take the day off and look up the whore with the beautiful fur whom I was talking to earlier in the day. After that I began to think about another woman, the wife of one of my friends who always twitted me about my indifference. And then I began to think about one after the other – all those whom I had passed up for one reason or another – until finally I fell sound asleep and in the midst of it I had a wet dream. At seven-thirty the alarm went off as usual and as usual I looked at my torn shirt hanging over the chair and I said to myself what's the use and I turned over. At eight o'clock the telephone rang and it was Hymie. Better get over quickly, he said, because there's a strike on. And that's how it went, day after day, and there was no reason for it, except that the whole country was cock-eyed and what I relate was going on everywhere, either on a smaller scale or a larger scale, but the same thing everywhere, because it was all chaos and all meaningless.

It went on and on that way, day in and day out for almost five solid years. The continent itself perpetually wracked by cyclones, tornadoes, tidal waves, floods, droughts, blizzards, heat waves, pests, strikes, hold-ups, assassinations, suicides . . . a continuous fever and torment, an eruption, a whirlpool. I was like a man sitting in a lighthouse: below me the wild waves, the rocks, the reefs, the debris of shipwrecked fleets. I could give the danger signal but I was powerless to avert catastrophe. I *breathed* danger and catastrophe. At times the sensation of it was so strong that it belched like fire from my nostrils. I longed to be free of it all and yet I was irresistibly attracted. I was violent and phlegmatic at the same time. I was like the lighthouse itself – secure in the midst of the most turbulent sea. Beneath me was solid rock, the same shelf of rock on which the towering skyscrapers were reared. My foundations went deep into the earth and the armature of my body was made of steel riveted with hot bolts. Above all I was an eye, a huge searchlight which scoured far and wide, which revolved ceaselessly, pitilessly. This eye so wide awake seemed to have made all my other faculties dormant; all my powers were used up in the effort to see, to take in the drama of the world.

If I longed for destruction it was merely that this eye might be extinguished. I longed for an earthquake, for some cataclysm of nature which would plunge the lighthouse into the sea. I wanted a metamorphosis, a change to fish, to leviathan, to destroyer. I wanted the earth to open up, to swallow everything in one engulfing yawn. I wanted to see the city buried fathoms deep in the bosom of the sea. I wanted to sit in a cave and read by candlelight. (I wanted that eye extinguished so that I might have a change to know my own body, my own desires. I wanted to be alone for a thousand years in order to reflect on what I had seen and heard – *and in order to forget*. I wanted something of the earth which was not of man's doing, something absolutely divorced from the human of which I was surfeited. I wanted something purely terrestrial and absolutely divested of idea. I wanted to feel the blood running back into my veins, even at the cost of annihilation. I wanted to shake the stone and the light out of my system. I wanted the dark fecundity of nature, the deep well of the womb, silence, or else the lapping of the black waters of death. I wanted to be that night which the remorseless eye illuminated, a night diapered with stars and trailing comets. To be of night so frighteningly silent, so utterly incomprehensible and eloquent at the same time. Never more to speak or to listen or to think. To be englobed and encompassed and to encompass and to englobe at the same time. No more pity, no more tenderness. To be human only terrestrially, like a plant or a worm or a brook. To be decomposed, divested of light and stone, variable as the molecule, durable as the atom, heartless as the earth itself.

It was just about a week before Valeska committed suicide that I ran into Mara. The week or two preceding that event was a veritable nightmare. A series of sudden deaths and strange encounters with women. First of all there was Pauline Janowski, a little Jewess of sixteen or seventeen who was without a home and without friends or relatives. She came to the office looking for a job. It was towards closing time and I didn't have the heart to turn her down cold. For some reason or other I took it into my head to bring her home for dinner and if possible try to persuade the wife to put her up for a while. What attracted me to her was her passion for Balzac. All the way home she was talking to me about *Lost Illusions*. The car was packed and we were jammed so tight together that it didn't make any difference what we were talking about because we were both thinking of only one thing. My wife of course was stupefied to see me standing at the door with a beautiful young girl. She was polite and courteous in her frigid way but I could see immediately that it was no use asking her to put the girl up. It was about all she could do to sit through the dinner with us. As soon as we had finished she excused herself and went to the movies. The girl started to weep. We were still sitting at the table, the dishes piled up in front of us. I went over to her and I put my arms around her. I felt genuinely sorry for her and I was perplexed as to what to do for her. Suddenly she threw her arms around my neck and she kissed me passionately. We stood there for a long while embracing each other and then I thought to myself no, it's a crime, and besides maybe the wife didn't go to the movies at all, maybe she'll be ducking back any minute. I told the kid to pull herself together, that we'd take a trolley ride somewhere. I saw the child's bank lying on the mantelpiece and I took it to the toilet and emptied it silently. There was only about seventy-five cents in it. We got on a trolley and went to the beach. Finally we found a deserted spot and we lay down in the sand. She was hysterically passionate and there was nothing to do but to do it. I thought she would reproach me afterwards, but she didn't. We lay there a while and she began talking about Balzac again. It seems she had ambitions to be a writer herself. I asked her what she was going to do. She said she hadn't the least idea. When we got up to go she asked me to put her on the highway. Said she thought she would go to Cleveland or some place. It was after midnight when I left her standing in front of a gasoline station. She had about thirty-five cents in her pocket-book. As I started homeward I began cursing my wife for the mean son of a bitch that she was. I wished to Christ it was she whom I had left standing on the highway with no place to go to. I knew that when I got back she wouldn't even mention the girl's name.

I got back and she was waiting up for me. I thought she was going to give me hell again. But no, she had waited up because there was an important message from O'Rourke. I was to telephone him soon as I got home. However, I decided not to telephone. I decided to get undressed and go to bed. Just when I had gotten comfortably settled the telephone rang. It was O'Rourke. There was a telegram for me at the office – he wanted to know if he should open it and read it to me. I said of course. The telegram was signed Monica. It was from Buffalo. Said she was arriving at the Grand Central in the morning with her mother's body. I thanked him and went back to bed. No questions from the wife. I lay there wondering what to do. If I were to comply with the request that would mean starting things all over again. I had just been thanking my stars that I had gotten rid of Monica. And now she was coming back with her mother's corpse. Tears and reconciliation. No, I didn't like the prospect at all. Supposing I didn't show up? What then? There was always somebody around to take care of a corpse. Especially if the bereaved were an attractive young blonde with sparkling blue eyes. I wondered if she'd go back to her job in the restaurant. If she hadn't known Greek and Latin I would never have been mixed up with her. But my curiosity got the better of me. And then she was so god-damned poor, that too got me. Maybe it wouldn't have been so bad if her hands hadn't smelled greasy. That was the fly in the ointment – the greasy hands. I remember the first night I met her and we strolled through the park. She was ravishing to look at, and she was alert and intelligent. It was just the time when women were wearing short skirts and she wore then to advantage. I used to go to the restaurant night after night just to watch her moving around, watch her bending over to serve or stooping down to pick up a fork.

And with the beautiful legs and the bewitching eyes a marvellous line about Homer, with the pork and sauerkraut a verse of Sappho's, the Latin conjugations, the Odes of Pindar, with the desert perhaps the *Rubaiyat* or *Cynara*. But the greasy hands and the frowsy bed in the boarding house opposite the market place – Whew! I couldn't stomach it. The more I shunned her the more clinging she became. Ten page letters about love with footnotes on *Thus Spake Zarathustra*. And then suddenly silence and me congratulating myself heartily. No, I couldn't bring myself to go to the Grand Central Station in the morning. I rolled over and I fell sound asleep. In the morning I would get the wife to telephone the office and say I was ill. I hadn't been ill now for over a week – it was coming to me.

At noon I find Kronski waiting for me outside the office. He wants me to have lunch with him . . . there's an Egyptian girl he wants me to meet. The girl turns out to be a Jewess, but she came from Egypt and she looks like an Egyptian. She's hot stuff and the two of us are working on her at once. As I was supposed to be ill I decided not to return to the office but to take a stroll through the East Side. Kronski was going back to cover me up. We shook hands with the girl and we each went our separate ways. I headed towards the river where it was cool, having forgotten about the girl almost immediately. I sat on the edge of a pier with my legs dangling over the stringpiece. A scow passed with a load of red bricks. Suddenly Monica came to my mind. Monica arriving at the Grand Central Station with a corpse. A corpse f.o.b. New York! It seemed so incongruous and ridiculous that I burst out laughing. What had she done with it? Had she checked it or had she left it on a siding? No doubt she was cursing me out roundly. I wondered what she would really think if she could have imagined me sitting there at the dock with my legs dangling over the stringpiece. It was warm and sultry despite the breeze that was blowing off the river. I began to snooze. As I dozed off Pauline came to my mind. I imagined her walking along the highway with her hand up. She was a brave kid, no doubt about it. Funny that she didn't seem to worry about getting knocked up. Maybe she was so desperate she didn't care. And Balzac! That too was highly incongruous. Why Balzac? Well, that was her affair. Anyway she'd have enough to eat with, until she met another guy. But a kid like that thinking about becoming a writer! Well, why not? Everybody had illusions of one sort or another. Monica too wanted to be a writer. Everybody was becoming a writer. A writer! Jesus, how futile it seemed!

I dozed off . . . When I woke up I had an erection. The sun seemed to be burning right into my fly. I got up and I washed my face at a drinking fountain. It was still as hot and sultry as ever. The asphalt was soft as mush, the flies were biting, the garbage was rotting in the gutter. I walked about between the pushcarts and looked at things with an empty eye. I had a sort of lingering hard-on all the while, but no definite object in mind. It was only when I got back to Second Avenue that I suddenly remembered the Egyptian Jewess from lunch time. I remembered her saying that she lived over the Russian restaurant near Twelfth Street. Still I hadn't any definite idea of what I was going to do. Just browsing about, killing time. My feet nevertheless were dragging me northward, towards Fourteenth Street. When I got abreast of the Russian restaurant I paused a moment and then I ran up the stairs three at a time. The hall door was open. I climbed up a couple of flights scanning the names on the doors. She was on the top floor and there was a man's name under hers. I knocked softly. No answer. I knocked again, a little harder. This time I heard someone moving about. Then a voice close to the door, asking who is it and at the same time the knob turning. I pushed the door open and stumbled into the darkened room. Stumbled right into her arms and felt her naked under the half-opened kimono. She must have come out of a sound sleep and only half realized who was holding her in his arms. When she realized it was me she tried to break away but I had her tight and I began kissing her passionately and at the same time backing her up towards the couch near the window. She mumbled something about the door being open but I wasn't taking any chance on letting her slip out of my arms. So I made a slight detour and little by little I edged her towards the door and made her shove it with her ass. I locked it with my one free hand and then I moved her into the centre of the room and with the free hand I unbuttoned my fly and got my pecker out and into position. She was so drugged with sleep that it was almost like working on an automaton. I could see too that she was enjoying the idea of being fucked half asleep. The only thing was that every time I made a lunge she grew more wide awake. And as she grew more conscious she became more frightened. It was difficult to know how to put her to sleep again without losing a good fuck. I managed to tumble her on to the couch without losing ground and she was hot as hell now, twisting and squirming like an eel. From the time I had started to maul her I don't think she had opened her eyes once. I kept saying to myself – 'an Egyptian fuck . . . an Egyptian fuck' – and so as not to shoot off immediately I deliberately began thinking about the corpse that Monica had dragged to the Grand Central Station and about the thirty-five cents that I had left with Pauline on the highway. Then bango! a loud knock on the door and with that she opens her eyes and looks at me in utmost terror. I started to pull away quickly but to my surprise she held me tight. 'Don't move,' she whispered in my ear. 'Wait!' There was another loud knock and then I heard Kronski's voice saying 'It's me, Thelma . . . it's me *Izzy.*' At that I almost burst out laughing. We slumped back again into a natural position and as her eyes softly closed I moved it around inside her, gently, so as not to wake her up again. It was one of the most wonderful fucks I ever had in my life. I thought it was going to last for ever. Whenever I felt in danger of going off I would stop moving and think – think for example of where I would like to spend my vacation, if I got one, or think of the shirts lying in the bureau drawer, or the patch in the bedroom carpet just at the foot of the bed. Kronski was still standing at the door – I could hear him changing about from one position to another. Every time I became aware of him standing there I jibbed her a little for good measure and in her half sleep she answered back, humorously, as though she understood what I meant by this put-and-take language. I didn't dare to think what she might be thinking or I'd have come immediately. Sometimes I skirted dangerously close to it, but the saving trick was always Monica and the corpse at the Grand Central Station. The thought of that, the humorousness of it, I mean, acted like a cold douche.

When it was all over she opened her eyes wide and stared at me as though she was taking me in for the first time. I hadn't a word to say to her; the only thought in my head was to get out as quickly as possible. As we were washing up I noticed a note on the floor near the door. It was from Kronski. His wife had just been taken to the hospital – he wanted her to meet him at the hospital. I felt relieved! It meant that I could break away without wasting any words.

There is a condition of misery which is irremediable – because its origin is lost in obscurity. Bloomingdale's, for example, can bring about this condition. All department stores are symbols of sickness and emptiness, but Bloomingdale's is my special sickness, my incurable obscure malady. In the chaos of Bloomingdale's there is an order, but this order is absolutely crazy to me: it is the order which I would find on the head of a pin if I were to put it under the microscope. It is the order of an accidental series of accidents accidentally conceived. This order has, above all, an odour – and it is the odour of Bloomingdale's which strikes terror into my heart. In Bloomingdale's

I fall apart completely: I dribble on to the floor, a helpless mess of guts and bones and cartilage. There is the smell, not of decomposition, but of misalliance. Man, the miserable alchemist, has welded together, in a million forms and shapes, substances and essences which have nothing in common. Because in his mind there is a tumour which is eating him away insatiably; he has left the little canoe which was taking him blissfully down the river in order to construct a bigger, safer boat in which there may be room for every one. His labours take him so far afield that he has lost all remembrance of why he left the little canoe. The ark is so full of bric-à-brac that it has become a stationary building above a subway in which the smell of linoleum prevails and predominates. Gather together all the significance hidden away in the interstitial miscellany of Bloomingdale's and put it on the head of a pin and you will have left a universe in which the grand constellations move without the slightest danger of collision. It is this microscopic chaos which brings on my morganatic ailments. In the street I begin to stab horses at random, or I lift a skirt here and there looking for a letter-box, or I put a postage stamp across a mouth, an eye, a vagina. Or I suddenly decide to climb a tall building, like a fly, and once having reached the roof I do fly with real wings and I fly and fly and fly, covering towns like Weehawken, Hoboken, Hackensack, Canarsie, Bergen Beach in the twinkling of an eye. Once you become a real schizerino flying is the easiest thing in the world; the trick is to fly with the etheric body, to leave behind in Bloomingdale's your sack of bones, guts, blood and cartilage; to fly only with your immutable self which, if you stop a moment to reflect, is always equipped with wings. Flying this way, in full daylight, has advantages over the ordinary night-flying which everybody indulges in. You can leave off from moment to moment, as quick and decisive as stepping on a brake; there is no difficulty in finding your other self, because the moment you leave off, you *are* your other self, which is to say, the so-called whole self. Only, as the Bloomingdale experience goes to prove, this whole self, about which so much boasting has been done, falls apart very easily. The smell of linoleum, for some strange reason, will always make me fall apart and collapse on the floor. It is the smell of all the unnatural things which were glued together in me, which were assembled, so to say, by negative consent.

It is only after the third meal that the morning gifts, bequeathed by the phony alliances of the ancestors, begin to drop away and the true rock of the self, the happy rock sheers up out of the muck of the soul. With nightfall the pinhead universe begins to expand. It expands organically, from an infinitesimal nuclear speck, in the way that minerals or star-clusters form. It eats into the surrounding chaos like a rat boring through store cheese. All chaos could be gathered together on a pinhead, but the self, microscopical at the start, works up to a universe from any point in space. This is not the self about which books are written, but the ageless self which has been farmed out through millenary ages to men with names and dates, the self which begins and ends as a worm, which *is* the worm in the cheese called the world. Just as the slightest breeze can set a vast forest in motion so, by some unfathomable impulse from within, the rock-like self can begin to grow, and in this growth nothing can prevail against it. It's like Jack Frost at work, and the whole world a windowpane. No hint of labour, no sound, no struggle, no rest; relentless, remorseless, unremitting, the growth of the self goes on. Only two items on the bill of fare: the self and the not-self. And an eternity in which to work it out. In this eternity, which has nothing to do with time or space, there are interludes in which something like a thaw sets in. The form of the self breaks down, but the self, like climate, remains. In the night the amorphous matter of the self assumes the most fugitive forms; error seeps in through the portholes and the wanderer is unlatched from his door. This door which the body wears, if opened out on to the world, leads to annihilation. It is the door in every fable out of which the magician steps; nobody has ever read of him returning home through the selfsame door. If opened inward there are infinite doors, all resembling trapdoors: no horizons are visible, no airlines, no rivers, no maps, no tickets. Each *couche* is a halt for the night only, be it five minutes or ten thousand years. The doors have no handles and they never wear out. Most important to note – there is no end in sight. All these halts for the night, so to speak, are like abortive explorations of a myth. One can feel his way about, take bearings, observe passing phenomena; one can even feel at home. But there is no taking root. Just at the moment when one begins to feel 'established' the whole terrain founders, the soil underfoot is afloat, the constellations are shaken loose from their moorings, the whole known universe, including the imperishable self, starts moving silently, ominously, shudderingly serene and unconcerned, towards an unknown, unseen destination. All the doors seem to be opening at once; the pressure is so great that an implosion occurs and in the swift plunge the skeleton bursts asunder. It was some such gigantic collapse which Dante must have experienced when he situated himself in Hell; it was not a bottom which he touched, but a core, a dead centre from which time itself is reckoned. Here the comedy begins, for here it is seen to be divine.

All this by way of saying that in going through the revolving door of the Amarillo dance hall one night, some twelve or fourteen years ago, the great event took place. The interlude which I think of as the Land of Fuck, a realm of time more than of space, is for me the equivalent of that Purgatory which Dante has described in nice detail. As I put my hand on the brass rail of the revolving door to leave the Amarillo dance hall, all that I had previously been, was, and about to be, foundered. There was nothing unreal about it; the very time in which I was born passed away, carried off by a mightier stream. Just as I had previously been bundled out of the womb, so now I was shunted back to some timeless vector where the process of growth is kept in abeyance. I passed into the world of effects. There was no fear, only a feeling of fatality. My spine was socketed to the node; I was up against the coccyx of an implacable new world. In the plunge the skeleton blew apart, leaving the immutable ego as helpless as a squashed louse.

If from this point I do not begin, it is because there is no beginning. If I do not fly at once to the bright land it is because wings are of no avail. It is zero hour and the moon is at nadir . . .

Why I think of Maxie Schnadig I don't know, unless it is because of Dostoievski. The night I sat down to read Dostoievski for the first time was a most important event in my life, even more important than my first love. It was the first deliberate, conscious act which had significance for me; it changed the whole face of the world. Whether it is true that the clock stopped that moment when I looked up after the first deep gulp I don't know any more. But the world stopped dead for a moment, that I know. It was my first glimpse into the soul of a man, or shall I say simply that Dostoievski was the first man to reveal his soul to me? Maybe I have been a bit queer before that, without realizing it, but from the moment that I dipped into Dostoievski I was definitely, irrevocably, contentedly queer. The ordinary, waking, work-a-day world was finished for me. Any ambition or desire I had to write was also killed – for a long time to come. I was like those men who have been too long in the trenches, too long under fire. Ordinary human suffering, ordinary human jealousy, ordinary human ambitions – it was just so much shit to me.

I can visualize best my condition when I think of my relations with Maxie and his sister Rita. At the time Maxie and I were both interested in sport. We used to go swimming together a great deal, that I remember well. Often we passed the whole day and night at the beach. I had only met Maxie's sister once or twice; whenever I brought up her name Maxie would rather frantically begin to talk about something else. That annoyed me because I was really bored to death with Maxie's company, tolerating him only because he loaned me money readily and bought me things which I needed. Every time we started for the beach I was in hopes his sister would turn up unexpectedly. But no, he always managed to keep her out of reach. Well, one day as we were undressing in the bath house and he was showing me what a fine tight scrotum he had, I said to him right out of the blue – 'listen, Maxie, that's all right about your nuts, they're fine and dandy, and there's nothing to worry about but where in hell is Rita all the time, why don't you bring her along some time and let me take a good look at her quim . . . yes, *quim*, you know what I mean.' Maxie, being a Jew from Odessa, had never heard the word quim before. He was deeply shocked by my words and yet at the same time intrigued by this new word. In a sort of daze he said to me – 'Jesus, Henry, you oughtn't to say a thing like that to me!' 'Why not?' I answered. 'She's got a cunt, your sister, hasn't she?' I was about to add something else when he broke into a terrific fit of laughter. That saved the situation, for the time being. But Maxie didn't like the idea at all deep down. All day long it bothered him, though he never referred to our conversation again. No, he was very silent that day. The only form of revenge he could think of was to urge me to swim far beyond the safety zone in the hope of tiring me out and letting me drown. I could see so clearly what was in his mind that I was possessed with the strength of ten men. Damned if I would go drown myself just because his sister like all other women happened to have a cunt.

It was at Far Rockaway where this took place. After we had dressed and eaten a meal I suddenly decided that I wanted to be alone and so, very abruptly, at the corner of a street, I shook hands and said goodbye. And there I was! Almost instantaneously I felt alone in the world, alone as one feels only in moments of extreme anguish. I think I was picking my teeth absentmindedly when this wave of loneliness hit me full on, like a tornado. I stood there on the street corner and sort of felt myself all over to see if I had been hit by something. It was inexplicable, and at the same time it was very wonderful, very exhilarating, like a double tonic, I might say. When I say that I was at Far Rockaway I mean that I was standing at the end of the earth, at a place called Xanthos, if there be such a place, and surely there ought to be a word like this to express no place at all. If Rita had come along then I don't think I would have recognized her. I had become an absolute stranger standing in the very midst of my own people. They

106

looked crazy to me, my people, with their newly sunburned faces and their flannel trousers and their clockwork stockings. They had been bathing like myself because it was a pleasant, healthy recreation and now like myself they were full of sun and food and a little heavy with fatigue. Up until this loneliness hit me I too was a bit weary, but suddenly, standing there completely shut off from the world, I woke up with a start. I became so electrified that I didn't dare move for fear I would charge like a bull or start to climb the wall of a building or else dance and scream. Suddenly I realized that all this was because I was really a brother to Dostoievski, that perhaps I was the only man in all America who knew what he meant in writing those books. Not only that, but I felt all the books I would one day write myself germinating inside me: they were bursting inside like ripe cocoons. And since up to this time I had written nothing but fiendishly long letters about everything and nothing, it was difficult for me to realize that there must come a time when I should begin, when I should put down the first word, *the first real word*. And this time was now! That was what dawned on me.

I used the word Xanthos a moment ago. I don't know whether there is a Xanthos or not, and I really don't care one way or another, but there must be a place in the world, perhaps in the Grecian islands, where you come to the end of the known world and you are thoroughly alone and yet you are not frightened of it but rejoice, because at this dropping off place you can feel the old ancestral world which is eternally young and new and fecundating. You stand there, wherever the place is, like a newly hatched chick beside its eggshell. This place is Xanthos, or as it happened in my case, Far Rockaway.

There I was! It grew dark, a wind came up, the streets became deserted, and finally it began to pour cats and dogs. Jesus, that finished me! When the rain came down, and I got it smack in the face staring at the sky, I suddenly began to bellow with joy. I laughed and laughed and laughed, exactly like an insane man. Nor did I know what I was laughing about. I wasn't thinking of a thing. I was just overwhelmed with joy, just crazy with delight in finding myself absolutely alone. If then and there a nice juicy quim had been handed me on a platter, if all the quims in the world had been offered me for to make my choice, I wouldn't have batted an eyelash. I had what no quim could give me. And just about at that point, thoroughly drenched but still exultant, I thought of the most irrelevant thing in the world – *carfare*! Jesus, the bastard Maxie had walked off without leaving me a sou. There I was with my fine budding antique world and not a penny in my jeans. Herr Dostoievski Junior had now to begin to walk here and there peering into friendly and unfriendly faces to see if he could pry loose a dime. He walked from one end of Far Rockaway to the other but nobody seemed to give a fuck about handing out carfare in the rain. Walking about in that heavy animal stupor which comes with begging I got to thinking of Maxie the window-trimmer and how the first time I spied him he was standing in the show-window dressing a mannikin. And from that in a few minutes to Dostoievski, then the world stopped dead, and then, like a great rose bush opening in the night, his sister Rita's warm, velvety flesh.

Now this is what is rather strange . . . A few minutes after I thought of Rita, her private and extraordinary quim, I was in the train bound for New York and dozing off with a marvellous languid erection. And stranger still, when I got out of the train, when I had walked but a block or two from the station, whom should I bump into rounding a corner but Rita herself. And as though she had been informed tele-pathically of what was going on in my brain, Rita too was hot under the whiskers. Soon we were sitting in a chop suey joint, seated side by side in a little booth, behaving exactly like a pair of rabbits in rut. On the dance floor we hardly moved. We were wedged in tight and we stayed that way, letting them jog and jostle us about as they might. I could have taken her home to my place, as I was alone at the time, but no, I had a notion to bring her back to her own home, stand her up in the vestibule and give her a fuck right under Maxie's nose – which I did. In the midst of it I thought again of the mannikin in the show window and of the way he had laughed that afternoon when I let drop the word quim. I was on the point of laughing aloud when suddenly I felt that she was coming, one of those long drawn-out orgasms such as you get now and then in a Jewish cunt. I had my hands under her buttocks, the tips of my fingers just inside her cunt, in the lining, as it were; as she began to shudder I lifted her from the ground and raised her gently up and down on the end of my cock. I thought she would go off her nut completely, the way she began to carry on. She must have had four or five orgasms like that in the air, before I put her feet down on the ground. I took it out without spilling a drop and made her lie down in the vestibule. Her hat had rolled off into a corner and her bag had spilled open and a few coins had tumbled out. I note this because just before I gave it to her good and proper I made a mental note to pocket a few coins for my carfare home. Anyway, it was only a few hours since I had said to Maxie in the bath house that I would like to take a look at his sister's quim, and here it was now smack up against me, sopping wet and throwing out one squirt after another. If she had been fucked before she had never been fucked properly, that's a cinch. And I myself was never in such a fine cool scientific frame of mind as now lying on the floor of the vestibule right under Maxie's nose, pumping it into the private, sacred, and extraordinary quim of his sister Rita. I could have held it in indefinitely – it was incredible how detached I was and yet thoroughly aware of every quiver and jolt she made. But somebody had to pay for making me walk around in the rain grubbing a dime. Somebody had to pay for the ecstasy produced by the germination of all those unwritten books inside me. Somebody had to verify the authenticity of this private, concealed cunt which had been plaguing me for weeks and months. Who better qualified than I? I thought so hard and fast between orgasms that my cock must have grown another inch or two. Finally I decided to make an end of it by turning her over and back-scuttling her. She balked a bit at first, but when she felt the thing slipping out of her she nearly went crazy. 'Oh yes, oh yes, do it, do it!' she gibbered, and with that I really got excited, I had hardly slipped it into her when I felt it coming, one of those long agonizing spurts from the tip of the spinal column. I shoved it in so deep that I felt as if something had given way. We fell over, exhausted, the both of us, and panted like dogs. At the same time, however, I had the presence of mind to feel around for a few coins. Not that it was necessary, because she had already loaned me a few dollars, but to make up for the carfare which I was lacking in Far Rockaway. Even then, by Jesus, it wasn't finished. Soon I felt her groping about, first with her hands, then with her mouth. I had still a sort of semi hard-on. She got it into her mouth and she began to caress it with her tongue. I saw stars. The next thing I knew her feet were around my neck and my tongue up her twat. And then I had to get over her again and shove it in, up to the hilt. She squirmed around like an eel, so help me God. And then she began to come again, long, drawn-out, agonizing orgasms, with a whimpering and gibbering that was hallucinating. Finally I had to pull it out and tell her to stop. What a quim! And I had only asked to take a look at it!

Maxie with his talk of Odessa revived something which I had lost as a child. Though I had never a very clear picture of Odessa the aura of it was like the little neighbourhood in Brooklyn which meant so much to me and from which I had been torn away too soon. I get a very definite feeling of it every time I see an Italian painting without perspective; if it is a picture of a funeral procession, for example, it is exactly the sort of experience which I knew as a child, one of intense immediacy. If it is a picture of the open street, the women sitting in the windows are sitting *on* the street and not above it and away from it. Everything that happens is known immediately by everybody, just as among primitive people. Murder is in the air, chance rules.

Just as in the Italian primitives this perspective is lacking, so in the little old neighbourhood from which I was uprooted as a child there were these parallel vertical planes on which everything took place and through which, from layer to layer, everything was communicated, as if by osmosis. The frontiers were sharp, clearly defined, but they were not impassable. I lived then, as a boy, close to the boundary between the north and the south side. I was just a little bit over on the north side, just a few steps from a broad thoroughfare called North Second Street, which was for me the real boundary line between the north and the south side. The actual boundary was Grand Street, which led to Broadway Ferry, but this street meant nothing to me, except that it was already beginning to be filled with Jews. No, North Second Street was the mystery street, the frontier between two worlds. I was living, therefore, between two boundaries, the one real, the other imaginary – as I have lived all my life. There was a little street, just a block long which lay between Grand Street and North Second Street, called Fillmore Place. This little street was obliquely opposite the house my grandfather owned and in which we lived. It was the most enchanting street I have ever seen in all my life. It was the ideal street – for a boy, a lover, a maniac, a drunkard, a crook, a lecher, a thug, an astronomer, a musician, a poet, a tailor, a shoemaker, a politician. In fact this was just the sort of street it was, containing just such representatives of the human race, each one a world unto himself and all living together harmoniously and inharmoniously, *but together*, a solid corporation, a close-knit human spore which could not disintegrate unless the street itself disintegrated.

So it seemed, at least. Until the Williamsburg Bridge was opened, whereupon there followed the invasion of the Jews from Delancey Street, New York. This brought about the disintegration of our little world, of the little street called Fillmore Place, which like the name itself was a street of value, of dignity, of light, of surprises. The Jews came, as I say, and like moths they began to eat into the fabric of our lives until there was nothing left by this moth-like presence which they brought with them everywhere. Soon the street began to smell bad, soon the real people moved away, soon the houses began to deteriorate and even the stoops fell away, like the paint. Soon the street looked like a dirty mouth with all the prominent teeth missing,

110

with ugly charred stumps gaping here and there, the lips rotting, the palate gone. Soon the garbage was knee deep in the gutter and the fire escapes filled with bloated bedding, with cockroaches, with dried blood. Soon the Kosher sign appeared on the shop windows and there was poultry everywhere and lax and sour pickles and enormous loaves of bread. Soon there were baby-carriages in every areaway and on the stoops and in the little yards and before the shop fronts. And with the change the English language also disappeared; one heard nothing but Yiddish, nothing but this sputtering, choking, hissing tongue in which God and rotten vegetables sound alike and mean alike.

Truth lies in this knowledge of the end which is ruthless and remorseless. We can know the truth and accept it, or we can refuse the knowledge of it and neither die nor be born again. In this manner it is possible to live forever, a negative life as solid and complete, or as dispersed and fragmentary, as the atom. And if we pursue this road far enough, even this atomic eternity can yield to nothingness and the universe itself fall apart.

For years now I have been trying to tell this story; each time I have started out I have chosen a different route. I am like an explorer who, wishing to circumnavigate the globe, deems it unnecessary to carry even a compass. Moreover, from dreaming over it so long, the story itself has come to resemble a vast, fortified city, and I who dream it over and over, am outside the city, a wanderer, arriving before one gate after another too exhausted to enter. And as with the wanderer, this city in which my story is situated eludes me perpetually. Always in sight it nevertheless remains unattainable, a sort of ghostly citadel floating in the clouds. From the soaring, crenellated battlements flocks of huge white geese swoop down in steady, wedge-shaped formation. With the tips of their blue-white wings they brush the dreams that dazzle my vision. My feet move confusedly; no sooner do I gain a foothold than I am lost again. I wander aimlessly, trying to gain a solid, unshakeable foothold whence I can command a view of my life, but behind me there lies only a welter of criss-crossed tracks, a groping, confused encircling, the spasmodic gambit of the chicken whose head has just been lopped off.

Whenever I try to explain to myself the peculiar pattern which my life has taken, when I reach back to the first cause, as it were, I think inevitably of the girl I first loved. It seems to me that everything dates from that aborted affair. A strange, masochistic affair it was, ridiculous and tragic at the same time. Perhaps I had the pleasure of kissing

111

her two or three times, the sort of kiss one reserves for a goddess. Perhaps I saw her alone several times. Certainly she could never have dreamed that for over a year I walked past her home every night hoping to catch a glimpse of her at the window. Every night after dinner I would get up from the table and take the long route which led to her home. She was never at the window when I passed and I never had the courage to stand in front of the house and wait. Back and forth I passed, back and forth, but never hide nor hair of her. Why didn't I write her? Why didn't I call her up? Once I remember summoning enough pluck to invite her to the theatre. I arrived at her home with a bunch of violets, the first and only time I ever bought flowers for a woman. As we were leaving the theatre the violets dropped from her corsage, and in my confusion I stepped on them. I begged her to leave them there, but she insisted on gathering them up. I was thinking how awkward I was – it was only long afterwards that I recalled the smile she had given me as she stooped down to pick up the violets.

It was a complete fiasco. In the end I ran away. Actually I was running away from another woman, but the day before leaving town I decided to see her once again. It was mid-afternoon and she came out to talk to me in the street, in the little areaway which was fenced off. She was already engaged to another man; she pretended to be happy about it but I could see, blind as I was, that she wasn't as happy as she pretended to be. If I had only said the word I am sure she would have dropped the other fellow; perhaps she would even have gone away with me. I preferred to punish myself. I said goodbye nonchalantly and I went down the street like a dead man. The next morning I was bound for the Coast, determined to start a new life.

The new life was also a fiasco. I ended up on a ranch in Chula Vista, the most miserable man that ever walked the earth. There was this girl I loved and there was the other woman, for whom I felt only a profound pity. I had been living with her for two years, this other woman, but it seemed like a lifetime. I was twenty-one and she admitted to be thirty-six. Every time I looked at her I said to myself – when I am thirty she will be forty-five, when I am forty she will be fifty-five, when I am fifty, she will be sixty-five. She had fine wrinkles under the eyes, laughing wrinkles, but wrinkles just the same. When I kissed her they magnified a dozen times. She laughed easily, but her eyes were sad, terribly sad. They were Armenian eyes. Her hair, which had been red once, was now a peroxide blonde. Otherwise she was adorable – a Venusian body, a Venusian soul, loyal, lovable, grateful, everything a woman should be, *except that she was fifteen years older*. The fifteen years difference drove me crazy. When I went out with her I thought only – how will it be ten years hence? Or else, what age does she seem to have now? Do I look old enough for her? Once we got back to the house it was all right. Climbing the stairs I would run my fingers up her crotch, which used to make her whinny like a horse. If her son, who was almost my age, were in bed we would close the doors and lock ourselves in the kitchen. She'd lie on the narrow kitchen table and I'd slough into her. It was marvellous. And what made it more marvellous was that with each performance I would say to myself – This is the last time . . . *tomorrow I will beat it!* And then, since she was the janitress, I would go down to the cellar and roll the ash barrels out for her. In the morning, when the son had left for work, I would climb up to the roof and air the bedding. Both she and the son had TB . . . Sometimes there were no table bouts. Sometimes the hopelessness of it all got me by the throat and I would put on my things and go for a walk. Now and then I forgot to return. And when I did that I was more miserable than ever, because I knew that she would be waiting for me with those large sorrowful eyes. I'd go back to her like a man who had a sacred duty to perform. I'd lie down on the bed and let her caress me; I'd study the wrinkles under her eyes and the roots of her hair which were turning red. Lying there like that, I would often think about the other one, the one I loved, would wonder if she were lying down for it too, or . . . Those long walks I took 365 days of the year! – I would go over them in my mind lying beside the other woman. How many times since have I relived these walks! The dreariest, bleakest, ugliest streets man ever created. In anguish I relive these walks, these streets, these first smashed hopes. The window is there, but no Melisande; the garden too is there, but no sheen of gold. Pass and repass, the window always vacant. The evening star hangs low; Tristan appears, then Fidelio, and then Oberon. The hydra-headed dog barks with all his mouths and though there are no swamps I hear the frogs croaking everywhere. Same houses, same car-lines, same everything. She is hiding behind the curtain, she is waiting for me to pass, she is doing this or doing that . . . *but she is not there, never, never, never*. Is it a grand opera or is it a hurdygurdy playing? It is Amato bursting his golden lung; it is the Rubaiyat, it is Mount Everest, it is a moonless night, it is a sob at dawn, it is a boy making believe, it is Puss in the Boot, it is Mauna Loa, it is fox or astrakhan, it is of no stuff and no time, it is endless and it begins over and over, under the heart, in the back of the throat, in the soles of the feet, and why not just once, just once, for the love of

Christ, just a shadow or a rustle of the curtain, or a breath on the window-pane, something once, if only a lie, something to stop the pain, to stop this walking up and down, up and down . . . Walking homeward. Same houses, same lamp posts, same everything. I walk past my own home, past the cemetery, past the gas tanks, past the car barns, past the reservoir, out into the open country. I sit beside the road with my head in my hands and sob. Poor bugger that I am, I can't contract my heart enough to burst the veins. I would like to suffocate with grief but instead I give birth to a rock.

Meanwhile the other one is waiting. I can see her again as she sat on the low stoop waiting for me, her eyes large and dolorous, her face pale and trembling with eagerness. *Pity* I always thought it was that brought me back, but now as I walk towards her and see the look in her eyes I don't know any more what it is, only that we will go inside and lie together and she will get up half weeping, half laughing, and she will grow very silent and watch me, study me as I move about, and never ask me what is torturing me, never, never, because that is the one things she fears, the one thing she dreads to know. *I don't love you!* Can't she hear me screaming it? *I don't love you!* Over and over I yell it, with lips tight, with hatred in my heart, with despair, with hopeless rage. But the words never leave my lips. I look at her and I am tongue-tied. I can't do it . . . Time, time, endless time on our hands and nothing to fill it but lies.

Well, I don't want to rehearse the whole of my life leading up to the fatal moment – it is too long and too painful. Besides, did my life really lead up to this culminating moment? I doubt it. I think there were innumerable moments when I had the chance to make a beginning, but I lacked the strength and the faith. On the night in question I deliberately walked out on myself: I walked right out of the old life and into the new. There wasn't the slightest effort involved. I was thirty then. I had a wife and child and what is called a 'responsible' position. These are the facts and facts mean nothing. The truth is my desire was so great it became a reality. At such a moment what a man *does* is of no great importance, it's what he *is* that counts. It's at such a moment that a man becomes an angel. That is precisely what happened to me: *I became an angel.* It is not the purity of an angel which is so valuable, as the fact it can fly. An angel can break the pattern anywhere at any moment and find its heaven; it has the power to descend into the lowest matter and to extricate itself at will. The night in question I understood it perfectly. I was pure and inhuman, I was detached, I had wings. I was de-possessed of the past and I had no concern about the future. I was beyond ecstasy. When I left the office I folded my wings and hid them beneath my coat.

The dance hall was just opposite the side entrance of the theatre where I used to sit in the afternoons instead of looking for work. It was a street of theatres and I used to sit there for hours at a time dreaming the most violent dreams. The whole theatrical life of New York was concentrated in that one street, so it seemed. It was Broadway, it was success, fame, glitter, paint, the asbestos curtain and the hole in the curtain. Sitting on the steps of the theatre I used to stare at the dance hall opposite, at the string of red lanterns which even in the summer afternoons were lit up. In every window there was a spinning ventilator which seemed to waft the music into the street, where it was broken by the jangled din of traffic. Opposite the other side of the dance hall was a comfort station and here too I used to sit now and then, hoping either to make a woman or make a touch. Above the comfort station, on the street level, was a kiosk with foreign papers and magazines; the very sight of these papers, of the strange languages in which they were printed, was sufficient to dislocate me for the day.

Without the slightest premeditation I climbed the stairs to the dance hall, went directly to the little window of the booth where Nick, the Greek, sat with a roll of tickets in front of him. Like the urinal below and the steps of the theatre, this hand of the Greek now seems to me a separate and detached thing – the enormous, hairy hand of an ogre borrowed from some horrible Scandinavian fairy-tale. It was the hand which spoke to me always, the hand which said 'Miss Mara will not be here tonight,' or 'Yes, Miss Mara is coming late tonight.' It was this hand which I dreamt of as a child when I slept in the bedroom with the barred window. In my fevered sleep suddenly this window would light up, to reveal the ogre clutching at the bars. Night after night the hairy monster visited me, clutching at the bars and gnashing its teeth. I would awake in a cold sweat, the house dark, the room absolutely silent.

Standing at the edge of the dance floor I notice her coming towards me; she is coming with sails spread, the large full face beautifully balanced on the long, columnar neck. I see a woman perhaps eighteen, perhaps thirty, with blue-black hair and a large white face, a full white face in which the eyes shine brilliantly. She has on a tailored blue suit of duveteen. I remember distinctly now the fullness of her body, and that her hair was fine and straight, parted on the side, like a man's. I remember the smile she gave me – knowing, mysterious, fugitive – a smile that sprang up suddenly, like a puff of wind.

115

The whole being was concentrated in the face. I could have taken just the head and walked home with it; I could have put it beside me at night, on a pillow, and made love to it. The mouth and the eyes, when they opened up, the whole being glowed from them. There was an illumination which came from some unknown source, from a centre hidden deep in the earth. I could think of nothing but the face, the strange, womb-like quality of the smile, the engulfing immediacy of it. The smile was so painfully swift and fleeting that it was like the flash of a knife. This smile, this face, was borne aloft on a long white neck, the sturdy, swan-like neck of the medium – and of the lost and the damned.

I stand on the corner under the red lights, waiting for her to come down. It is about two in the morning and she is signing off. I am standing on Broadway with a flower in my buttonhole, feeling absolutely clean and alone. Almost the whole evening we have been talking about Strindberg, about a character of his named Henriette. I listened with such tense alertness that I fell into a trance. It was as if, with the opening phrase, we had started on a race – in opposite directions. Henriette! Almost immediately the name was mentioned she began to talk about herself, without ever quite losing hold of Henriette. Henriette was attached to her by a long, invisible string which she manipulated imperceptibly with one finger, like the street-hawker who stands a little removed from the black cloth, on the sidewalk, apparently indifferent to the little mechanism which is jiggling on the cloth, but betraying himself by the spasmodic movement of the little finger to which the black thread is attached. Henriette is me, my real self, she seemed to be saying. She wanted me to believe that Henriette was really the incarnation of evil. She said it so naturally, so innocently, with an almost subhuman candour – how was I to believe that she meant it? I could only smile, as though to show her I was convinced.

Suddenly I feel her coming. I turn my head. Yes, there she is coming full on, the sails spread, the eyes glowing. For the first time I see now what a carriage she has. She comes forward like a bird, a human bird wrapped in a big soft fur. The engine is going full steam: I want to shout, to give a blast that will make the whole world cock its ears. What a walk! It's not a walk, it's a glide. Tall, stately, full-bodied, self-possessed, she cuts the smoke and jazz and red-light glow like the queen mother of all the slippery Babylonian whores. On the corner of Broadway just opposite the comfort station, this is happening. Broadway – it's her realm. This is Broadway, this is New York,

116

this is America. She's America on foot, winged and sexed. She is the lubet, the abominate and the sublimate – with a dash of hydrochloric acid, nitro-glycerine, laudanum and powdered onyx. Opulence she has, and magnificence: it's America right or wrong, and the ocean on either side. For the first time in my life the whole continent hits me full force, hits me between the eyes. This is America, buffaloes or no buffaloes, America the emery wheel of hope and disillusionment. Whatever made America made her, bone, blood, muscle, eyeball, gait, rhythm; poise, confidence; brass and hollow gut. She's almost on top of me, the full face gleaming like calcium. The big soft fur is slipping from her shoulder. She doesn't notice it. She doesn't seem to care if her clothes should drop off. She doesn't give a fuck about anything. It's America moving like a streak of lightning towards the glass warehouse of red-blooded hysteria. Amurrica, fur or no fur, shoes or no shoes. Amurrica C.O.D. *And scram, you bastards, before we plug you!* It's got me in the guts. I'm quaking. Something's coming to me and there's no dodging it. She's coming head on, through the plate-glass window. If she would only stop a second, if she would only let me be for just one moment. But no, not a single moment does she grant me. Swift, ruthless, imperious, like Fate itself she is on me, a sword cutting me through and through . . .

She has me by the hand, she holds it tight. I walk beside her without fear. Inside me the stars are twinkling; inside me a great blue vault where a moment ago the engines were pounding furiously.

One can wait a whole lifetime for a moment like this. The woman whom you never hoped to meet now sits before you, and she talks and looks exactly like the person you dreamed about. But strangest of all is that you never realized before that you had dreamed about her. Your whole past is like a long sleep which would have been forgotten had there been no dream. And the dream too might have been forgotten had there been no memory, but remembrance is there in the blood and the blood is like an ocean in which everything is washed away but that which is new and more substantial even than life: REALITY.

We are seated in a little booth in the Chinese restaurant across the way. Out of the corner of my eye I catch the flicker of the illuminated letters running up and down the sky. She is still talking about Henriette, or maybe it is about herself. Her little black bonnet, her bag and fur are lying beside her on the bench. Every few minutes she lights a fresh cigarette which burns away as she talks. There is no beginning nor end; it spurts out of her like a flame and consumes everything within reach. No knowing how or where she began.

117

Suddenly she is in the midst of a long narrative, a fresh one, but it is always the same. Her talk is as formless as dream: there are no grooves, no walls, no exits, no stops. I have the feeling of being drowned in a deep mesh of words, of crawling painfully back to the top of the net, of looking into her eyes and trying to find there some reflection of the significance of her words – but I can find nothing, nothing except my own image wavering in a bottomless well. Though she speaks of nothing but herself I am unable to form the slightest image of her being. She leans forward, with elbows on the table, and her words inundate me; wave after wave rolling over me and yet nothing builds up inside me, nothing that I can seize with my mind. She's telling me about her father, about the strange life they led at the edge of Sherwood Forest where she was born, or at least she *was* telling me about this, but now it's about Henriette again, or is it Dostoievski? – I'm not sure – but anyway, suddenly I realize that she's not talking about any of these any more but about a man who took her home one night and as they stood on the stoop saying goodnight he suddenly reached down and pulled up her dress. She pauses a moment as though to reassure me that this is what she means to talk about. I look at her bewilderedly. I can't imagine by what route we got to this point. *What man?* What had he been saying to her? I let her continue, thinking that she will probably come back to it, but no, she's ahead of me again and now it seems the man, *this* man, is already dead; a suicide, and she is trying to make me understand that it was an awful blow to her, but what she really seems to convey is that she is proud of the fact that she drove a man to suicide. I can't picture the man as dead; I can only think of him as he stood on her stoop lifting her dress, a man without a name but alive and perpetually fixed in the act of bending down to lift up her dress. There is another man who was her father and I see him with a string of racehorses, or sometimes in a little inn just outside Vienna; rather I see him on the roof of the inn flying kites to while the time away. And between this man who was her father and the man with whom she was madly in love, I can make no separation. He is someone in her life about whom she would rather not talk, but just the same she comes back to him all the time, and though I'm not sure that it was *not* the man who lifted up her dress neither am I sure that it wasn't the man who committed suicide. Perhaps it's the man whom she started to talk about when we sat down to eat. Just as we were sitting down I remember now that she began to talk rather hectically about a man whom she had just seen entering the cafeteria. She even mentioned his name, but I forgot it immediately. But I

118

remember her saying that she had lived with him and that he had done something which she didn't like – she didn't say what – and so she had walked out on him, left him flat, without a word of explanation. And then, just as we were entering the Chop Suey joint, they ran into each other and she was still trembling over it as we sat down in the little booth . . . For one long moment I have the most uneasy sensation. Maybe every word she uttered was a lie! Not an ordinary lie, no, something worse, something indescribable. Only sometimes the truth comes out like that too, especially if you think you're never going to see the person again. Sometimes you can tell a perfect stranger what you would never dare reveal to your most intimate friend. It's like going to sleep in the midst of a party; you become so interested in yourself that you go to sleep. And when you're sound asleep you begin to talk to someone, someone who was in the same room with you all the time and therefore understands everything even though you begin in the middle of a sentence. And perhaps this other person goes to sleep also, or was always asleep, and that's why it was so easy to encounter him, and if he doesn't say anything to disturb you then you know that what you are saying is real and true and that you are wide-awake and there is no other reality except this being wide-awake asleep. Never before have I been so wide-awake and so sound asleep at the same time. If the ogre in my dreams had really pushed the bars aside and taken me by the hand I would have been frightened to death and consequently now dead, that is, forever asleep and therefore always at large, and nothing would be strange any more, nor untrue, even if what happened did not happen. What happened must have happened long ago, in the night undoubtedly, And what is now happening is also happening long ago, in the night, and this is no more true than the dream of the ogre and the bars which would not give, except that now the bars are broken and she whom I feared has me by the hand and there is no difference between that which I feared and what is, because I was asleep and now I am wide-awake asleep and there is nothing more to fear, nor to expect, nor to hope for, but just this which is and which knows no end.

She wants to go. To go . . . Again her haunch, that slippery glide as when she came down from the dance hall and moved into me. Again her words . . . 'suddenly, for no reason at all, he bent down and lifted up my dress.' She's slipping the fur around her neck; the little black bonnet sets her face off like a cameo. The round, full face, with Slavic cheek-bones. How could I dream this, never having seen it? How could I know that she would rise like this, close and full, the face full white and blooming like a magnolia? I tremble as the fullness of her thigh brushes me. She seems even a little taller than I, though she is not. It's the way she holds her chin. She doesn't notice where she's walking. She walks *over* things, on, on, with eyes wide open and staring into space. No past, no future. Even the present seems dubious. The self seems to have left her, and the body rushes forward, the neck full and taut, white as the face, full like the face. The talk goes on, in that low, throaty voice. No beginning, no end. I'm aware not of time nor the passing of time, but of timelessness. She's got the little womb in the throat hooked up to the big womb in the pelvis. The cab is at the kerb and she is still chewing the cosmological chaff of the outer ego. I pick up the speaking tube and connect with the double uterus. Hello, hello, are you there? Let's go! Let's get on with it – cabs, boats, trains, naptha launches; beaches, bedbugs, highways, byways, ruins; relics; old world, new world, pier, jetty; the high forceps; the swinging trapeze, the ditch, the delta, the alligators, the crocodiles, talk, talk; and more talk, then roads again and more dust in the eyes, more rainbows, more cloudbursts, more breakfast foods, more creams, more lotions. And when all the roads have been traversed and there is left only the dust of our frantic feet there will still remain the memory of your large full face so white, and the wide mouth with fresh lips parted, the teeth chalk white and each one perfect, and in this remembrance nothing can possibly change because this, like your teeth, is perfect . . .

It is Sunday, the first Sunday of my new life, and I am wearing the dog collar you fastened around my neck. A new life stretches before me. It begins with the day of rest. I lie back on a broad green leaf and I watch the sun bursting in your womb. What a clabber and clatter it makes! All this expressly for me, what? If only you had a million suns in you! If only I could lie here forever enjoying the celestial fireworks!

I lie suspended over the surface of the moon. The world is in a womb-like trance: the inner and the outer ego are in equilibrium. You promised me so much that if I never come out of this it will make no difference. It seems to me that it is exactly 25,960 years since I have been asleep in the black womb of sex. It seems to me that I slept perhaps 365 years too many. But at any rate I am now in the right house, among the sixes, and what lies behind me is well and what lies ahead is well. You come to me disguised as Venus, but you are Lilith, and I know it. My whole life is in the balance; I will enjoy the luxury of this for one day. Tomorrow I shall tip the scales. Tomorrow the equilibrium will be finished; if I ever find it again it will be in the blood and not in the stars. It is well that you promise me so much. I need to be promised nearly everything, for I have lived in the shadow of the sun too long. I want light and chastity – and a solar fire in the guts. I want to be deceived and disillusioned so that I may complete the upper triangle and not be continually flying off the planet into space. I believe everything you tell me, but I know also that it will all turn out differently. I take you as a star and a trap, as a stone to tip the scales, as a judge that is blindfolded, as a hole to fall into, as a path to walk, as a cross and an arrow. Up to the present I travelled the opposite way of the sun; henceforth I travel two ways, as sun and as moon. Henceforth I take on two sexes, two hemispheres, two skies, two sets of everything. Henceforth I shall be double-jointed and double-sexed. Everything that happens will happen twice. I shall be as a visitor to this earth, partaking of its blessings and carrying off its gifts. I shall neither serve nor be served. I shall seek the end in myself.

I look out again at the sun – my first full gaze. It is blood-red and men are walking about on the roof-tops. Everything above the horizon is clear to me. It is like Easter Sunday. Death is behind me and birth too. I am going to live now among the life maladies. I am going to live the spiritual life of the pygmy, the secret life of the little man in the wilderness of the bush. Inner and outer have changed places. Equilibrium is no longer the goal – the scales must be destroyed. Let me hear you promise again all those sunny things you carry inside you. Let me try to believe for one day, while I rest in the open, that the sun brings good tidings. Let me rot in splendour while the sun bursts in your womb. I believe all your lies implicitly. I take you as the personification of evil, as the destroyer of the soul, as the Maharanee of the night. Tack your womb up on my wall, so that I may remember you. We must get going. Tomorrow, tomorrow . . .

# From *Sexus*

It must have been a Thursday night when I met her for the first time –
at the dance hall. I reported to work in the morning, after an hour or
two's sleep, looking like a somnambulist. The day passed like a
dream. After dinner I fell asleep on the couch and awoke fully dressed
about six the next morning. I felt thoroughly refreshed, pure at heart,
and obsessed with one idea – to have her at any cost. Walking through
the park I debated what sort of flowers to send with the book I had
promised her (*Winesburg, Ohio*). I was approaching my thirty-third
year, the age of Christ crucified. A wholly new life lay before me, had I
the courage to risk all. Actually there was nothing to risk: I was at the
bottom rung of the ladder, a failure in every sense of the word.

It was a Saturday morning, then, and for me Saturday has always
been the best day of the week. I come to life when others are dropping
off with fatigue; my week begins with the Jewish day of rest. That this
was to be the grand week of my life, to last for seven long years, I had
no idea of course. I knew only that the day was auspicious and
eventful. To make the fatal step, to throw everything to the dogs, is in
itself an emancipation: the thought of consequences never entered my
head. To make absolute, unconditional surrender to the woman one
loves is to break every bond save the desire not to lose her, which is the
most terrible bond of all.

I spent the morning borrowing right and left, dispatched the book
and flowers, then sat down to write a long letter to be delivered by a
special messenger. I told her that I would telephone her later in the
afternoon. At noon I quit the office and went home. I was terribly
restless, almost feverish with impatience. To wait until five o'clock
was torture. I went again to the park, oblivious of everything as I
walked blindly over the downs to the lake where the children were
sailing their boats. In the distance a band was playing; it brought back
memories of my childhood, stifled dreams, longings, regrets. A
sultry, passionate rebellion filled my veins. I thought of certain great
figures in the past, of all that they had accomplished at my age. What
ambitions I may have had were gone; there was nothing I wanted to do

except put myself completely in her hands. Above everything else I wanted to hear her voice, know that she was still alive, that she had not already forgotten me. To be able to put a nickel in the slot every day of my life henceforth, to be able to hear her say hello, that and nothing more was the utmost I dared hope for. If she would promise me that much, and keep her promise, it wouldn't matter what happened.

Promptly at five o'clock I telephoned. A strangely sad, foreign voice informed me that she was not at home. I tried to find out when she would be home but I was cut off. The thought that she was out of reach drove me frantic. I telephoned my wife that I would not be home for dinner. She greeted the announcement in her usual disgusted way, as though she expected nothing more of me than disappointments and postponements. 'Choke on it, you bitch,' I thought to myself as I hung up. 'At least I know that I don't want you, any part of you, dead or alive.' An open trolley was coming along; without a thought of its direction I hopped aboard and made for the rear seat. I rode around for a couple of hours in a deep trance; when I came to I recognized an Arabian ice-cream parlour near the waterfront, got off, walked to the wharf and sat on a stringpiece looking up at the humming fretwork of the Brooklyn Bridge. There were still several hours to kill before I dared venture to go to the dance hall. Gazing vacantly at the opposite shore my thoughts drifted ceaselessly, like a ship without a rudder.

When finally I picked myself up and staggered off I was like a man under an anaesthetic who has managed to slip away from the operating table. Everything looked familiar yet made no sense; it took ages to co-ordinate a few simple impressions which by ordinary reflex calculus would mean table, chair, building, person. Buildings emptied of their automatons are even more desolate than tombs; when the machines are left idle they create a void deeper than death itself. I was a ghost moving about in a vacuum. To sit down, to stop and light a cigarette, not to sit down, not to smoke, to think, or not to think, breathe or stop breathing, it was all one and the same. Drop dead and the man behind you walks over you; fire a revolver and another man fires at you; yell and you wake the dead, who, oddly enough, also have powerful lungs. Traffic is now going East and West; in a minute it will be going North and South. Everything is proceeding blindly according to rule and nobody is getting anywhere. Lurch and stagger in and out, up and down, some dropping out like flies, others swarming in like gnats. Eat standing up, with slots, levers, greasy nickels, greasy cellophane, greasy appetite. Wipe your mouth, belch, pick your teeth, cock your hat, tramp, slide, stagger, whistle, blow your brains out. In the next life I will be a vulture feeding on rich carrion: I will perch on top of the tall buildings and dive like a shot the moment I smell death. Now I am whistling a merry tune – the epigastric regions are at peace. *Hello, Mara, how are you?* And she will give me the enigmatic smile, throwing her arms about me in warm embrace. This will take place in a void under powerful klieg lights with three centimetres of privacy marking a mystic circle about us.

I mount the steps and enter the arena, the grand ballroom of the double-barrelled sex adepts, now flooded with a warm boudoir glow. The phantoms are waltzing in a sweet chewing-gum haze, knees slightly crooked, haunches taut, ankles swimming in powdered sapphire. Between drumbeats I hear the ambulance clanging down below, then fire engines, then police sirens. The waltz is perforated with anguish, little bullet holes slipping over the cogs of the mechanical piano which is drowned because it is blocks away in a burning building without fire escapes. She is not on the floor. She may be lying in bed reading a book, she may be making love with a prize fighter, or she may be running like mad through a field of stubble, one shoe on, one shoe off, a man named Corn Cob pursuing her hotly. Wherever she is I am standing in complete darkness; her absence blots me out.

I inquire of one of the girls if she knows when Mara will arrive. *Mara?* Never heard of her. How should she know anything about anybody since she's only had the job an hour or so and is sweating like a mare wrapped in six suits of woollen underwear lined with fleece. Won't I offer her a dance – she'll ask one of the other girls about this Mara. We dance a few rounds of sweat and rose water, the conversation running to corns and bunions and varicose veins, the musicians peering through the boudoir mist with jellied eyes, their faces spread in a frozen grin. The girl over there, Florrie, she might be able to tell me something about my friend. Florrie has a wide mouth and eyes of lapis lazuli; she's as cool as a geranium, having just come from an all-afternoon fucking fiesta. Does Florrie know if Mara will be coming soon? She doesn't think so . . . she doesn't think she'll come at all this evening. *Why?* She thinks she has a date with someone. Better ask the Greek – he knows everything.

The Greek says yes, Miss Mara will come . . . yes, just wait a while. I wait and wait. The girls are steaming, like sweating horses standing in a field of snow. Midnight. No sign of Mara. I move slowly, unwillingly, towards the door. A Puerto Rican lad is buttoning his fly on the top step.

In the subway I test my eyesight reading the ads at the farther end of the car. I cross-examine my body to ascertain if I am exempt from any of the ailments which civilized man is heir to. Is my breath foul? Does my heart knock? Have I a fallen instep? Are my joints swollen with rheumatism? No sinus trouble? No pyorrhea? How about constipation? Or that tired feeling after lunch? No migraine, no acidosis, no intestinal catarrh, no lumbago, no floating bladder, no corns or bunions, no varicose veins? As far as I know I'm sound as a button, and yet . . . Well, the truth is I lack something, something vital . . . .

I'm lovesick. Sick to death. A touch of dandruff and I'd succumb like a poisoned rat.

My body is heavy as lead when I throw it into bed. I pass immediately into the lowest depth of dream. This body, which has become a sarcophagus with stone handles, lies perfectly motionless; the dreamer rises out of it, like a vapour, to circumnavigate the world. The dreamer seeks vainly to find a form and shape that will fit his ethereal essence. Like a celestial tailor, he tries on one body after another, but they are all misfits. Finally he is obliged to return to his own body, to reassume the leaden mould, to become a prisoner of the flesh, to carry on in torpor, pain and ennui.

Sunday morning. I awaken fresh as a daisy. The world lies before me, unconquered, unsullied, virgin as the Arctic zones. I swallow a little bismuth and chloride of lime to drive away the last leaden fumes of inertia. I will go directly to her home, ring the bell, and walk in. Here I am, take me – or stab me to death. Stab the heart, stab the brain, stab the lungs, the kidneys, the viscera, the eyes, the ears. If only one organ be left alive you are doomed – doomed to be mine, forever, in this world and the next and all the worlds to come. I'm a desperado of love, a scalper, a slayer. I'm insatiable. I eat hair, dirty wax, dry blood clots, anything and everything you call yours. Show me your father, with his kites, his racehorses, his free passes for the opera: I will eat them all, swallow them alive. Where is the chair you sit in, where is your favourite comb, your toothbrush, your nail file? Trot them out that I may devour them at one gulp. You have a sister more beautiful than yourself, you say. Show her to me – I want to lick the flesh from her bones.

Riding towards the ocean, towards the marshland where a little house was built to hatch a little egg which, after it had assumed the proper form, was christened Mara. That one little drop escaping from a man's penis should produce such staggering results! I believe in God the Father, in Jesus Christ his only begotten Son, in the blessed Virgin Mary, the Holy Ghost, in Adam Cadmium, in chrome nickel, the oxides and the mercurochromes, in waterfowls and watercress, in epileptoid seizures, in bubonic plagues, in devachan, in planetary conjunctions, in chicken tracks and stick-throwing, in revolutions, in stock crashes, in wars, earthquakes, cyclones, in Kali Yuga and in hula-hula. *I believe. I believe.* I believe because not to believe is to become as lead, to lie prone and rigid, forever inert, to waste away . . . .

Looking out on the contemporary landscape. Where are the beasts of the field, the crops, the manure, the roses that flower in the midst of corruption? I see railroad tracks, gas stations, cement blocks, iron girders, tall chimneys, automobile cemeteries, factories, warehouses, sweatshops, vacant lots. Not even a goat in sight. I see it all clearly and distinctly: it spells desolation, death, death everlasting. For thirty years now I have worn the iron cross of ignominious servitude, serving but not believing, working but taking no wages, resting but knowing no peace. Why should I believe that everything will suddenly change, just having her, just loving and being loved?

Nothing will be changed except myself.

As I approach the house I see a woman in the back yard hanging up clothes. Her profile is turned to me; it is undoubtedly the face of the woman with the strange, foreign voice who answered the telephone. I don't want to meet this woman, I don't want to know who she is, I don't want to believe what I suspect. I walk round the block and when I come again to the door she is gone. Somehow my courage too is gone.

I ring the bell hesitantly. Instantly the door is yanked open and the figure of a tall, menacing young man blocks the threshold. She is not in, can't say when she'll be back, who are you, what do you want of her? Then goodbye and bang! The door is staring me in the face. Young man, you'll regret this. One day I'll return with a shotgun and blow your testicles off . . . . So that's it! Everybody on guard, everybody tipped off, everybody trained to be elusive and evasive. Miss Mara is never where she's expected to be, nor does anybody know where she might be expected to be. Miss Mara inhabits the airs: volcanic ash blown hither and thither by the trade winds. Defeat and mystery for the first day of the Sabbatical year. Gloomy Sunday amongst the Gentiles, amongst the kith and kin of accidental birth. Death to all Christian brethren! Death to the phony status quo!

A few days passed without any sign of life from her. In the kitchen, after my wife had retired, I would sit and write voluminous letters to her. We were living then in a morbidly respectable neighbourhood, occupying the parlour floor and basement of a lugubrious brownstone house. From time to time I tried to write but the gloom which my wife created around her was too much for me. Only once did I succeed in breaking the spell which she had cast over the place; that was during a high fever which lasted for several days when I refused to see a doctor, refused to take any medicine, refused to take any nourishment. In a corner of the room upstairs I lay in a wide bed and fought off a delirium which threatened to end in death. I had never really been ill since childhood and the experience was delicious. To make my way to the toilet was like staggering through all the intricate passages of an ocean liner. I lived several lives in the few days that it lasted. That was my sole vacation in the sepulchre which is called home. The only other place I could tolerate was the kitchen. It was a sort of comfortable prison cell and, like a prisoner, here I often sat alone late into the night planning my escape. Here too my friend Stanley sometimes joined me, croaking over my misfortune and withering every hope with bitter and malicious barbs.

It was here I wrote the maddest letters ever penned. Anyone who thinks he is defeated, hopeless, without resources, can take courage from me. I had a scratchy pen, a bottle of ink and paper – my sole weapons. I put down everything which came into my head, whether it made sense or not. After I had posted a letter I would go upstairs and lie down beside my wife and, with eyes wide open, stare into the darkness, as if trying to read my future. I said to myself over and over that if a man, a sincere and desperate man like myself, loves a woman with all his heart, if he is ready to cut off his ears and mail them to her, if he will take his heart's blood and pump it out on paper, saturate her with his need and longing, besiege her everlastingly, she cannot possibly refuse him. The homeliest man, the weakest man, the most undeserving man must triumph if he is willing to surrender his last drop of blood. No woman can hold out against the gift of absolute love.

I went again to the dance hall and found a message waiting for me. The sight of her handwriting made me tremble. It was brief and to the point. She would meet me at Times Square, in front of the drugstore, at midnight the following day. I was to please stop writing her to her home.

I had a little less than three dollars in my pocket when we met. The greeting she gave me was cordial and brisk. No mention of my visit to the house or the letters or the gifts. Where would I like to go, she asked after a few words. I hadn't the slightest idea what to suggest. That she was standing there in the flesh, speaking to me, looking at me, was an event which I had not yet fully grasped. 'Let's go to Jimmy Kelly's place,' she said, coming to my rescue. She took me by the arm and walked me to the kerb where a cab was waiting for us. I sank back into the seat, overwhelmed by her mere presence. I made no attempt to kiss her or even to hold her hand. She had come – that was the paramount thing. That was everything.

We remained until the early hours of the morning, eating, drinking, dancing. We talked freely and understandingly. I knew no more about her, about her real life, than I knew before, not because of any secrecy on her part but rather because the moment was too full and neither past nor future seemed important.

When the bill came I almost dropped dead.

In order to stall for time I ordered more drinks. When I confessed to her that I had only a couple of dollars on me she suggested that I give them a cheque, assuring me that since she was with me there would be no question about its acceptance. I had to explain that I owned no chequebook, that I possessed nothing but my salary. In short, I made a full clearance.

While confessing this sad state of affairs to her an idea had germinated in my crop. I excused myself and went to the telephone booth. I called the main office of the telegraph company and begged the night manager, who was a friend of mine, to send a messenger to me immediately with a fifty-dollar bill. It was a lot of money for him to borrow from the till, and he knew I wasn't any too reliable, but I gave him a harrowing story, promising faithfully to return it before the day was out.

The messenger turned out to be another good friend of mine, old man Creighton, an ex-minister of the gospel. He seemed indeed surprised to find me in such a place at that hour. As I was signing the sheet he asked me in a low voice if I was sure I would have enough with the fifty. 'I can lend you something out of my own pocket,' he added. 'It would be a pleasure to be of assistance to you.'

'How much can you spare?' I asked, thinking of the task ahead of me in the morning.

'I can give you another twenty-five,' he said readily.

I took it and thanked him warmly. I paid the bill, gave the waiter a generous tip, shook hands with the manager, the assistant manager, the bouncer, the hat check girl, the doorman, and with a beggar who had his mitt out. We got into a cab and, as it wheeled around, Mara impulsively climbed over me and straddled me. We went into a blind fuck, with the cab lurching and careening, our teeth knocking, tongue bitten, and the juice pouring from her like hot soup. As we passed an open plaza on the other side of the river, just at daybreak, I caught the astonished glance of a cop as we sped by. 'It's dawn, Mara,' I said, trying gently to disengage myself. 'Wait, wait,' she begged, panting and clutching at me furiously, and with that she went into a prolonged orgasm in which I thought she would rub my cock off. Finally she slid off and slumped back into her corner, her dress still up over her knees. I leaned over to embrace her again and as I did so I ran my hand up her wet cunt. She clung to me like a leech, wiggling her slippery ass around in a frenzy of abandon. I felt the hot juice trickling through my fingers. I had all four fingers up her crotch, stirring up the liquid moss which was tingling with electrical spasms. She had two or three orgasms and then sank back exhausted, smiling up at me weakly like a trapped doe.

After a time she got out her mirror and began powdering her face. Suddenly I observed a startled expression on her face, followed by a quick turn of the head. In another moment she was kneeling on the seat, staring out of the back window. 'Someone's following us,' she said. 'Don't look!' I was too weak and happy to give a damn. 'Just a bit of hysteria,' I thought to myself, saying nothing but observing her attentively as she gave rapid, jerky orders to the driver to go this way and that, faster and faster. '*Please, please!*' she begged him, as though it were life and death. 'Lady,' I heard him say, as if from far off, from some other dream vehicle, 'I can't give her any more . . . I've got a wife and kid . . . I'm sorry.'

I took her hand and pressed it gently. She made an abortive gesture, as if to say – 'You don't know . . . you don't know . . . this is terrible.' It was not the moment to ask her questions. Suddenly I had the realization that we were in danger. Suddenly I put two and two together, in my own crazy fashion. I reflected quickly . . . nobody is following us . . . that's all coke and laudanum . . . but somebody's after her, that's definite . . . she's committed a crime, a serious one, and maybe more than one . . . nothing she says adds up . . . I'm in a web of lies . . . I'm in love with a monster, the most gorgeous monster imaginable . . . I should quit her now, immediately, without a word of explanation . . . otherwise I'm doomed . . . she's fathomless, impenetrable . . . I might have known that the one woman in the world whom I can't live without is marked with mystery . . . get out at once . . . jump . . . save yourself!

I felt her hand on my leg, rousing me stealthily. Her face was relaxed, her eyes wide open, full, shining with innocence . . .

129

'They've gone,' she said. 'It's all right now.'

Nothing is right, I thought to myself. We're only beginning. Mara, Mara, where are you leading me? It's fateful, it's ominous, but I belong to you body and soul, and you will take me where you will, deliver me to my keeper, bruised, crushed, broken. For us there is no final understanding. I feel the ground slipping from under me . . . .

My thoughts she was never able to penetrate, neither then nor later. She probed deeper than thought: she read blindly, as if endowed with antennae. She knew that I was meant to destroy, that I would destroy her too in the end. She knew that whatever game she might pretend to play with me she had met her match. We were pulling up to the house. She drew close to me and, as though she had a switch inside her which she controlled at will, she turned on me the full incandescent radiance of her love. The driver had stopped the car. She told him to pull up the street a little farther and wait. We were facing one another, hands clasped, knees touching. A fire ran through our veins. We remained thus for several minutes, as in some ancient ceremony, the silence broken only by the purr of the motor.

'I'll call you tomorrow,' she said, leaning forward impulsively for a last embrace. And then in my ear she murmured – 'I'm falling in love with the strangest man on earth. You frighten me, you're so gentle. Hold me tight . . . believe in me always . . . I feel almost as if I were with a god.'

Embracing her, trembling with the warmth of her passion, my mind jumped clear of the embrace, electrified by the tiny seed she had planted in me. Something that had been chained down, something that had struggled abortively to assert itself ever since I was a child and had brought my ego into the street for a glance around, now broke loose and went sky-rocketing into the blue. Some phenomenal new being was sprouting with alarming rapidity from the top of my head, from the double crown which was mine from birth.

After an hour or two's rest I got to the office, which was already jammed with applications. The telephones were ringing as usual. It seemed more than ever senseless to be passing my life away in the attempt to fill up a permanent leak. The officials of the cosmococcic telegraph world had lost faith in me and I had lost faith in the whole fantastic world which they were uniting with wires, cables, pulleys, buzzers and Christ only knows what. The only interest I displayed was in the pay cheque – and the much talked of bonus which was due any day. I had one other interest, a secret, diabolical one, and that was to work off a grudge which I had against Spivak, the efficiency expert whom they had brought in from another city expressly to spy on me. As soon as Spivak appeared on the scene, no matter in what remote, outlying office, I was tipped off. I used to lie awake nights thinking it out like a safecracker – how I would trip him up and bring about his dismissal. I made a vow that I would hang on to the job until I had knifed him. It gave me pleasure to send him phony messages under false names in order to give him a bum steer, covering him with ridicule and causing endless confusion. I even had people write him letters threatening his life. I would get Curley, my chief stooge, to telephone him from time to time, saying that his house was on fire or that his wife had been taken to the hospital – anything that would upset him and start him off on a fool's errand. I had a gift for this underhanded sort of warfare. It was a talent that had been developed since the tailoring days. Whenever my father said to me – 'Better cross his name off the books, he'll never pay up!' I interpreted it very much as would a young Indian brave if the old chief had handed him a prisoner and said – 'Bad pale face, give him the works!' (I had a thousand different ways of annoying a man without running foul of the law. Some men, whom I disliked on principle, I continued to plague long after they had paid their petty debts. One man, whom I especially detested, died of an apoplectic fit upon receiving one of my anonymous insulting letters which was smeared with cat shit, bird shit, dog shit and one or two other varieties, including the well-known human variety.) Spivak consequently was just my meat. I concentrated all my cosmococcic attention on the sole plan of annihilating him. When we met I was polite, deferential, apparently eager to co-operate with him in every way. Never lost my temper with him, though every word he uttered made my blood boil. I did everything possible to bolster his pride, inflate his ego, so that when the moment came to puncture the bag the noise would be heard far and wide.

Towards noon Mara telephoned. The conversation must have lasted a quarter of an hour. I thought she'd never hang up. She said she had been rereading my letters; some of them she had read aloud to her aunt, or rather parts of them. (Her aunt had said that I must be a poet.) She was disturbed about the money I had borrowed. Would I be able to pay it back all right or should she try and borrow some? It was strange that I should be poor – I behaved like a rich man. But she was glad I was poor. Next time we would take a trolley ride somewhere. She didn't care about night clubs; she preferred a walk in the country or a stroll along the beach. The book was wonderful – she had only begun it this morning. Why didn't I try to write? She was sure I could write a great book. She had ideas for a book which she would tell me about when we met again. If I liked, she would introduce me to some writers she knew – they would be only too glad to help me . . . .

She rambled on like that interminably. I was thrilled and worried at the same time. I had rather she put it down on paper. But she seldom wrote letters, so she said. *Why* I couldn't understand. Her fluency was marvellous. She would say things at random, intricate, flamelike, or slide off into a parenthetical limbo peppered with fireworks – admirable linguistic feats which a practised writer might struggle for hours to achieve. And yet her letters – I remember the shock I received when I opened the first one – were almost childlike.

Two or three days later I met Mara for the first time in broad daylight. I was waiting for her in the Long Island depot over in Brooklyn. It was about six in the afternoon, daylight-saving time, which is a strange sunlit rush hour that enlivens even such a gloomy crypt as the waiting room of the Long Island Railroad. I was standing near the door when I spotted her crossing the car tracks under the elevated line; the sunlight filtered through the hideous structure in shafts of powdered gold. She had on a dotted Swiss dress which made her full figure seem even more opulent; the breeze blew lightly through her glossy black hair, teasing the heavy chalk-white face like spray dashing against a cliff. In that quick lithe stride, so sure, so alert, I sensed the animal breaking through the flesh with flowery grace and fragile beauty. This was her daytime self, a fresh, healthy creature who dressed with utter simplicity, and talked almost like a child.

We had decided to spend the evening at the beach. I was afraid it would be too cool for her in that light dress but she said she never felt the cold. We were so frightfully happy that the words just babbled out of our mouths. We had crowded together in the motorman's compartment, our faces almost touching and glowing with the fiery rays of the setting sun. How different this ride over the rooftops from the lonely anxious one that Sunday morning when I set out for her home! Was it possible that in such a short span of time the world could take on such a different hue?

That fiery sun going down in the West – what a symbol of joy and warmth! It fired our hearts, illumined our thoughts, magnetized our souls. Its warmth would last far into the night, would flow back from below the curved horizon in defiance of the night. In this fiery blaze I handed her the manuscript to read. I couldn't have chosen a more favourable moment or a more favourable critic. It had been conceived in darkness and it was being baptized in light. As I watched her expression I had such a strong feeling of exaltation that I felt as if I had handed her a message from the Creator himself. I didn't need to know her opinion, I could read it on her face. For years I cherished this souvenir, reviving it in those dark moments when I had broken with everyone, walking back and forth in a lonely attic in a foreign city, reading the freshly written pages and struggling to visualize on the faces of all my coming readers this expression of unreserved love and admiration. When people ask me if I have a definite audience in mind when I sit down to write I tell them no, I have no one in mind, but the truth is that I have before me the image of a great crowd, an anonymous crowd, in which perhaps I recognize here and there a friendly face: in that crowd I see accumulating the slow, burning warmth which was once a single image: I see it spread, take fire, rise into a great conflagration. (The only time a writer receives his due reward is when someone comes to him burning with this flame which he fanned in a moment of solitude. Honest criticism means nothing: what one wants is unrestrained passion, fire for fire.)

Back in town I found a note on Ulric's bell, from Mara. She had arrived shortly after we left. Had been sitting on the steps waiting for me, waiting for hours, if I were to believe her words. A postscript informed me that she was off to Rockaway with her two friends. I was to call her there as soon as I could.

I arrived at dusk and found her waiting for me at the station; she was in a bathing suit over which she had thrown a mackintosh. Florrie and Hannah were sleeping it off again at the hotel; Hannah had lost her beautiful new set of false teeth and was in a state of nervous prostration. Florrie, she said, was going back to the woods again; she had fallen hard for Bill, one of the backwoodsmen. But first she had to have an abortion performed. It was nothing – not for Florrie anyway. The only thing that bothered her was that she seemed to grow larger down there with each abortion; soon she wouldn't be able to take on anything but niggers.

She led me to another hotel where we were to pass the night together. We sat talking awhile in the lugubrious dining room over a glass of beer. She looked queer in that mackintosh – like a person who's been driven out of the house by fire in the middle of the night. We were itching to get to bed but in order not to arouse suspicion we had to pretend to be in no great hurry. I had lost all sense of place: it seemed as if we had made a rendezvous in a dark room by the Atlantic

Ocean in the wake of an exodus. Two or three other couples slipped in noiselessly, sipped their drinks, and chatted furtively in subdued whispers. A man walked through with a bloody meat cleaver, holding a decapitated chicken by the legs; the blood dripped on the floor, leaving a zigzag trail – like the passage of a drunken whore who is menstruating freely.

Finally we were shown to a cell at the end of a long corridor. It was like the terminus of a bad dream, or the missing half of a Chirico painting. The corridor formed the axis of two wholly unrelated worlds; if you were to go left instead of right you might never find your way back again. We undressed and fell on the iron cot in a sexual sweat. We went at it like a pair of wrestlers who have been left to untangle themselves in an empty arena after the lights are out and the crowd dispersed. Mara was struggling frantically to bring on an orgasm. She had somehow become detached from her sexual apparatus; it was night and she was lost in the dark; her movements were those of a dreamer desperately struggling to re-enter the body which had begun the act of surrender. I got up to wash myself, to cool it off with a little cold water. There was no sink in the room. In the yellow light of an almost extinct bulb I saw myself in a cracked mirror; I had the expression of a Jack the Ripper looking for a straw hat in a pisspot. Mara lay prone on the bed, panting and sweating; she had the appearance of a battered odalisque made of jagged pieces of mica. I slipped into my trousers and staggered through the funnel-like corridor in search of the washroom. A bald-headed man, stripped to the waist, stood before a marble basin washing his trunk and armpits. I waited patiently until he had finished. He snorted like a walrus in performing his ablutions; when he had done he opened a can of talcum powder and sprinkled it generously over his torso, which was creased and caked like an elephant's hide.

When I returned I found Mara smoking a cigarette and playing with herself. She was burning up with desire. We went at it again, trying it dog-fashion this time, but still it was no go. The room began to heave and bulge, the walls were sweating, the mattress which was made of straw was almost touching the floor. The performance began to take on all the aspects and proportions of a bad dream. From the end of the corridor came the broken wheeze of an asthmatic; it sounded like the tail end of a gale whizzing through a corrugated rat hole.

Just as she was about to come we heard someone fumbling at the door. I slid off her and poked my head out. It was a drunk trying to find his room. A few minutes later, when I went to the washroom to give my cock another cool spritz-bath, he was still looking for his room. The transoms were all open and from them came a stertorous cacophony which resembled the epiphany of John the locust-eater. When I returned to resume the ordeal my cock felt as if it were made of old rubber bands. I had absolutely no more feeling at that end; it was like pushing a piece of stiff suet down a drainpipe. What's more, there wasn't another charge left in the battery; if anything was to happen now it would be in the nature of gall and leathery worms or a drop of pus in a solution of thin pot cheese. What surprised me was that it continued to stand up like a hammer; it had lost all the appearance of a sexual implement; it looked disgustingly like a cheap gadget from the five-and-ten-cent store, like a bright-coloured piece of fishing tackle minus the bait. And on this bright and slippery gadget Mara twisted like an eel. She wasn't any longer a woman in heat, she wasn't even a woman; she was just a mass of undefinable contours wriggling and squirming like a piece of fresh bait seen upside down through a convex mirror in a rough sea.

I had long ceased to be interested in her contortions; except for the part of me that was in her I was as cool as a cucumber and remote as the Dog Star. It was like a long-distance death message concerning someone whom you had forgotten long ago. All I was waiting for was to feel that incredibly aborted explosion of wet stars which drop back to the floor of the womb like dead snails.

Towards dawn, Eastern Standard Time, I saw by that frozen condensed-milk expression about the jaw that it was happening. Her face went through all the metamorphoses of early uterine life, only in reverse. With the last dying spark it collapsed like a punctured bag, the eyes and nostrils smoking like toasted acorns in a slightly wrinkled lake of pale skin. I fell off her and dove straight into a coma which ended towards evening with a knock on the door and fresh towels. I looked out the window and saw a collection of tar-covered roofs spotted here and there with doves of taupe. From the ocean front came the boom of surf followed by a frying pan symphony of exasperated sheet metal cooling off in a drizzle at a hundred and thirty-nine degrees centigrade. The hotel was droning and purring like a fat and moribund swamp fly in the solitude of a pine forest. Along the axis of the corridor there had been a further sag and recess during the interim. The Grade A world to the left was all sealed and boarded, like those colossal bathhouses along the boardwalk which, in the off season, curl up on themselves and expire in gasps through endless chinks and slats. The other nameless world to the right had already been chewed off by a triphammer, the work doubtless of some maniac who had endeavoured to justify his existence as a day labourer. Underfoot it was slimy and slippery, as if an army of zippered seals had been weaving it back and forth to the washroom all day long. Here and there an open door revealed the presence of grotesquely plastic water nymphs who had managed to squeeze their mammiferous trundles of avoirdupois into sylphlike fish nets made of spun glass and ribbons of wet clay. The last roses of Summer were fading away into goitrous udders with arms and legs. Soon the epidemic would be over and the ocean would resume its air of gelatinous grandeur, or mucilaginous dignity, of sullen and spiteful solitude.

We stretched ourselves out in the hollow of a suppurating sand dune next to a bed of waving stinkweed on the lee side of a macadamized road over which the emissaries of progress and enlightenment were rolling along with that familiar and soothing clatter which accompanies the smooth locomotion of spitting and farting contraptions of tin woven together by steel knitting needles. The sun was setting in the West as usual, not in splendour and radiance however but in disgust, like a gorgeous omelette engulfed by clouds of snot and phlegm. It was the ideal setting for love, such as the drugstores sell or rent between the covers of a handy pocket edition. I took off my shoes and leisurely deposited my big toe in the first notch of Mara's crotch. Her head was pointed South, mine North; we pillowed them on folded hands, our bodies relaxed and floating effortlessly in the magnetic drift, like two enormous twigs suspended on the surface of a gasoline lake. A visitor from the Renaissance, coming upon us unexpectedly, might well have assumed that we had become dislodged from a painting depicting the violent end of the mangy retinue of a Sybaritic doge. We were lying at the edge of a world in ruins, the composition being a rather precipitate study of perspective and foreshortening in which our prostrated figures served as a picaresque detail.

The conversation was thoroughly desultory, spluttering out with a dull thud like a bullet encountering muscle and sinew. We weren't talking, we were simply parking our sexual implements in the free-parking void of anthropoid chewing-gum machines on the edge of a gasoline oasis. Night would fall poetically over the scene, like a shot of ptomaine poison wrapped in a rotten tomato. Hannah would find her false teeth behind the mechanical piano; Florrie would appropriate a rusty can-opener with which to start the blood flowing.

The wet sand clung to our bodies with the tenacity of fresh-laid wallpaper. From the factories and hospitals nearby came the ingratiating aroma of exhausted chemicals, of hair soaked in peepee, of useless organs plucked out alive and left to rot slowly through an eternity in sealed vessels labelled with great care and veneration. A brief twilight sleep in the arms of Morpheus the Danubian dachshund.

When I got back to town Maude inquired in her polite fishlike way if I had had a pleasant holiday. She remarked that I looked rather haggard. She added that she was thinking of taking a little vacation herself; she had received an invitation from an old convent friend to pass a few days at her home in the country. I thought it an excellent idea.

Two days later I accompanied her and the child to the station. She asked me if I wouldn't care to ride part of the way with them. I saw no reason why I shouldn't. Besides, I thought maybe she had something of importance to tell me. I boarded the train and rode some distance into the country, talking about things of no consequence and wondering all the time when she would come out with it. Nothing happened. I finally got off the train and waved goodbye. 'Say goodbye to daddy,' she urged the child. 'You won't see him again for several weeks.' Bye-bye! Bye-bye! I waved good-naturedly, like any suburban papa seeing his wife and child off. Several weeks, she had said. That would be excellent. I walked up and down the platform waiting for the train and pondering on all the things I would do in her absence. Mara would be delighted. It would be like having a private honeymoon: we could do a million wonderful things in a stretch of several weeks.

The following day I awoke with a frightful earache. I telephoned Mara and urged her to meet me at the doctor's office. The doctor was one of the wife's demonic friends. He had almost murdered the child once with his medieval instruments of torture. Now it was my turn. I left Mara to sit it out on a bench near the entrance to the park.

The doctor seemed delighted to see me; engaging me in a pseudo-literary discussion, he put his instruments up to boil. Then he tested out an electrically run glass cage which looked like a transparent ticker but which was actually some devilish sort of inhuman bloodsucking contraption which he intended to try out as a parting fillip.

So many doctors had tinkered with my ear that I was quite a veteran by this time. Each fresh irruption meant that the dead bone was drawing closer and closer to the brain. Finally there would be a grand conjunction, the mastoid would become like a wild mustang, there would be a concert of silver saws and silver mallets, and I would be shipped home with my face twisted to one side like a hemiplegic rhapsodist.

'You don't hear any more with that ear, of course?' said he, plunging a hot wire into the very core of my skull without a word of warning.

'No, not at all,' I answered, almost sliding off the seat with pain.

'Now this is going to hurt a bit,' said he, manipulating a diabolical-looking fishhook.

It went on like that, each operation a little more painful than the last, until I was so beside myself with pain that I wanted to kick him in the guts. Still there remained the electrical cage: that was to irrigate the canals, extract the last iota of pus, and send me out into the street rearing like a bronco.

'It's a nasty business,' he said, lighting a cigarette in order to give me a breathing spell. 'I wouldn't want to go through with it myself. If it gets any worse you'd better let me operate on you.'

I settled down for the irrigation. He inserted the nozzle and turned on the switch. It felt as though he were irrigating my brain with a solution of prussic acid. The pus was coming out and with it a thin stream of blood. The pain was excruciating.

'Does it really hurt as much as that?' he exclaimed, seeing that I had become white as a sheet.

'It hurts worse than that,' I said. 'If you don't stop soon I'll smash it. I'd rather have triple mastoids and look like a demented frog.'

He pulled the nozzle out and with it the lining of my ear, of my cerebellum, of one kidney and the marrow of my coccyx.

'A fine job,' said I. 'When do I come again?'

He thought it best to come tomorrow – just to see how it was progressing.

Mara had a fright when she saw me. She wanted to take me home at once and nurse me. I was so used up I couldn't stand having anyone near me. Hurriedly I said goodbye. 'Meet me tomorrow!'

I staggered home like a drunk and fell on the couch, into a deep drugged sleep. When I awoke it was dawning. I felt excellent. I got up and went for a stroll through the park. The swans were coming to life: their mastoids were nonexistent.

When pain lets up life seems grand, even without money or friends or high ambitions. Just to breathe easily, to walk without a sudden spasm or twitch. Swans are very beautiful then. Trees too. Even automobiles. Life moves along on roller skates; the earth is pregnant and constantly churning up new magnetic fields of space. See how the wind bends the tiny blades of grass! Each little blade is sentient; everything responds. If the earth itself were in pain we could do nothing about it. The planets never have an earache; they are immune, though bearing within them untold pain and suffering.

For once I was at the office ahead of time. I worked like a Trojan without feeling the slightest fatigue. At the appointed time I met Mara. She would sit again on the park bench, in the same spot.

This time the doctor merely took a look at the ear, picked away a fresh scab, swabbed it with a soothing ointment, and plugged it up. 'Looks fine,' he mumbled. 'Come back in a week.'

We were in good spirits, Mara and I. We had dinner in a roadhouse and with it some Chianti. It was a balmy evening, just made for a stroll over the downs. After a time we lay down in the grass and gazed up at the stars. 'Do you think she'll really stay away several weeks?' asked Mara.

It seemed too good to be true.

'Maybe she'll never come back,' I said. 'Maybe that's what she wanted to tell me when she asked me to ride part of the way with her. Maybe she lost her nerve at the last minute.'

Mara didn't think she was the sort to make a sacrifice like that. It didn't matter anyway. For a while we could be happy, could forget that she existed.

'I wish we could get away from this country altogether,' said Mara. 'I wish we could go to some other country, somewhere where nobody knows us.'

I agreed that that would be ideal. 'We'll do it eventually,' I said. 'There isn't a soul here whom I care about. My whole life has been meaningless – until you came along.'

'Let's go and row in the lake,' said Mara suddenly. We got up and sauntered over to the boats. Too late, the boats were all padlocked. We started strolling aimlessly along a path by the water; soon we came to a little resthouse built out over the water. It was deserted. I sat down on the rough bench and Mara seated herself on my lap. She had on the stiff dotted Swiss dress which I liked so much. Underneath it not a stitch. She got off my lap a moment and lifting her dress she straddled me. We had a wonderful close-knit fuck. When it was over we sat for a while without unhitching, just silently chewing one another's lips and ears.

Then we got up and, at the edge of the lake, we washed ourselves with our handkerchiefs. I was just drying my cock with the tail of my shirt when Mara suddenly grasped my arm and pointed to something

139

moving behind a bush. All I could see was a gleam of something bright. I quickly buttoned up my pants and taking Mara by the arm we regained the gravel path and started slowly walking in the opposite direction.

'It was a cop, I'm sure,' said Mara. 'They do that, the dirty perverts. They're always hiding in the bushes spying on people.'

In a moment, sure enough, we heard the heavy tread of a thick-witted Mick.

'Just a minute, you two,' he said, 'Where do you think you're going?'

'What do you mean?' said I, pretending to be annoyed. 'We're taking a walk, can't you see?'

'It's about time you took a walk,' he said. 'I've a good mind to walk you back to the station with me. What do you think this is – a stud farm?'

I pretended I didn't know what he was talking about. Being a Mick, that enraged him.

'None of your lip,' said he. 'Better get that dame out of here before I run you in.'

'She's my wife.'

'So . . . your wife, is it? Well now, ain't that nice? Just doing a little billing and cooing, eh? Washing your private parts in public too – I'll be damned if I ever saw the likes of it. Now don't be in too great a hurry. You're guilty of a grave offence, me lad, and if this is your wife she's in for it too.'

'Look here, you don't mean to say . . .'

'What's your name?' he demanded cutting me short, and making to reach for his little notebook.

I told him.

'And where do you live?'

I told him.

'And her name?'

'The same as mine – she's my wife, I told you.'

'So you did,' he said, with a dirty leer. 'All right. Now then, what do you do for a living? Are you working?'

I pulled out my wallet and showed him the Cosmodemonic pass which I always carried and which entitled me to ride free of charge on all subways, elevated and streetcar lines of the city of Greater New York. He scratched his head at this and tilted his cap back on his head. 'So you're the employment manager, are you? That's a pretty responsible position for a young man like you.' Heavy pause. 'I suppose you'd like to keep your job a little longer, wouldn't you?'

Suddenly I had visions of seeing my name plastered in headlines over the morning papers. A fine story the reporters could make of it if they wanted to. It was time to do something.

'Look here, Officer,' said I, 'let's talk the thing over quietly. I live nearby – why don't you walk over to the house with me? Maybe my wife and I were a little reckless – we're not married very long. We shouldn't have carried on like that in a public place, but it was dark and there was nobody around . . .'

'Well, there might be a way of fixing it,' says he. 'You don't want to lose your job, do you?'

'No, I don't,' says I, wondering at the same time how much I had in my pocket and whether he would sneeze at it or not.

Mara was fumbling in her bag.

'Now don't be in such a hurry, lad. You know you can't bribe an officer of the law. By the way, what church do you go to, if I'm not too inquisitive?'

I answered quickly, giving the name of the Catholic church on our corner.

'Then you're one of Father O'Malley's boys! Well, why didn't you tell me that in the first place? Shure, you wouldn't want to disgrace the parish now, would you?'

I told him it would kill me were Father O'Malley to hear of it.

'And you were married in Father O'Malley's church?'

'Yes, Fath – I mean Officer. We were married last April.'

I was trying to count the bills in my pocket without extracting them. It seemed as if there were only three or four bucks. I was wondering how much Mara might have. The cop had started walking and we fell in with him. Presently he stopped short. He pointed ahead with his club. And with his club in the air and his head slightly averted, he began a slow monologue about a coming novena to Our Lady of the Flying Buttress or something of the sort, saying as he held out his left hand that the shortest way out of the park was straight ahead and mind you, be on your good behaviour and so forth.

Mara and I hastily stuffed a few bills in his hand and, thanking him for his kindness, we lit out like a bolt.

'I think you'd better come home with me,' I said. 'If it wasn't enough we gave him he may be coming to pay us a visit. I don't trust these dirty bastards . . . . Father O'Malley, *shit!*'

We hurried home and locked ourselves in. Mara was still trembling. I dug up a little port wine which was hidden away in a cupboard.

'The thing to happen now,' I said, as I downed a glassful, 'is for Maude to come back and surprise us.'

'She wouldn't do that, would she?'

'Christ only knows what she might do.'

'I think we'd better sleep down here,' said Mara. 'I wouldn't like to sleep in her bed.'

We finished the wine and got undressed. Mara came out of the bathroom in Maude's silk kimono. It gave me a start to see her in Maude's outfit. 'I'm your wife, am I not?' she said, putting her arms around me. It gave me a thrill to hear her say that. She walked about the room examining the things.

'Where do you write?' she asked. 'At that little table?'

I nodded.

'You ought to have a big table and a room of your own. How can you write here?'

'I have a big desk upstairs.'

'Where? In the bedroom?'

'No, in the parlour. It's wonderfully lugubrious up there – would you like to see it?'

'No,' she said quickly, 'I'd rather not go up there. I'll always think of you sitting here in this corner by the window . . . . Is this where you wrote me all those letters?'

'No,' I said, 'I wrote you from the kitchen.'

'Show me,' she said. 'Show me just where you sat. I want to see how you looked.'

I took her by the hand and led her back to the kitchen. I sat down and pretended I was writing her a letter. She bent over me and putting her lips to the table she kissed the spot encircled by my arms.

'I never dreamt I would see your home,' she said. 'It's strange to see the place which is to have such an effect upon your life. It's a holy place. I wish we could take this table with us and this chair – everything – even the stove. I wish we could move the whole room and build it into our own home. It belongs to us, this room.'

We went to bed on the divan in the basement. It was a warm night and we went to sleep in the raw. About seven in the morning, as we lay entwined in each other's arms, the rolling doors were violently pushed open and there stood my darling wife, the landlord who lived upstairs, and his daughter. In flagrant delectation we were caught. I sprang out of bed stark naked. Snatching a towel which was on the chair beside the couch I flung it around me and waited for the verdict. Maude motioned to her witnesses to step in and take a look at Mara, who was lying there holding a sheet over her bosom.

'I'll ask you to please get this woman out of here as quickly as possible,' said Maude, and with that she turned on her heel and went upstairs with her witnesses.

Had she been sleeping upstairs in our own bed all night? If so, why had she waited until morning?

'Take it easy, Mara. The goose is cooked now. We may as well stay and have breakfast.'

I dressed hurriedly and ran out to get some bacon and eggs.

'God, I don't see how you can take it so calmly,' she said, sitting at the table with a cigarette to her lips, watching me prepare the breakfast. 'Haven't you any feelings?'

'Sure I have. My feeling is that everything has worked out splendidly. *I'm free*, do you realize that?'

'What are you going to do now?'

'I'm going to work, for one thing. This evening I'll go to Ulric's place – you might meet me there. I have an idea my friend Stanley is behind all this. We'll see.'

At the office I sent a telegram to Stanley to meet me at Ulric's that evening. During the day I had a telephone call from Maude suggesting that I find myself a room. She said she would get the divorce as soon as possible. No comments upon the situation, just a pure businesslike statement. I was to let her know when I wished to call for my things.

Ulric took it rather gravely. It meant a change of life and all changes were serious to him. Mara on the other hand was thoroughly in possession of herself and already looking forward to the new life. It remained to see how Stanley would take it.

Presently the bell rang and there he was, sinister-looking as usual and drunk as a pope. I hadn't seen him that way for years. He had decided that it was an event of the first importance and that it should be celebrated. As far as getting any details from him was concerned it was absolutely impossible. 'I told you I'd fix it for you,' he said. 'You walked into it like a fly into a web. I had it figured out to a T. I didn't ask you any questions, did I? I knew just what you'd do.'

He took a swig from a flask which he was carrying in his inside coat pocket. He didn't even bother to remove his hat. I could see him now as he must have looked when at Fort Oglethorpe. He was the sort of fellow I would have given a wide berth, seeing him in that state.

The telephone rang. It was Dr Kronski asking for *Mister* Miller. 'Congratulations!' he shouted. 'I'm coming over there to see you in a few minutes. I have something to tell you.'

'By the way,' I said, 'do you know anybody who has an extra room to let?'

'That's just what I was going to talk to you about. I've got a place all picked out for you – up on the Bronx. It's a friend of mine – he's a doctor. You can have a whole wing of the house to yourself. Why don't you take Mara with you? You'll like it there. He's got a billiard room on the ground floor, and a good library, and . . .'

'Is he Jewish?' I asked.

'*Is he?* He's a Zionist, an anarchist, a Talmudist and an abortionist. A damned fine chap – and if you're in need of help he'll give you his shirt. I was just around to your house – that's how I found out. Your wife seems to be tickled to death. She'll live pretty comfortably on the alimony you'll have to pay her.'

I told Mara what he had said. We decided to have a look at the place immediately. Stanley had disappeared. Ulric thought he might have gone to the bathroom.

I went to the bathroom and knocked. No answer. I pushed the door open. Stanley was lying in the tub fully dressed, his hat over his eye, the empty bottle in his hand. I left him lying there.

'He's gone, I guess,' I shouted to Ulric as we sailed out.

The Bronx! We had been promised a whole wing of the house – a turkey wing, with feathers and goose pimples thrown in. Kronski's idea of a haven.

It was a suicidal period which began with cockroaches and hot pastrami sandwiches and ended à la Newburg in a cubbyhole on Riverside Drive where Mrs Kronski the Second began her thankless task of illustrating a vast cycloramic appendix to the insanities.

It was under Kronski's influence that Mara decided to change her name again – from Mara to Mona. There were other, more significant changes which also had their origin here in the purlieus of the Bronx.

We had come in the night to Dr Onirifick's hide-out. A light snow had fallen and the coloured panes of glass in the front door were covered with a mantle of pure white. It was just the sort of place I had imagined Kronski *would* select for our 'honeymoon'. Even the cockroaches, which began scurrying up and down the walls as soon as we turned on the lights, seemed familiar – and ordained. The billiard table, which stood in a corner of the room, was at first disconcerting, but when Dr Onirifick's little boy casually opened his fly and began to make peepee against the leg of the table everything seemed quite as it should be.

The front door opened directly on to our room, which was equipped with a billiard table, as I say, a large brass bedstead with eiderdown quilts, a writing desk, a grand piano, a hobbyhorse, a fireplace, a cracked mirror covered with flyspecks, two cuspidors and a settee. There were in all no less than eight windows in our room. Two of them had shades which could be pulled down about two-thirds of the way; the others were absolutely bare and festooned with cobwebs. It was very jolly. No one ever rang the bell or knocked first; everyone walked in unannounced and found his way about as best he could. It was 'a room with a view' both inside and out.

Here we began our life together. A most auspicious debut! The only thing lacking was a sink in which we could urinate to the sound of running water. A harp might have come in handy, too, especially on those droll occasions when the members of Dr Onirifick's family, tired of sitting in the laundry downstairs, would waddle up to our room like auks and penguins and watch us in complete silence as we ate or bathed or made love or combed the lice out of one another's hair. What language they spoke we never knew. They were as mute as the reindeer and nothing could frighten or astound them, not even the sight of a mangy foetus.

Dr Onirifick was always very busy. Children's diseases were his speciality, but the only children we ever noticed during our stay were embryonic ones which he chopped into fine pieces and threw down the drains. He had three children of his own. They were all three supernormal, and on this account were allowed to behave as they pleased. The youngest, about five years of age and already a wizard at algebra, was definitely on his way to becoming a pyromaniac as well as a supermathematician. Twice he had set fire to the house. His latest exploit revealed a more ingenious turn of mind: it was to set fire to a perambulator containing a tender infant and then push the perambulator downhill towards a congested traffic lane.

Yes, a jolly place to begin life anew. There was Ghompal, an ex-messenger whom Kronski had salvaged from the Cosmodemonic Telegraph Company when that institution began to weed out its non-Caucasian employees. Ghompal, being of Dravidian stock and dark as sin, had been one of the first to get the gate. He was a tender soul, extremely modest, humble, loyal and self-sacrificing – almost painfully so. Dr Onirifick cheerfully made a place for him in his vast household – as a glorified chimney sweep. Where Ghompal ate and slept was a mystery. He moved about noiselessly in the performance of his duties, effacing himself, when he deemed it necessary, with the celerity of a ghost. Kronski prided himself on having rescued in the person of this outcast a scholar of the first water. 'He's writing a history of the world,' he told us impressively. He omitted mentioning that, in addition to his duties as secretary, nurse, chambermaid, dishwasher and errand boy, Ghompal also stoked the furnace, hauled the ashes, shovelled the snow, papered the walls and painted the spare rooms.

Nobody attempted to wrestle with the problem of roaches. There were millions of them hidden away beneath the mouldings, the wood-work, the wallpaper. One had only to turn on the light and they streamed out in double, triple, file, column after column, from walls, ceiling, floor, crannies, crevices – veritable armies of them parading, deploying, manoeuvering, as if obeying the commands of some unseen super-roach of a drillmaster. At first it was disgusting, then nauseating, and finally, as with the other strange, disturbing phenomena which distinguished Dr Onirifick's household, their presence among us was accepted by all and sundry as inevitable.

The piano was completely out of tune. Kronski's wife, a timid, mouselike creature whose mouth seemed to be curled in a perpetual deprecatory smile, used to sit and practise the scales on this instru-ment, oblivious apparently of the hideous dissonances which her nimble fingers produced. To hear her play 'The Barcarolle', for example, was excruciating. She seemed not to hear the sour notes, the jangled chords; she played with an expression of utter serenity, her soul enrapt, her senses numbed and bewitched. It was a venomous composure which deceived no one, not even herself, for the moment her fingers ceased wandering she became what in truth she was – a petty, mean, spiteful, malevolent little bitch.

It was curious to see the way in which Kronski pretended to have found a jewel in this second wife. It would have been pathetic, not to say tragic, were he not such a ridiculous figure. He cavorted about her like a porpoise attempting to be elfish. Her digs and barbs served only to galvanize the ponderous, awkward figure in which was hidden a hypersensitive soul. He writhed and twisted like a wounded dolphin, the saliva dripping from his mouth, the sweat pouring from his brow and flooding his all too liquid eyes. It was a horrible charade he gave us on these occasions; though one pitied him one had to laugh, to laugh until the tears came to one's eyes.

If Curley were around he would turn on Curley savagely, in the very midst of his antics, and vent his spleen. He had a loathing for Curley that was inexplicable. Whether it was envy or jealousy which provoked these uncontrollable rages, whatever it was, Kronski would, in these moments, act like a man possessed. Like a huge cat, he would circle around poor Curley, taunting him, baiting him, stinging him with rebukes, slanders, insults, until he was actually foaming at the mouth.

'Why don't you do something, say something?' he would sneer. 'Put up your dukes! Give me a crack, why don't you? You're yeller, aren't you? You're just a worm, a cad, a stooge.'

Curley would leer at him with a contemptuous smile, saying not a word, but poised and ready to strike should Kronski lose all control.

Nobody understood why these ugly scenes took place. Ghompal especially. He had evidently never witnessed such situations in his native land. They left him pained, wounded, shocked. Kronski felt this keenly, loathing himself even more than he loathed Curley. The more he fell in Ghompal's estimation the harder he strove to ingratiate himself with the Hindu.

'There's a really fine soul,' he would say to us. 'I would do anything for Ghompal – anything.'

There were lots of things he might have done to alleviate the latter's burdens, but Kronski gave the impression that when the time came he would do something magnificent. Until then nothing less would satisfy him. He hated to see anyone lend Ghompal a helping hand. 'Trying to salve your conscience, eh?' he would snarl. 'Why don't you put your arms around him and kiss him? Afraid of contamination, is that it?'

Once, just to make him uncomfortable, I did exactly that. I walked up to Ghompal and, putting my arms around him, I kissed him on the brow. Kronski looked at us shamefacedly. Everyone knew that Ghompal had syphilis.

There was Dr Onirifick himself, of course, a presence which made itself felt throughout the house, rather than a human being. What went on in that office of his on the second floor? None of us really knew. Kronski, in his elaborate, melodramatic way, gave crude imaginative pictures of abortion and seduction, bloody jigsaw puzzles which only a monster could put together. On the few occasions when we met, Dr Onirifick impressed me as being nothing more than a mild, goodhearted man with a smattering of learning and a deep interest in music. Only for a few minutes did I see him lose his poise, and that altogether justifiable. I had been reading a book by Hilaire Belloc dealing with the persecution of the Jew throughout the centuries. It was like waving a red flag in front of him to even mention the book and I immediately regretted the blunder. In diabolical fashion Kronski tried to widen the breach. 'Why are we harbouring this snake in the grass?' he seemed to say, arching his eyebrows and twitching and squirming in his customary way. Dr Onirifick, however, passed it off by treating me as if I were merely another gullible idiot who had fallen for the arch casuistry of a diseased Catholic mind.

'He was upset tonight,' Kronski volunteered after the doctor had retired. 'You see, he's after that twelve-year-old niece of his and his wife is on to him. She's threatening to turn him over to the district attorney if he doesn't stop running after the girl. She's jealous as the devil and I don't blame her. Besides, she hates to think of the abortions that are pulled off every day, right under her nose, polluting her home, as it were. She swears there's something wrong with him. There's something wrong with her too, if you notice. If you ask me, I think she's afraid he'll cut her open some night. She looks at his hands all the time, as if he always came to her fresh from a murder.'

He paused a moment to let these observations sink in. 'There's something else preying on her mind,' he resumed. 'The daughter is growing up . . . she'll be a young woman before long. Well, with a husband like that you can see what's bothering her. It's not just the idea of incest –horrible enough – but the further thought, that . . . that he'll come to her some night with bloody hands . . . the hands that murdered the life in her own daughter's womb. . . . Complicated, what? But not impossible. Not with that guy! Such a fine fellow. A sensitive, delicate chap, really. She's right. And what makes it worse is that he's almost Christlike. You can't talk to him about the sex mania because he won't admit a word you say. He pretends to be absolutely innocent. But he's in deep. Someday the police will come and take him away – there'll be a hell of a stink, you'll see. . . .'

That Dr Onirifick had made it possible for Kronski to pursue his medical studies I knew. And that Kronski had to find some extraordinary way of paying Dr Onirifick back I was also aware of. Nothing would suit him better than to have his friend disintegrate completely. Then Kronski would come to the rescue in magnificent fashion. He would do something wholly unexpected, something no man had ever done for another. That was how his mind worked. Meanwhile, by spreading rumours, by slandering and maligning his friend, by undermining him, he was only hastening a downfall which was inevitable. He was positively itching to get to work on his friend, to rehabilitate him, to repay him superabundantly for the kindness he had shown him in putting him through college. He would pull the house down about his friend's ears in order to rescue him from the ruins. A curious attitude. A sort of perverted Galahad. A meddler. A super-meddler. Always doing his damnedest to make things go from bad to worse so that at the last ditch he, Kronski, might step in and magically transform the situation. Even so, it was not gratitude he desired but recognition, recognition of superior powers, recognition of his uniqueness.

While he was still an intern I used to visit him occasionally at the hospital where he was serving his time. We used to play billiards with the other interns. I only visited the hospital when I was in a desperate mood, when I wanted a meal or the loan of a few dollars. I hated the atmosphere of the place; I loathed his associates, their manners, their conversation, their very aims even. The great healing art meant nothing to them; they were looking for a snug berth, that was all. Most of them had as little flair for medicine as a politician has for statesmanship. They didn't even have that fundamental prerequisite of the healer – the love of humankind. They were callous, heartless, utterly self-centred, utterly disinterested in anything but their own advancement. They were worse boors than the butchers in the slaughterhouse.

Kronski was thoroughly at home in this environment. He knew more than the others, could outtalk them, outsmart them, outshout them. He was a better billiard player, a better crapshooter, a better chess player, a better everything. He knew it all and he loved to spew it forth, parade up and down in his own vomit.

Naturally he was heartily detested. Of a gregarious nature he managed, despite his obnoxious traits, to keep himself surrounded by his kind. Had he been obliged to live alone he would have fallen apart. He knew that he was not wanted: nobody ever sought him out except to ask a favour of him. Alone, the realization of his plight must have caused him bitter moments. It was difficult to know how he really appraised himself because in the presence of others he was all gusto, merriment, bluster, bravado, grandeur and grandiloquence. He behaved as though he were rehearsing a part before an invisible mirror. How he loved himself! Yes, and what loathing there was behind that facade, that *amour-propre*! 'I smell bad!' – that's what he must have said to himself every night when alone in his room. 'But I'll do something magnificent yet . . . just watch!'

At intervals there came moods of dejection. He was a pitiful object then – something quite inhuman, something not of the animal world but of the vegetable kingdom. He would plop himself down somewhere and let himself rot. In this condition tumours sprouted from him, as from some gigantic mouldy potato left to perish in the dark. Nothing could stir him from his lethargy. Wherever he was put he would stay, inert, brooding incessantly, as though the world were coming to an end.

As far as one could make out he had no personal problems. He was a monster who had emerged from the vegetable kingdom without passing through the animal stage. His body, almost insentient, was invested with a mind which ruled him like a tyrant. His emotional life was a mush which he ladled out like a drunken Cossack. There was something almost anthropophagous about his tenderness; he demanded not the promptings and stirrings of the heart but the heart itself, and with it, if possible, the gizzard, the liver, the pancreas and other tender, edible portions of the human organism. In his exalted moments he seemed not only eager to devour the object of his tenderness but to invite the other to devour him also. His mouth would wreathe itself in a veritable mandibular ecstasy; he would work himself up until the very soul of him came forth in a spongy ectoplasmic substance. It was a horrible state of affection, terrifying because it knew no bounds. It was a depersonalized glut or slop, a hang-over from some archaic condition of ecstasy – the residual memory of crabs and snakes, or their prolonged copulations in the protoplasmic slime of ages long forgotten.

And now, in Cockroach Hall, as we called it, there was preparing itself a delicious sexual omelette which we were all to savour, each in his own particular way. There was something intestinal about the atmosphere of the establishment, for it was an establishment more than a home. It was the clinic of love, so to speak, where embryos sprouted like weeds and, like weeds, were pulled up by the roots or chopped down with the scythe.

How the employment manager of the great Cosmodemonic Telegraph Company had ever allowed himself to be ensnared and trapped in this blood-soaked den of sex surpasses understanding. The moment I got off the train at the elevated station and started descending the stairs into the heart of the Bronx I became a different person. It was a walk of a few blocks to Dr Onirifick's establishment, just sufficient to disorient me, to give me time to slip into the role of the sensitive genius, the romantic poet, the happy mystic who had found his true love and who was ready to die for her.

There was a frightful discordance between this new inner state of being and the physical atmosphere of the neighbourhood through which I had to plunge each night. Everywhere the grim, monotonous walls loomed up; behind them lived families whose life centred about a job. Industrious, patient, ambitious slaves whose one aim was emancipation. In the interim putting up with anything; oblivious of discomfort, immune to ugliness. Heroic little souls whose very obsession to liberate themselves from the thralldom of work served only to magnify the squalor and the misery of their lives.

What proof had I that poverty could bear another face? Only the dim, fuzzy memory of my childhood in the 14th Ward, Brooklyn. The memory of a child who had been sheltered, who had been given every opportunity, who had known nothing but joy and freedom – until he was ten years of age.

Why had I made that blunder in talking to Dr Onirifick? I had not intended to talk about the Jews that evening – I had intended to talk about *The Path to Rome*. That was the book of Belloc's which had really set me on fire. A sensitive man, a scholar, a man for whom the history of Europe was a living memory, he had decided to walk from Paris to Rome with nothing but a knapsack and a stout walking stick. And he did. En route, all those things happened which always happen en route. It was my first understanding of the difference between process and goal, my first awareness of the truth that the goal of life is the living of it. How I envied Hilaire Belloc his adventure! Even to this day I can see in the corner of his pages the little pencil sketches he made of walls and spires, of turrets and bastions. I have only to think of the title of his book and I am sitting in the fields again, or standing on a quaint medieval bridge, or snoozing beside a quiet canal in the heart of France. I never dreamed that it would be possible for me to see that land, to walk through those fields, stand on those same bridges, follow those same canals. That could never happen to *me*! I was doomed.

When I think now of the ruse by which I was liberated, when I think that I was released from this prison because the one I loved wanted to get rid of me, what a sad, baffled, mystifying smile comes over my features. How confused and intricate everything is! We are grateful to those who stab us in the back; we run away from those who would help us; we congratulate ourselves on our good luck, never dreaming that our good luck may be a quagmire from which it will be impossible to extricate ourselves. We run forward with head turned; we rush blindly into the trap. We never escape, except into a cul-de-sac.

I am walking through the Bronx, five or six blocks, just time and space enough to twist myself into a corkscrew. Mona will be there waiting for me. She will embrace me warmly, as if we had never embraced before. We will have only a couple of hours together and then she will leave – to go to the dance hall where she still works as a taxi girl. I will be sound asleep when she returns at three or four in the morning. She will pout and fret if I don't awaken, if I don't throw my arms around her passionately and tell her I love her. She has so much to tell me each night and there is no time to tell it. Mornings, when I leave, she is sound asleep. We come and go like railroad trains. This is the beginning of our life together.

I love her, heart and soul. She is everything to me. And yet she is nothing like the women I dreamed of, like those ideal creatures whom I worshipped as a boy. She corresponds to nothing I had conceived out of my own depths. She is a totally new image, something foreign, something which Fate whirled across my path from some unknown sphere. As I look at her, as I get to love her morsel by morsel, I find that the totality of her escapes me. My love adds up like a sum, but she, the one I am seeking with desperate, hungry love, escapes like an elixir. She is completely mine, almost slavishly so, but I do not possess her. It is I who am possessed. I am possessed by a love such as was never offered me before – an engulfing love, a total love, a love of my very toenails and the dirt beneath them – and yet my hands are forever fluttering, forever grasping and clutching, seizing nothing.

Coming home one evening, I observed out of the corner of my eye one of those soft, sensuous creatures of the ghetto who seem to emerge from the pages of the Old Testament. She was one of the Jewesses whose name must be Ruth or Esther. Or perhaps *Miriam*.

Miriam, yes! That was the name I was searching for. Why was that name so wonderful to me? How could such a simple appellation evoke such powerful emotions? I kept asking myself this question.

Miriam is the name of names. If I could mould all women into the perfect ideal, if I could give this ideal all the qualities I seek in woman, her name would be Miriam.

I had forgotten completely the lovely creature who inspired these reflections. I was on the track of something, and as my pace quickened, as my heart thumped more madly, I suddenly recalled the face, the voice, the figure, the gestures of the Miriam I knew as a boy of twelve. Miriam Painter, she called herself. Only fifteen or sixteen, but full-blown, radiantly alive, fragrant as a flower and – untouchable. She was not a Jewess, nor did she even remotely suggest the memory of those legendary creatures of the Old Testament. (Or perhaps I had not then read the Old Testament.) She was the young woman with long chestnut hair, with frank, open eyes and rather generous mouth who greeted me cordially whenever we met on the street. Always at ease, always giving herself, always radiant with health and good nature; withal wise, sympathetic, full of understanding. With her it was unnecessary to make awkward overtures: she always came towards me beaming with this secret inner joy, always welling over. She swallowed me up and carried me along; she enfolded me like a mother, warmed me like a mistress, dispatched me like a fairy. I never had an impure thought about her: never desired her, never craved for a caress. I loved her so deeply, so completely, that each time I met her it was like being born again. All I demanded was that she should remain alive, be of this earth, be somewhere, anywhere, in this world, and never die. I hoped for nothing, I wanted nothing of her. Her mere existence was all-sufficing. Yes, I used to run into the house, hide myself away, and thank God aloud for having sent Miriam to this earth of ours. What a miracle! And what a blessed thing to love like this!

I don't know how long this went on. I haven't the slightest idea whether she was aware of my adoration or not. What matter? I was in love, with love. To love! To surrender absolutely, to prostrate oneself before the divine image, to die a thousand imaginary deaths, to annihilate every trace of self, to find the whole universe embodied and enshrined in the living image of another! Adolescent, we say. Rot! This is the germ of the future life, the seed which we hide away, which we bury deep within us, which we smother and stifle and do our utmost to destroy as we advance from one experience to another and flutter and flounder and lose our way.

By the time I meet the second ideal – Una Gifford – I am already diseased. Only fifteen years of age and the canker is gnawing at my vitals. How explain it? Miriam had dropped out of my life, not dramatically, but quietly, unostentatiously. She simply disappeared, was seen no more. I didn't even realized what it meant. I didn't think about it. People came and went; objects appeared and disappeared. I was in the flux, like the others, and it was all natural even if inexplicable. I was beginning to read, to read too much. I was turning inward, closing in on myself, as flowers close up in the night.

Una Gifford brings nothing but pain and anguish. I want her, I need her, I can't live without her. She says neither Yes or No, for the simple reason that I have not the courage to put the question to her. I will be sixteen shortly and we are both still in school – we are only going to graduate next year. How can a girl your own age, to whom you only nod, or stare at, be the woman without whom life is impossible? How can you dream of marriage before you have crossed the threshold of life? But if I had eloped with Una Gifford then, at the age of fifteen, if I had married her and had ten children by her, it would have been right, dead right. What matter if I became something utterly different, if I sank down to the bottom rung? What matter if it meant premature old age? I had a need for her which was never answered, and that need was like a wound which grew and grew until it became a gaping hole. As life went on, as that desperate need grew more intense, I dragged everything into the hole and murdered it.

I was not aware, when I first knew Mona, how much she needed me. Nor did I realize how great a transformation she had made of her life, her habits, her background, her antecedents, in order to offer me that ideal image of herself which she all too quickly suspected that I had created. She had changed everything – her name, her birthplace, her mother, her upbringing, her friends, her tastes, even her desires. It was characteristic of her that she should want to change my name too, which she did. I was now Val, the diminutive of Valentine, which I had always been ashamed of – it seemed like a sissy's name – but now that it issued from her lips it sounded like the name which suited me. Nobody else called me Val, though they heard Mona repeat it endlessly. To my friends I was what I always had been; they were not hypnotized by a mere change of name.

Of transformations. . . . I remember vividly the first night we passed at Dr Onirifick's place. We had taken a shower together, shuddering at the sight of the myriad of roaches which infested the bathroom. We got into bed beneath the eiderdown quilt. We had had an ecstatic fuck in this strange public room filled with bizarre objects. We were drawn very close together that night. I had separated from my wife and she had separated from her parents. We hardly knew why we had accepted to live in this outlandish house; in our proper senses neither of us would have dreamed of choosing such a setting. But we were not in our right senses. We were feverish to begin a new life, and we felt guilty, both of us, for the crimes we had committed in order to embark on the great adventure. Mona felt it more than I, in the beginning. She felt that she had been responsible for the break. It was the child which I had left behind, not my wife, whom she felt sorry for. It preyed on her mind. With it was the fear, no doubt, that I would wake up one day and realize that I had made a mistake. She struggled to make herself indispensable, to love me with such devotion, such complete self-sacrifice, that the past would be annihilated. She didn't do it deliberately. She wasn't even aware of what she was doing. But she clung to me desperately, so desperately that when I think of it now the tears come to my eyes. Because it was unnecessary: I needed her even more than she needed me.

And so, as we were falling off to sleep that night, as she rolled over to turn her back on me, the cover slipped off and I became aware, from the animal-like crouch she had assumed, of the massive quality of her back. I ran my two hands over her flesh, caressed her back as one would caress the flanks of a lioness. It was curious that I had never been aware of her superb back. We had slept together many times and we had fallen asleep in all sorts of postures, but I had noticed nothing. Now, in this huge bed which seemed to float in the wan light of the big room, her back became engraved in my memory. I had no definite thoughts about it – just vague pleasure sensations of the strength and the vitality that was in her. *One who could support the world on her back!* I didn't formulate anything so definite as that, but it was there, the thought, in some vague, obscure region of my consciousness. In my fingertips more likely.

Under the shower I had teased her about her tummy, which was growing rather generous, and I realized at once that she was extremely sensitive about her figure. But I was not critical of her opulent flesh – I was delighted to discover it. It carried a promise, I thought. And then, under my very eyes, this body which had been so generously endowed began to shrink. The inner torture was beginning to take its toll. At the same time the fire that was in her began to burn more brightly. Her flesh was consumed by the passion that ravaged her. Her strong, columnar neck, the part of her body which I most admired, grew slenderer and slenderer, until the head seemed like a giant peony swaying on its fragile stem.

'You're not ill?' I would ask, alarmed by this swift transformation.

'Of course not!' she would say. 'I'm reducing.'

'But you're carrying it too far, Mona.'

'I was like this as a girl,' she would answer. 'It's natural for me to be thin.'

'But I don't want you to grow thin. I don't want you to change.

Look at your neck – do you want to have a scrawny neck?'

'My neck isn't scrawny,' she would say, jumping up to look at herself in the mirror.

'I didn't say it was, Mona . . . but it may get that way if you keep on in this reckless fashion.'

'Please Val, don't talk about it. You don't understand. . . .'

'Mona, don't talk that way. I'm not criticizing you. I only want to protect you.'

'You don't like me this way . . . is that it?'

'Mona, I like you *any* way. I love you. I adore you. But please be reasonable. I'm afraid you're going to fade away, evaporate in thin air. I don't want you to get ill. . . .'

'Don't be silly, Val. I never felt better in my life.'

'By the way,' she added, 'are you going to see the little one this Saturday?' She would never mention either my wife or the child by name. Also, she preferred to think that I was visiting only the child on these weekly expeditions to Brooklyn.

I said I thought I would go . . . why, was there any reason not to?

'No, no!' she said, jerking her head strangely and turning away to look for something in the bureau drawer.

I stood behind her, as she was leaning over, and clasped my arms around her waist.

'Mona, tell me something. . . . Does it hurt you very much when I go over there? Tell me honestly. Because if it does, I'll stop going. It has to come to an end someday anyway.'

'You know I don't want you to stop. Have I ever said anything against it?'

'No-o-o,' I said, lowering my head and gazing intently at the carpet. 'No-o-o, you never say anything. But sometimes I wish you would . . . .'

'Why do you say that?' she cried sharply. She looked almost indignant. 'Haven't you a right to see your own daughter? I would do it, if I were in your place.' She paused a moment and then, unable to control herself, she blurted out: 'I would never have left her if she had been mine. I wouldn't have given her up, not for anything!'

'Mona! What are you saying? What does this mean?'

'Just that. I don't know how you can do it. I'm not worth such a sacrifice. Nobody is.'

'Let's drop it,' I said. 'We're going to say things we don't mean. I tell you, I don't regret anything. It was no sacrifice, understand that. I wanted you and I got you. I'm happy. I could forget everybody if it

156

were necessary. You're the whole world to me, and you know it.'

I seized her and pulled her to me. A tear rolled down her cheek.

'Listen, Val, I don't ask you to give up anything, but . . .'

'But what?'

'Couldn't you meet me once in a while at night when I quit work?'

'At two in the morning?'

'I know . . . it *is* an ungodly hour . . . but I feel terribly lonely when I leave the dance hall. Especially after dancing with all those men, all those stupid, horrible creatures who mean nothing to me. I come home and you're asleep. What have I got?'

'Don't say that, *please*. Yes, of course I'll meet you – now and then.'

'Couldn't you take a nap after dinner and . . .'

'Sure I could. Why didn't you tell me sooner? It was selfish of me not to think of that.'

'You're not selfish, Val.'

'I am too. . . . Listen, supposing I ride down with you this evening? I'll come back, take a snooze, and meet you at closing time.'

'You're sure it won't be too tiring?'

'No, Mona, it'll be wonderful.'

On the way home, however, I began to realize what it would mean to arrange my hours thus. At two o'clock we would catch a bite somewhere. An hour's ride on the elevated. In bed Mona would chat awhile before going to sleep. It would be almost five o'clock by that time and by seven I would have to be up again ready for work.

I got into the habit of changing my clothes every evening, in preparation for the rendezvous at the dance hall. Not that I went every evening – no, but I went as often as possible. Changing into old clothes – a khaki shirt, a pair of moccasins, sporting one of the canes which Mona had filched from Carruthers – my romantic self asserted itself. I led two lives: one at the Cosmodemonic Telegraph Company and another with Mona.

While the divorce proceedings were pending events rolled up as at the end of an epoch. It only needed a war to top it off. First of all the Satanic Majesties of the Cosmodemoniacal Telegraph Company had seen fit to shift my headquarters once again, this time to the top of an old loft building in the twine and paper-box district. My desk stood in the centre of an enormous deserted floor which was used as a drill room by the messenger brigade after hours. In the adjoining room, equally large and empty, a sort of combination clinic, dispensary and gymnasium was established. All that was needed to complete the picture was the installation of a few pool tables. Some of the half-wits brought their roller skates along to while away the 'rest periods'. It was an infernal racket they made all day long, but I was so utterly disinterested now in all the company's plans and projects that, far from disturbing me, it afforded me great amusement. I was thoroughly isolated now from the other offices. The snooping and spying had abated; I was in quarantine, so to speak. The hiring and firing went on in dreamy fashion; my staff had been cut down to two – myself and the ex-pugilist who had formerly been the wardrobe attendant. I made no effort to keep the files in order, nor did I investigate references, nor did I conduct any correspondence. Half the time I didn't bother to answer the telephone; if there were anything very urgent there was always the telegraph.

The atmosphere of the new quarters was distinctly dementia praecox. They had relegated me to hell and I was enjoying it. As soon as I got rid of the day's applicants I would go into the adjoining room and watch the shenanigans. Now and then I would put on a pair of skates myself and do a twirl with the goofy ones. My assistant looked on askance, unable to comprehend what had happened to me. Sometimes, in spite of his austerity, his 'code' and other detracting psychological elements, he would break out into a laugh which would prolong itself to the verge of hysteria. Once he asked me if I was having 'trouble at home'. He feared that the next step would be drink, I suppose.

As a matter of fact, I did begin to indulge rather freely about this time, what with one thing and another. It was a harmless sort of drinking, which began only at the dinner table. By sheer accident I had discovered a French-Italian restaurant in the back of a grocery store. The atmosphere was most convivial. Everyone was a 'character', even the police sergeants and the detectives who gorged themselves disgracefully at the proprietor's expense.

I had to have some place to while away the evenings, now that Mona had sneaked into the theatre by the back door. Whether Monahan had found her the job or whether, as she said, she had just lied her way in, I was never able to discover. At any rate, she had given herself a new name, one that would suit her new career, and with it a complete new history of her life and antecedents. She had become English all of a sudden, and her people had been connected with the theatre as far back as she could remember, which was often amazingly far. It was in one of the little theatres which then flourished that she made her entrance into that world of make-believe which so well suited her.

Since they paid her scarcely anything they could afford to act gullible.

Arthur Raymond and his wife were at first inclined to disbelieve the news. Another one of Mona's inventions, they thought. Rebecca, always poor at dissembling, practically laughed in Mona's face. But when she came home with the script of a Schnitzler play one evening and seriously began to rehearse her role their incredulity gave way to consternation. And when Mona, by some inexplicable legerdemain, succeeded in attaching herself to the Theatre Guild, the atmosphere of the household became supersaturated with envy, spite and malevolence. The play was becoming too real – there was a very real danger now that Mona might become the actress she pretended to be.

The rehearsals were endless, it seemed. I never knew what hour Mona would return home. When I did spend an evening with her it was like listening to a drunk. The glamour of the new life had completely intoxicated her. Now and then I would stay in of an evening and try to write, but it was no go. Arthur Raymond was always there, lying in wait like an octopus. 'What do you want to write for?' he would say. 'God, aren't there enough writers in the world?' And then he would begin to talk about writers, the writers he admired, and I would sit before the machine, as if ready to resume my work the moment he left me. Often I would do nothing more than write a letter – to some famous author, telling him how greatly I admired his work, hinting that, if he had not already heard of me, he would soon. In this way it fell about one day that I received an astonishing letter from that Dostoievski of the North, as he was called: Knut Hamsun. It was written by his secretary, in broken English, and for a man who was shortly to receive the Nobel prize, it was to say the least a puzzling piece of dictation. After explaining that he had been pleased, even touched, by my homage, he went on to say (through his wooden mouthpiece) that his American publisher was not altogether satisfied with the financial returns from the sale of his books. They feared that they might not be able to publish any more of his books – unless the public were to show a more lively interest. His tone was that of a giant in distress. He wondered vaguely what could be done to retrieve the situation, not so much for himself as for his dear publisher, who was truly suffering because of him. And then, as the letter progressed, a happy idea seemed to take hold of him and forthwith he gave expression to it. It was this – once he had received a letter from a Mr Boyle, who also lived in New York and whom I doubtless knew(!). He thought perhaps Mr Boyle and myself might get together, rack our brains over the situation, and quite possibly come to some brilliant solution. Perhaps we could tell other people in America that there existed in the wilds and fens of Norway a writer named Knut Hamsun whose books had been conscientiously translated into English and were now languishing on the shelves of his publisher's stock room. He was sure that if he could only increase the sales of his books by a few hundred copies his publisher would take heart and have faith in him again. He had been to America, he said, and though his English was too poor to permit him to write me in his own hand, he was confident that his secretary could make clear his thoughts and intentions. I was to look up Mr Boyle, whose address he no longer remembered. Do what you can, he urged. Perhaps there were several other people in New York who had heard of his work and with whom we could operate. He closed on a dolorous but majestic note. . . . I examined the letter carefully to see if perhaps he hadn't shed a few tears over it.

If the envelope hadn't borne the Norwegian postmark, if the letter itself hadn't been signed in his own scrawl, which I later confirmed, I would have thought it a hoax. Tremendous discussions ensued amid boisterous laughter. It was considered that I had been royally paid out for my foolish hero worship. The idol had been smashed and my critical faculties reduced to zero. No one could possibly see how I could ever read Knut Hamsun again. To tell the honest truth, I felt like weeping. Some terrible miscarriage had occurred, just how I couldn't fathom, but despite the evidence to the contrary, I simply could not bring myself to believe that the author of *Hunger, Pan, Victoria, Growth of the Soil*, had dictated that letter. It was entirely conceivable that he had left the matter to his secretary, that he had signed his name in good faith without bothering to be told the contents. A man as famous as he undoubtedly received dozens of letters a day from admirers all over the world. There was nothing in my youthful panegyric to interest a man of his stature. Besides, he probably despised the whole American race, having had a bitter time of it here during the years of his pilgrimage. Most likely he had tole his dolt of a secretary on more than one occasion that his American sales were negligible. Perhaps his publishers had been pestering him – publishers are known to have only one concern in dealing with their authors, namely sales. Perhaps he had remarked disgustedly, in the presence of his secretary, that Americans had money to spend on everything but the things worth while in life. And she, poor imbecile, probably worshipful of the master, had decided to avail herself of the opportunity and offer a few crackbrained suggestions in order to

160

ameliorate the painful situation. She was more than likely no Dagmar, no Edwige. No, not even a simple soul like Martha Gude, who tried so desperately not to be taken in by Herr Nagel's romantic flights and overtures. She was probably one of those educated Norwegian head-cheeses who are emancipated in everything but the imagination. She was probably hygienic and scientific-minded, capable of keeping her house in order, doing harm to no one, mindful of her own business, and dreaming one day of becoming the head of a fertilizing establishment or a crèche for bastard children.

No, I was thoroughly disillusioned in my god. I purposely reread some of his books and, naive soul that I was, I wept again over certain passages. I was so deeply impressed that I began to wonder if I had dreamed the letter.

The repercussions from this 'miscarriage' were quite extra-ordinary. I became savage, bitter, caustic. I became a wanderer who played on muted strings of iron. I impersonated one after another of my idol's characters. I talked sheer rot and nonsense; I poured hot piss over everything. I became two people – myself and my impersonations, which were legion.

The divorce trial was impending. That made me even more savage and bitter, for some inexplicable reason. I hated the farce which has to be gone through in the name of justice. I loathed and despised the lawyer whom Maude had retained to protect her interests. He looked like a corn-fed Romain Rolland, a *chauve-souris* without a crumb of humour or imagination. He seemed to be charged with moral indig-nation; he was a prick through and through, a coward, a sneak, a hypocrite. He gave me the creeps.

We had it out about him the day of the outing. Lying in the grass somewhere near Mineola. The child running about gathering flowers. It was warm, very warm, and there was a hot dry wind blowing which made one nervous and rooty. I had taken my prick out and put it in her hand. She examined it shyly, not wishing to be too clinical about it and yet dying to convince herself that there was nothing wrong. After a while she dropped it and rolled over on her back, her knees up, and the warm wind licking her bottom. I jockeyed her into a favourable position, made her pull her panties off. She was in one of her protest-ing moods again. Didn't like being mauled like that in an open field. But there's not a soul around, I insisted. I made her spread her legs farther apart; I ran my hand up her cunt. It was gooey.

I pulled her to me and tried to get it in. She balked. She was worried about the child. I looked around. 'She's all right,' I said. 'She's having a good time. She's not thinking about us.'

'But supposing she comes back . . . and finds us. . . .'

'She'll think we're sleeping. She won't know what we're doing. . . .'

With this she pushed me away violently. It was outrageous. 'You'd take me in front of your own child! It's horrible.'

'It's not horrible at all. You're the one who's horrible I tell you, it's innocent. Even if she should remember it – when she's grown up – she'll be a woman then and she'll understand. There's nothing dirty about it. It's your dirty mind, that's all.'

By this time she was slipping her panties on. I hadn't bothered to shove my prick back in my trousers. It was getting limp now; it fell on the grass, dejected.

'Well, let's have something to eat then,' I said. 'If we can't fuck we can always eat.'

'Yes, *eat*! You can eat any time. That's all you care about, eating and sleeping.'

'*Fucking*,' I said, 'not sleeping.'

'I wish you'd stop talking to me that way.' She began to undo the lunch. 'You have to spoil everything. I thought we might have a peaceful day, just once. You always said you wanted to take us out on a picnic. You never did. Not once. You thought of nothing but yourself, your friends, your women. I was a fool to think you might change. You don't care about your child – you've hardly noticed her. You can't even restrain yourself in her presence. You'd take me in front of her and pretend that it was innocent. You're vile . . . I'm glad it's all over. By this time next week I'll be free . . . I'll be rid of you for ever. You've poisoned me. You've made me bitter and hateful. You make me despise myself. Since I've known you I don't recognize myself any more. I've become what you wanted me to become. You never loved me . . . *never*. All you wanted was to satisfy your desires. You've treated me like an animal. You take what you want and you go. You go from me to the next woman – any woman – just so long as she'll open her legs for you. You haven't an ounce of loyalty or tenderness or consideration in you. . . . Here, take it!' she said, shoving a sandwich in my fist. 'I hope you choke on it!'

As I brought the sandwich to my mouth I smelled the odour of her cunt on my fingers. I sniffed my fingers while looking up at her with a grin.

'You're disgusting!' she said.

'Not so very, my lady. It smells good to me, even if you are a hateful sourpuss. I like it. It's the only thing about you I like.'

She was furious now. She began to weep.

'Weeping because I said I liked your cunt! What a woman! Jesus, I'm the one who ought to do the despising. What sort of woman are you?'

Her tears became more copious. Just then the child came running up. What was the matter? Why was mother crying?

'It's nothing,' said Maude, drying her tears. 'I turned my ankle.' A few dry sobs belched from her despite her efforts to restrain herself. She bent over the basket and selected a sandwich for the child.

'Why don't you do something, Henry?' said the child. She sat there looking from one to the other with a grave, puzzled look.

I got to my knees and rubbed Maude's ankle.

'Don't touch me!' she said harshly.

'But he wants to make it better,' said the child.

'Yes, daddy'll make it better,' I said, rubbing the ankle gently, and then patting the calf of her leg.

'Kiss her,' said the child. 'Kiss her and make the tears go away.'

I bent forward and kissed Maude on the cheek. To my astonishment she flung her arms around me and kissed me violently on the mouth. The child also put her arms around us and kissed us.

Suddenly Maude had a fresh spasm of weeping. This time it was really pitiful to behold. I felt sorry for her. I put my arms around her tenderly and comforted her.

'God,' she sobbed, 'what a farce!'

'But it isn't,' I said. 'I mean it sincerely. I'm sorry, sorry for everything.'

'Don't cry any more,' begged the child. 'I want to eat. I want Henry to take me over there,' and she pointed with her little hand to a copsewood at the edge of the field. 'I want you to come too.'

'To think this is the only time . . . and it had to be like this.' She was sniffing now.

'Don't say that, Maude. The day isn't over yet. Let's forget about all that. Come on, let's eat.'

Reluctantly, wearily, it seemed, she picked up a sandwich and held it to her mouth. 'I can't eat,' she murmured, dropping the sandwich.

'Come on, yes you can!' I urged, putting my arm around her again.

'You act this way now . . . and later you'll do something to spoil it.'

'No I won't . . . I promise you.'

'Kiss her again,' said the child.

I leaned over and kissed her softly and gently on the lips. She seemed really placated now. A soft light came into her eyes.

'Why can't you be like this always?' she said, after a brief pause.

'I am,' I said, 'when I'm given a chance. I don't like to fight with you. Why should I? We're not man and wife any longer.'

'Then why do you treat me the way you do? Why do you always make love to me? Why don't you leave me alone?'

'I'm not making love to you,' I answered. 'It's not love, it's passion. That's not a crime, is it? For God's sake, let's not start that all over again. I'm going to treat you the way you want to be treated – today. I won't touch you again.'

'I don't ask that. I don't say you shouldn't touch me. But it's the *way* you do it . . . you don't show any respect for me . . . for my person. That's what I dislike. I know you don't love me any more, but you can behave decently towards me, even if you don't care any more. I'm not the prude you pretend I am. I have feelings too . . . maybe deeper, stronger than yours. I can find someone else to replace you, don't think that I can't. I just want a little time . . .'

She was munching her sandwich halfheartedly. Suddenly there was a gleam in her eye. She put on a coy, roguish expression.

'I could get married tomorrow, if I wanted to,' she continued. 'You never thought of that, did you? I've had three proposals already, as a matter of fact. The last one was from. . . .' and here she mentioned the lawyer's name.

'*Him?*' I said, unable to repress a disdainful smile.

'Yes, *him*,' she said. 'And he's not what you think he is. I like him very much.'

'Well, that explains things. Now I know why he's taken such a passionate interest in the case.'

I knew she didn't care for him, this Rocambolesque, any more than she cared for the doctor who explored her vagina with a rubber finger. She didn't care for anybody really; all she wanted was peace, surcease from pain. She wanted a lap to sit on in the dark, a prick to enter her mysteriously, a babble of words to drown her unmentionable desires. Lawyer what's-his-name would do of course. Why not? He would be as faithful as a fountain pen, as discreet as a rat trap, as provident as an insurance policy. He was a walking briefcase with pigeonholes in his belfry; he was a salamander with a heart of pastrami. He was shocked, was he, to learn that I had brought another woman to my own home? Shocked to learn that I had left the used condoms on the edge of the sink? Shocked that I had stayed for breakfast with my paramour? A snail is shocked when a drop of rain hits its shell. A general is shocked when he learns that his garrison has been massacred in his absence. God himself is shocked doubtless when He sees how revoltingly stupid and insensitive the human beast really is. But I doubt if angels are ever shocked – not even by the presence of the insane.

I was trying to give her the dialectics of moral dynamism. I twisted my tongue in the endeavour to make her understand the marriage of the animal and the divine. She understood about as well as a layman understands when you explain the fourth dimension. She talked about delicacy and respect, as if they were pieces of angel cake. Sex was an animal locked up in a zoo which one visited now and then in order to study evolution.

Towards evening we rode back to the city, the last stretch in the elevated train, the child asleep in my arms. Mamma and Papa returning from the picnic grounds. Below, the city spread out with senseless geometrical rigidity, an evil dream rearing itself architecturally. A dream from which it is impossible to awaken. Mr and Mrs Megalopolitan with their offspring. Hobbled and fettered. Suspended in the sky like so much venison. A pair of every kind hanging by the hocks. At one end of the line starvation; at the other end bankruptcy. Between stations the pawnbroker, with three golden balls to signify the triune God of birth, buggery and blight. Happy days. A fog rolling in from Rockaway. Nature folding up like a dead leaf – at Mineola. Every now and then the doors open and shut: fresh batches of meat for the slaughterhouse. Little scraps of conversation, like the twittering of titmice. Who would think that the chubby little youngster beside you will in ten or fifteen years be shitting his brains out with fright on a foreign field? All day long you make innocent little gadgets; at night you sit in a dark hall and watch phantoms move across a silver screen. Maybe the realest moments you know are when you sit alone in the toilet and make caca. That doesn't cost anything or commit you in any way. Not like eating or fucking, or making works of art. You leave the toilet and you step into the big shithouse. Whatever you touch is shitty. Even when it's wrapped in cellophane the smell is there. *Caca*! The philosopher's stone of the industrial age. Death and transfiguration – into shit! The department-store life – with filmy silks on one counter and bombs on the other counter. No matter what interpretation you put on it, every thought, every deed, is cash-registered. You're fucked from the moment you draw your first breath. One grand international business machine corporation. *Logistics*, as they say.

# Part III

# Paris

# From *Tropic of Cancer*

I am living at the Villa Borghese. There is not a crumb of dirt anywhere, nor a chair misplaced. We are all alone here and we are dead.

Last night Boris discovered that he was lousy. I had to shave his armpits and even then the itching did not stop. How can one get lousy in a beautiful place like this? But no matter. We might never have known each other so intimately, Boris and I, had it not been for the lice.

Boris has just given me a summary of his views. He is a weather prophet. The weather will continue bad, he says. There will be more calamities, more death, more despair. Not the slightest indication of a change anywhere. The cancer of time is eating us away. Our heroes have killed themselves, or are killing themselves. The hero, then, is not Time, but Timelessness. We must get in step, a lock step, towards the prison of death. There is no escape. The weather will not change.

It is now the fall of my second year in Paris. I was sent here for a reason I have not yet been able to fathom.

I have no money, no resources, no hopes. I am the happiest man alive. A year ago, six months ago, I thought that I was an artist. I no longer think about it, I *am*. Everything that was literature has fallen from me. There are no more books to be written, thank God.

This then? This is not a book. This is libel, slander, defamation of character. This is not a book, in the ordinary sense of the word. No, this is a prolonged insult, a gob of spit in the face of Art, a kick in the pants to God, Man, Destiny, Time, Love, Beauty . . . what you will. I am going to sing for you, a little off key perhaps, but I will sing. I will sing while you croak, I will dance over your dirty corpse. . . .

To sing you must first open your mouth. You must have a pair of lungs, and a little knowledge of music. It is not necessary to have an accordion, or a guitar. The essential thing is to *want* to sing. This then is a song. I am singing.

★

It is to you, Tania, that I am singing. I wish that I could sing better, more melodiously, but then perhaps you would never have consented to listen to me. You have heard the others sing and they have left you cold. They sang too beautifully, or not beautifully enough.

It is the twenty-somethingth of October. I no longer keep track of the date. Would you say – my dream of the 14th November last? There are intervals, but they are between dreams, and there is no consciousness of them left. The world around me is dissolving, leaving here and there spots of time. The world is a cancer eating itself away. . . . I am thinking that when the great silence descends upon all and everywhere music will at last triumph. When into the womb of time everything is again withdrawn chaos will be restored and chaos is the score upon which reality is written. You, Tania, are my chaos. It is why I sing. It is not even I, it is the world dying, shedding the skin of time. I am still alive, kicking in your womb, a reality to write upon.

Dozing off. The physiology of love. The whale with his six-foot penis, in repose. The bat – *penis libre*. Animals with a bone in the penis. Hence, *a bone on*. . . . 'Happily,' says Gourmont, 'the bony structure is lost in man.' Happily? Yes, happily. Think of the human race walking around with a bone on. The kangaroo has a double penis – one for weekdays and one for holidays. Dozing. A letter from a female asking if I have found a title for my book. Title? To be sure: 'Lovely Lesbians'.

*Your anecdotal life!* A phrase of M. Borowski's. It is on Wednesdays that I have lunch with Borowski. His wife, who is a dried-up cow, officiates. She is studying English now – her favourite word is 'filthy'. You can see immediately what a pain in the ass the Borowskis are. But wait. . . .

Borowski wears corduroy suits and plays the accordion. An invincible combination, especially when you consider that he is not a bad artist. He puts on that he is a Pole, but he is not, of course. He is a Jew, Borowski, and his father was a philatelist. In fact, almost all Montparnasse is Jewish, or half-Jewish, which is worse. There's Carl and Paula, and Cronstadt and Boris, and Tania and Sylvester, and Moldorf and Lucille. All except Fillmore. Henry Jordan Oswald turned out to be a Jew also. Louis Nichols is a Jew. Even Van Norden and Chérie are Jewish. Frances Blake is a Jew, or a Jewess. Titus is a Jew. The Jews then are snowing me under. I am writing this for my friend Carl whose father is a Jew. All this is important to understand.

Of them all the loveliest Jew is Tania, and for her sake I too would become a Jew. Why not? I already speak like a Jew. And I am as ugly as a Jew. Besides, who hates the Jews more than the Jew?

Twilight hour. Indian blue, water of glass, trees glistening and liquescent. The rails fall away into the canal at Jaurès. The long caterpillar with lacquered sides dips like a roller coaster. It is not Paris. It is not Coney Island. It is a crepuscular melange of all the cities of Europe and Central America. The railroad yards below me, the tracks black, webby, not ordered by the engineer but cataclysmic in design, like those gaunt fissures in the polar ice which the camera registers in degrees of black.

Food is one of the things I enjoy tremendously. And in this beautiful Villa Borghese there is scarcely ever any evidence of food. It is positively appalling at times. I have asked Boris time and again to order bread for breakfast, but he always forgets. He goes out for breakfast, it seems. And when he comes back he is picking his teeth and there is a little egg hanging from his goatee. He eats in the restaurant out of consideration for me. He says it hurts to eat a big meal and have me watch him.

I like Van Norden but I do not share his opinion of himself. I do not agree, for instance, that he is a philosopher, or a thinker. He is cunt-struck, that's all. And he will never be a writer. Nor will Sylvester ever be a writer, though his name blaze in 50,000-candlepower red lights. The only writers about me for whom I have any respect, at present, are Carl and Boris. They are possessed. They glow inwardly with a white flame. They are mad and tone deaf. They are sufferers.

Moldorf, on the other hand, who suffers too in his peculiar way, is not mad. Moldorf is word drunk. He has no veins or blood vessels, no heart or kidneys. He is a portable trunk filled with innumerable drawers and in the drawers are labels written out in white ink, brown ink, red ink, blue ink, vermilion, saffron, mauve, sienna, apricot, turquoise, onyx, Anjou, herring, Corona, verdigris, gorgonzola. . . .

I have moved the typewriter into the next room where I can see myself in the mirror as I write.

Tania is like Irène. She expects fat letters. But there is another Tania, a Tania like a big seed, who scatters pollen everywhere – or, let us say, a little bit of Tolstoy, a stable scene in which the foetus is dug up. Tania is a fever, too – *les voies urinaires*, Café de la Liberté, Place des Vosges, bright neckties on the Boulevard Montparnasse, dark bathrooms, Porto Sec, Abdullah cigarettes, the adagio sonata *Pathétique*, aural amplificators, anecdotal seances, burnt sienna breasts, heavy garters, what time is it, golden pheasants stuffed with chestnuts, taffeta fingers, vaporish twilights turning to ilex, acromegaly, cancer and delirium, warm veils, poker chips, carpets of blood and soft thighs. Tania says so that every one may hear: 'I love him!' And while Boris scalds himself with whisky she says: 'Sit down here! O Boris . . . *Russia* . . . what'll I do? I'm bursting with it!'

At night when I look at Boris' goatee lying on the pillow I get hysterical. O Tania, where now is that warm cunt of yours, those fat, heavy garters, those soft, bulging thighs? There is a bone in my prick six inches long. I will ream out every wrinkle in your cunt, Tania, big with seed. I will send you home to your Sylvester with an ache in your belly and your womb turned inside out. Your Sylvester! Yes, he knows how to build a fire, but I know how to inflame a cunt. I shoot hot bolts into you, Tania, I make your ovaries incandescent. Your Sylvester is a little jealous now? He feels something, does he? He feels the remnants of my big prick. I have set the shores a little wider, I have ironed out the wrinkles. After me you can take on stallions, bulls, rams, drakes, St Bernards. You can stuff toads, bats, lizards up your rectum. You can shit arpeggios if you like, or string a zither across your navel. I am fucking you, Tania, so that you'll stay fucked. And if you are afraid of being fucked publicly I will fuck you privately. I will tear off a few hairs from your cunt and paste them on Boris' chin. I will bite into your clitoris and spit out two franc pieces. . . .

Indigo sky swept clear of fleecy clouds, gaunt trees infinitely extended, their black boughs gesticulating like a sleepwalker. Sombre, spectral trees, their trunks pale as cigar ash. A silence supreme and altogether European. Shutters drawn, shops barred. A red glow here and there to mark a tryst. Brusque the facades, almost forbidding; immaculate except for the splotches of shadow cast by the trees. Passing by the Orangerie I am reminded of another Paris, the Paris of Maugham, of Gauguin, Paris of George Moore. I think of that terrible Spaniard who was then startling the world with his acrobatic leaps from style to style. I think of Spengler and of his terrible pronunciamentos, and I wonder if style, style in the grand manner, is done for. I say that my mind is occupied with these thoughts, but it is not true; it is only later, after I have crossed the Seine, after I have put behind me the carnival of lights, that I allow my mind to play with these ideas. For the moment I can think of nothing – except that I am a sentient being stabbed by the miracle of these waters that reflect a forgotten world. All along the banks the trees lean heavily over the tarnished mirror; when the wind rises and fills them with a rustling murmur they will shed a few tears and shiver as the water swirls by. I am suffocated by it. No one to whom I can communicate even a fraction of my feelings. . . .

The trouble with Irène is that she has a valise instead of a cunt. She wants fat letters to shove in her valise. Immense, *avec des choses inouïes*. Llona now, she had a cunt. I know because she sent us some hairs from down below. Llona – a wild ass snuffing pleasure out of the wind. On every high hill she played the harlot – and sometimes in telephone booths and toilets. She bought a bed for King Carol and a shaving mug with his initials on it. She lay in Tottenham Court Road with her dress pulled up and fingered herself. She used candles, Roman candles, and door knobs. Not a prick in the land big enough for her . . . *not one*. Men went inside her and curled up. She wanted extension pricks, self-exploding rockets, hot boiling oil made of wax and creosote. She would cut off your prick and keep it inside her forever, if you gave her permission. One cunt out of a million, Llona! A laboratory cunt and no litmus paper that could take her colour. She was a liar, too, this Llona. She never bought a bed for her King Carol. She crowned him with a whisky bottle and her tongue was full of lice and tomorrows. Poor Carol, he could only curl up inside her and die. She drew a breath and he fell out – like a dead clam.

Enormous, fat letters, *avec des choses inouïes*. A valise without straps. A hole without a key. She had a German mouth, French ears, Russian ass. Cunt international. When the flag waved it was red all the way back to the throat. You entered on the Boulevard Jules-Ferry and came out at the Porte de la Villette. You dropped your sweetbreads into the tumbrils – red tumbrils with two wheels, naturally. At the confluence of the Ourcq and Marne, where the water sluices through the dikes and lies like glass under the bridges. Llona is lying there now and the canal is full of glass and splinters; the mimosas weep, and there is a wet, foggy fart on the windowpanes. One cunt out of a million Llona! All cunt and a glass ass in which you can read the history of the Middle Ages.

It is the caricature of a man which Moldorf first presents. Thyroid eyes. Michelin lips. Voice like pea soup. Under his vest he carries a little pear. However you look at him it is always the same panorama: netsuke snuffbox, ivory handle, chess piece, fan, temple motif. He has fermented so long now that he is amorphous. Yeast despoiled of its vitamins. Vase without a rubber plant.

173

The females were sired twice in the ninth century, and again during the Renaissance. He was carried through the great dispersions under yellow bellies and white. Long before the Exodus a Tatar spat in his blood.

His dilemma is that of the dwarf. With his pineal eye he sees his silhouette projected on a screen of incommensurable size. His voice, synchronized to the shadow of a pinhead, intoxicates him. He hears a roar where others hear only a squeak.

There is his mind. It is an amphitheatre in which the actor gives a protean performance. Moldorf, multiform and unerring, goes through his roles – clown, juggler, contortionist, priest, lecher, mountebank. The amphitheatre is too small. He puts dynamite to it. The audience is drugged. He scotches it.

I am trying ineffectually to approach Moldorf. It is like trying to approach God, for Moldorf *is* God – he has never been anything else. I am merely putting down words. . . .

I have had opinions about him which I have discarded; I have had other opinions which I am revising. I have pinned him down only to find that it was not a dung-beetle I had in my hands, but a dragonfly. He has offended me by his coarseness and then overwhelmed me with his delicacy. He has been voluble to the point of suffocation, then quiet as the Jordan.

When I see him trotting forward to greet me, his little paws outstretched, his eyes perspiring, I feel that I am meeting. . . . No, this is not the way to go about it!

*'Comme un oeuf dansant sur un jet d'eau.'*

He has only one cane – a mediocre one. In his pocket scraps of paper containing prescriptions for *Weltschmerz*. He is cured now, and the little German girl who washed his feet is breaking her heart. It is like Mr Nonentity toting his Gujarati dictionary everywhere. *'Inevitable for everyone'* – meaning, no doubt, *indispensable*. Borowski would find all this incomprehensible. Borowski has a different cane for each day in the week, and one for Easter.

We have so many points in common that it is like looking at myself in a cracked mirror.

I have been looking over my manuscripts, pages scrawled with revisions. Pages of *literature*. This frightens me a little. It is so much like Moldorf. Only I am a Gentile, and Gentiles have a different way of suffering. They suffer without neuroses and, as Sylvester says, a man

174

who has never been afflicted with a neurosis does not know the meaning of suffering.

I recall distinctly how I enjoyed my suffering. It was like taking a cub to bed with you. Once in a while he clawed you – and then you really were frightened. Ordinarily you had no fear – you could always turn him loose, or chop his head off.

There are people who cannot resist the desire to get into a cage with wild beasts and be mangled. They go in even without revolver or whip. Fear makes them fearless. . . . For the Jew the world is a cage filled with wild beasts. The door is locked and he is there without whip or revolver. His courage is so great that he does not even smell the dung in the corner. The spectators applaud but he does not hear. The drama, he thinks, is going òn inside the cage. The cage, he thinks, is the world. Standing there alone and helpless, the door locked, he finds that the lions do not understand his language. Not one lion has ever heard of Spinoza. Spinoza? Why they can't even get their teeth into him. 'Give us meat!' they roar, while he stands there petrified, his ideas frozen, his *Weltanschauung* a trapeze out of reach. A single blow of the lion's paw and his cosmogony is smashed.

The lions, too, are disappointed. They expected blood, bones, gristle, sinews. They chew and chew, but the words are chicle and chicle is indigestible. Chicle is a base over which you sprinkle sugar, pepsin, thyme, licorice. Chicle, when it is gathered by *chicleros*, is OK. The *chicleros* came over on the ridge of a sunken continent. They brought with them an algebraic language. In the Arizona desert they met the Mongols of the North, glazed like eggplants. Time shortly after the earth had taken its gyroscopic lean – when the Gulf Stream was parting ways with the Japanese current. In the heart of the soil they found tufa rock. They embroidered the very bowels of the earth with their language. They ate one another's entrails and the forest closed in on them, on their bones and skulls, on their lace tufa. Their language was lost. Here and there one still finds the remnants of a menagerie, a brain plate covered with figures.

What has all this to do with you, Moldorf? The word in your mouth is anarchy. Say it, Moldorf, I am waiting for it. Nobody knows, when we shake hands, the rivers that pour through our sweat. Whilst you are framing your words, your lips half parted, the saliva gurgling in your cheeks, I have jumped halfway across Asia. Were I to take your cane, mediocre as it is, and poke a little hole in your side, I could collect enough material to fill the British Museum. We stand on five minutes and devour centuries. You are the sieve through which my anarchy strains, resolves itself into words. Behind the word is chaos. Each word a stripe, a bar, but there are not and never will be enough bars to make the mesh.

In my absence the window curtains have been hung. They have the appearance of Tyrolean tablecloths dipped in lysol. The room sparkles. I sit on the bed in a daze, thinking about man before his birth. Suddenly bells begin to toll, a weird, unearthly music, as if I had been translated to the steppes of Central Asia. Some ring out with a long, lingering roll, some erupt drunkenly, maudlinly. And now it is quiet again, except for a last note that barely grazes the silence of the night – just a faint, high gong snuffed out like a flame.

I have made a silent compact with myself not to change a line of what I write. I am not interested in perfecting my thoughts, nor my actions. Beside the perfection of Turgenev I put the perfection of Dostoievski. (Is there anything more perfect than *The Eternal Husband*?) Here, then, in one and the same medium, we have two kinds of perfection. But in Van Gogh's letters there is a perfection beyond either of these. It is the triumph of the individual over art.

There is only one thing which interests me vitally now, and that is the recording of all that which is omitted in books. Nobody, so far as I can see, is making use of those elements in the air which give direction and motivation to our lives. Only the killers seem to be extracting from life some satisfactory measure of what they are putting into it. The age demands violence, but we are getting only abortive explosions. Revolutions are nipped in the bud, or else succeed too quickly. Passion is quickly exhausted. Men fall back on ideas, *comme d'habitude*. Nothing is proposed that can last more than twenty-four hours. We are living a million lives in the space of a generation. In the study of entomology, or of deep sea life, or cellular activity, we derive more . . .

The telephone interrupts this thought which I should never have been able to complete. Someone is coming to rent the apartment. . . .

It looks as though it were finished, my life at the Villa Borghese. Well, I'll take up these pages and move on. Things will happen elsewhere. Things are always happening. It seems wherever I go there is drama. People are like lice – they get under your skin and bury themselves there. You scratch and scratch until the blood comes, but you can't get permanently deloused. Everywhere I go people are making a mess of their lives. Everyone has his private tragedy. It's in the blood now – misfortune, ennui, grief, suicide. The atmosphere is saturated with disaster, frustration, futility. Scratch and scratch – until there's no skin left. However, the effect upon me is exhilarating. Instead of being discouraged, or depressed, I enjoy it. I am crying for more and more disasters, for bigger calamities, for grander failures. I want the whole world to be out of whack, I want everyone to scratch himself to death.

So fast and furiously am I compelled to live now that there is scarcely time to record even these fragmentary notes. After the telephone call, a gentleman and his wife arrived. I went upstairs to lie down during the transaction. Lay there wondering what my next move would be. Surely not to go back to the fairy's bed and toss about all night flicking bread crumbs with my toes. That puking little bastard! If there's anything worse than being a fairy it's being a miser. A timid, quaking little bugger who lived in constant fear of going broke some day – the 18th of March perhaps, or the 25th of May precisely. Coffee without milk or sugar. Bread without butter. Meat without gravy, or no meat at all. Without this and without that! That dirty little miser! Open the bureau drawer one day and find money hidden away in a sock. Over two thousand francs – and cheques that he hadn't even cashed. Even that I wouldn't have minded so much if there weren't always coffee grounds in my beret and garbage on the floor, to say nothing of the cold cream jars and the greasy towels and the sink always stopped up. I tell you, the little bastard he smelled bad – except when he doused himself with cologne. His ears were dirty, his eyes were dirty, his ass was dirty. He was double-jointed, asthmatic, lousy, picayune, morbid. I could have forgiven him everything if only he had handed me a decent breakfast! But a man who has two thousand francs hidden away in a dirty sock and refuses to wear a clean shirt or smear a little butter over his bread, such a man is not just a fairy, nor even just a miser – he's an imbecile!

But that's neither here nor there, about the fairy. I'm keeping an ear open as to what's going on downstairs. It's a Mr Wren and his wife who have called to look at the apartment. They're talking about taking it. Only *talking* about it, thank God. Mrs Wren has a loose laugh – complications ahead. Now *Mister* Wren is talking. His voice is raucous, scraping, booming, a heavy blunt weapon that wedges its way through flesh and bone and cartilage.

Boris calls me down to be introduced. He is rubbing his hands, like a pawnbroker. They are talking about a story Mr Wren wrote, a story about a spavined horse.

'But I thought Mr Wren was a painter?'

'To be sure,' says Boris, with a twinkle in his eye, 'but in the wintertime he writes. And he writes well . . . remarkably well.'

I try to induce Mr Wren to talk, to say something, anything, to talk about the spavined horse, if necessary. But Mr Wren is almost inarticulate. When he essays to speak of those dreary months with the pen he becomes unintelligible. Months and months he spends before setting a word to paper. (And there are only three months of winter!) What does he cogitate all those months and months of winter? So help me God, I can't see this guy as a writer. Yet Mrs Wren says that when he sits down to it the stuff *just pours out*.

The talk drifts. It is difficult to follow Mr Wren's mind because he says nothing. *He thinks as he goes along* – so Mrs Wren puts it. Mrs Wren puts everything about Mr Wren in the loveliest light. 'He thinks as he goes along' – very charming, charming indeed, as Borowski would say, but really very painful, particularly when the thinker is nothing but a spavined horse.

Boris hands me money to buy liquor. Going for the liquor I am already intoxicated. I know just how I'll begin when I get back to the house. Walking down the street it commences, the grand speech inside me that's gurgling like Mrs Wren's loose laugh. Seems to me she had a slight edge on already. Listens beautifully when she's tight. Coming out of the wine shop I hear the urinal gurgling. Everything is loose and splashy. I want Mrs Wren to listen. . . .

Boris is rubbing his hands again. Mr Wren is still stuttering and spluttering. I have a bottle between my legs and I'm shoving the corkscrew in. Mrs Wren has her mouth parted expectantly. The wine is splashing between my legs, the sun is splashing through the bay window, and inside my veins there is a bubble and splash of a thousand crazy things that commence to gush out of me now pell-mell. I'm telling them everything that comes to mind, everything that was bottled up inside me and which Mrs Wren's loose laugh has somehow released. With that bottle between my legs and the sun splashing through the window I experience once again the splendour of those miserable days when I first arrived in Paris, a bewildered, poverty-stricken individual who haunted the streets like a ghost at a banquet. Everything comes back to me in a rush – the toilets that wouldn't work, the prince who shined my shoes, the Cinema Splendide where I slept on the patron's overcoat, the bars in the window, the feeling of suffocation, the fat cockroaches, the drinking and carousing that went on between times, Rose Cannaque and Naples dying in the sunlight. Dancing the streets on an empty belly and now and then calling on strange people – Madame Delorme, for instance. How I ever got to Madame Delorme's, I can't imagine any more. But I got there, got inside somehow, past the butler, past the maid with her little white apron, got right inside the palace with my corduroy trousers and my hunting jacket – and not a button on my fly. Even now I can taste again the golden ambiance of that room where Madame Delorme sat upon a throne in her mannish rig, the goldfish in the bowls, the maps of the ancient world, the beautifully bound books; I can feel again her heavy hand resting upon my shoulder, frightening me a little with her heavy Lesbian air. More comfortable down below in that thick stew pouring into the Gare St Lazare, the whores in the doorways, seltzer bottles on every table; a thick tide of semen flooding the gutters. Nothing better between five and seven than to be pushed around in that throng, to follow a leg or a beautiful bust, to move along with the tide and everything whirling in your brain. A weird sort of contentment in those days. No appointments, no invitations for dinner, no programme, no dough. The golden period, when I had not a single friend. Each morning the dreary walk to the American Express, and each morning the inevitable answer from the clerk. Dashing here and there like a bedbug, gathering butts now and then, sometimes furtively, sometimes brazenly; sitting down on a bench and squeezing my guts to stop the gnawing, or walking through the Jardin des Tuileries and getting an erection looking at the dumb statues. Or wandering along the Seine at night, wandering and wandering, and going mad with the beauty of it, the trees leaning to, the broken images in the water, the rush of the current under the bloody lights of the bridges, the women sleeping in doorways, sleeping on newspapers, sleeping in the rain; everywhere the musty porches of the cathedrals and beggars and lice and old hags full of St Vitus' dance; pushcarts stacked up like wine barrels in the side streets, the smell of berries in the market place and the old church surrounded with vegetables and blue arc lights, the gutters slippery with garbage and women in satin pumps staggering through the filth and vermin at the end of an all-night souse. The Place St Sulpice, so quiet and deserted, where towards midnight there came every night the woman with the busted umbrella and the crazy veil; every night she slept there on a bench under her torn umbrella, the ribs hanging down, her dress turning green, her bony fingers and the odour of decay oozing from her body; and in the morning I'd be sitting there myself, taking a quiet snooze in the sunshine, cursing the goddamned pigeons gathering up the crumbs everywhere. St Sulpice! The fat belfries, the garish posters over the door, the candles flaming inside. The Square so beloved of Anatole France, with that drone and buzz from the altar, the splash of the fountain, the pigeons cooing, the crumbs disappearing like magic and only a dull rumbling in the hollow of the guts. Here I would sit day after day thinking of Germaine and that dirty little street near the Bastille where she lived, and that buzz-buzz going on behind the altar, the buses whizzing by, the sun beating down into the asphalt and the asphalt working into me and Germaine, into the asphalt and all Paris in the big fat belfries.

And it was down the Rue Bonaparte that only a year before Mona and I used to walk every night, after we had taken leave of Borowski. St Sulpice not meaning much to me then, nor anything in Paris. Washed out with talk. Sick of faces. Fed up with cathedrals and squares and menageries and what not. Picking up a book in the red bedroom and the cane chair uncomfortable; tired of sitting on my ass all day long, tired of red wallpaper, tired of seeing so many people jabbering away about nothing. The red bedroom and the trunk always open; her gowns lying about in a delirium of disorder. The red bedroom with my galoshes and canes, the notebooks I never touched, the manuscripts lying cold and dead. Paris! Meaning the Café Select, the Dôme, the Flea Market, the American Express. Paris! Meaning Borowski's canes, Borowski's hats, Borowski's *gouaches*, Borowski's prehistoric fish – and prehistoric jokes. In that Paris of '28 only one night stands out in my memory – the night before sailing for America. A rare night, with Borowski slightly pickled and a little disgusted with me because I'm dancing with every slut in the place. But we're leaving in the morning! That's what I tell every cunt I grab hold of – leaving in the morning! That's what I'm telling the blonde with agate-coloured eyes. And while I'm telling her she takes my hand and squeezes it between her legs. In the lavatory I stand before the bowl with a tremendous erection; it seems light and heavy at the same time, like a piece of lead with wings on it. And while I'm standing there like that two cunts sail in – Americans. I greet them cordially, prick in hand. They give me a wink and pass on. In the vestibule, as I'm buttoning my fly, I notice one of them waiting for her friend to come out of the can. The music is still playing and maybe Mona'll be coming to fetch me, or Borowski with his gold-knobbed cane, but I'm in her arms now and she has hold of me and I don't care who comes or what happens.

We wriggle into the cabinet and there I stand her up, slap up against the wall, and I try to get it into her but it won't work and so we sit down on the seat and try it that way but it won't work either. No matter how we try it it won't work. And all the while she's got hold of my prick, she's clutching it like a lifesaver, but it's no use, we're too hot, too eager. The music is still playing and so we waltz out of the cabinet into the vestibule again and as we're dancing there in the shithouse I come all over her beautiful gown and she's sore as hell about it. I stumble back to the table and there's Borowski with his ruddy face and Mona with her disapproving eye. And Borowski says 'Let's all go to Brussels tomorrow,' and we agree, and when we get back to the hotel I vomit all over the place, in the bed, in the washbowl, over the suits and gowns and the galoshes and canes and the notebooks I never touched and the manuscripts cold and dead.

A few months later. The same hotel, the same room. We look out on the courtyard where the bicycles are parked, and there is the little room up above, under the attic, where some smart young Alec played the phonograph all day long and repeated clever little things at the top of his voice. I say 'we' but I'm getting ahead of myself, because Mona has been away a long time and it's just today that I'm meeting her at the Gare St Lazare. Towards evening I'm standing there with my face squeezed between the bars, but there's no Mona, and I read the cable over again but it doesn't help any. I go back to the Quarter and just the same I put away a hearty meal. Strolling past the Dôme a little later suddenly I see a pale, heavy face and burning eyes – and the little velvet suit that I always adore because under the soft velvet there were always her warm breasts, the marble legs, cool, firm, muscular. She rises up out of a sea of faces and embraces me, embraces me passionately – a thousand eyes, noses, fingers, legs, bottles, windows, purses, saucers all glaring at us and we in each other's arms oblivious. I sit down beside her and she talks – a flood of talk. Wild consumptive notes of hysteria, perversion, leprosy. I hear not a word because she is beautiful and I love her and now I am happy and willing to die.

We walk down the Rue du Château, looking for Eugene. Walk over the railroad bridge where I used to watch the trains pulling out and feel all sick inside wondering where the hell she could be. Everything soft and enchanting as we walk over the bridge. Smoke coming up between our legs, the tracks creaking, semaphores in our blood. I feel her body close to mine – all mine now – and I stop to rub my hands over the warm velvet. Everything around us is crumbling, crumbling and the warm body under the warm velvet is aching for me. . . .

181

Back in the very same room and fifty francs to the good, thanks to Eugene. I look out on the court but the phonograph is silent. The trunk is open and her things are lying around everywhere just as before. She lies down on the bed with her clothes on. Once, twice, three times, four times . . . I'm afraid she'll go mad . . . in bed, under the blankets, how good to feel her body again! But for how long? Will it last this time? Already I have a presentiment that it won't.

She talks to me so feverishly – as if there will be no tomorrow. 'Be quiet, Mona! Just look at me . . . *don't talk!*' Finally she drops off and I pull my arm from under her. My eyes close. Her body is there beside me . . . it will be there till morning surely . . . . It was in February I pulled out of the harbour in a blinding snowstorm. The last glimpse I had of her was in the window waving goodbye to me. A man standing on the other side of the street, at the corner, his hat pulled down over his eyes, his jowls resting on his lapels. A foetus watching me. A foetus with a cigar in its mouth. Mona at the window waving goodbye. White heavy face, hair streaming wild. And now it is a heavy bedroom, breathing regularly through the gills, sap still oozing from between her legs, a warm feline odour and her hair in my mouth. My eyes are closed. We breathe warmly into each other's mouth. Close together, America three thousand miles away. I never want to see it again. To have her here in bed with me, breathing on me, her hair in my mouth – I count that something of a miracle. Nothing can happen now till morning. . . .

I wake from a deep slumber to look at her. A pale light is trickling in. I look at her beautiful wild hair. I feel something crawling down my neck. I look at her again, closely. Her hair is alive. I pull back the sheet – more of them. They are swarming over the pillow.

It is a little after daybreak. We pack hurriedly and sneak out of the hotel. The cafés are still closed. We walk, and as we walk we scratch ourselves. The day opens in milky whiteness, streaks of salmon-pink sky, snails leaving their shells. Paris. Paris. Everything happens here. Old, crumbling walls and the pleasant sound of water running in the urinals. Men licking their moustaches at the bar. Shutters going up with a bang and little streams purling in the gutters. *Amer Picon* in huge scarlet letters. *Zigzag*. Which way will we go and why or where or what?

Mona is hungry, her dress is thin. Nothing but evening wraps, bottles of perfume, barbaric earrings, bracelets, depilatories. We sit down in a billiard parlour on the Avenue du Maine and order hot coffee. The toilet is out of order. We shall have to sit some time before we can go to another hotel. Meanwhile we pick bedbugs out of each other's hair. Nervous. Mona is losing her temper. Must have a bath. Must have this. Must have that. Must, must, must. . .

'How much money have you left?'

Money! Forgot all about that.

Hôtel des Etats-Unis. An *ascenseur*. We go to bed in broad daylight. When we get up it is dark and the first thing to do is to raise enough dough to send a cable to America. A cable to the foetus with the long juicy cigar in his mouth. Meanwhile there is the Spanish woman on the Boulevard Raspail – she's always good for a warm meal. By morning something will happen. At least we're going to bed together. No more bedbugs now. The rainy season has commenced. The sheets are immaculate. . . .

A new life opening up for me at the Villa Borghese. Only ten o'clock and we have already had breakfast and been out for a walk. We have an Elsa here with us now. 'Step softly for a few days,' cautions Boris.

The day begins gloriously: a bright sky, a fresh wind, the houses newly washed. On our way to the Post Office Boris and I discussed the book. *The Last Book* – which is going to be written anonymously.

A new day is beginning. I felt it this morning as we stood before one of Dufresne's glistening canvases, a sort of *déjeuner intime* in the thirteenth century, *sans vin*. A fine, fleshy nude, solid, vibrant, pink as a fingernail, with glistening billows of flesh; all the secondary characteristics, and a few of the primary. A body that sings, that has the moisture of dawn. A still life, only nothing is still, nothing dead here. The table creaks with food; it is so heavy it is sliding out of the frame. A thirteenth-century repast – with all the jungle notes that he has memorized so well. A family of gazelles and zebras nipping the fronds of the palms.

And now we have Elsa. She was playing for us this morning while we were in bed. *Step softly for a few days*. . . . Good! Elsa is the maid and I am the guest. And Boris is the big cheese. A new drama is beginning. I'm laughing to myself as I write this. He knows what is going to happen, that lynx, Boris. He has a nose for things too. *Step softly*. . . .

Boris is on pins and needles. At any moment now his wife may appear on the scene. She weighs well over 180 pounds, that wife of his. And Boris is only a handful. There you have the situation. He tries to explain it to me on our way home at night. It is so tragic and so ridiculous at the same time that I am obliged to stop now and then and laugh in his face. 'Why do you laugh so?' he says gently, and then he commences himself, with that whimpering, hysterical note in his voice, like a helpless wretch who realizes suddenly that no matter how many frock coats he puts on he will never make a man. He wants to run away, to take a new name. 'She can have everything, that cow, if only she leaves me alone,' he whines. But first the apartment has to be rented, and the deeds signed, and a thousand other details for which his frock coat will come in handy. But the size of her – that's what really worries him. If we were to find her suddenly standing on the doorstep when we arrive he would faint – that's how much he respects her!

And so we've got to go easy with Elsa for a while. Elsa is only there to make breakfast – and to show the apartment.

But Elsa is already undermining me. That German blood. Those melancholy songs. Coming down the stairs this morning, with the fresh coffee in my nostrils, I was humming softly. . . . *'Es wär' so schön gewesen.'* For breakfast, that. And in a little while the English boy upstairs with his Bach. As Elsa says – 'he needs a woman'. And Elsa needs something too. I can feel it. I didn't say anything to Boris about it, but while he was cleaning his teeth this morning Elsa was giving me an earful about Berlin, about the women who look so attractive from behind, and when they turn round – *wow, syphilis!*

It seems to me that Elsa looks at me rather wistfully. Something left over from the breakfast table. This afternoon we were writing, back to back, in the studio. She had begun a letter to her lover who is in Italy. The machine got jammed. Boris had gone to look at a cheap room he will take as soon as the apartment is rented. There was nothing for it but to make love to Elsa. She wanted it. And yet I felt a little sorry for her. She had only written the first line to her lover – I read it out of the corner of my eye as I bent over her. But it couldn't be helped. That damned German music, so melancholy, so sentimental. It undermined me. And then her beady little eyes, so hot and sorrowful at the same time.

After it was over I asked her to play something for me. She's a musician, Elsa, even though it sounded like broken pots and skulls clanking. She was weeping, too, as she played. I don't blame her. Everywhere the same thing, she says. Everywhere a man, and then she has to leave, and then there's an abortion and then a new job and then another man and nobody gives a fuck about her except to use her. All this after she's played Schumann for me – Schumann, that slobbery, sentimental German bastard! Somehow I feel sorry as hell for her and yet I don't give a damn. A cunt who can play as she does ought to have better sense than be tripped up by every guy with a big putz who happens to come along. But that Schumann gets into my blood. She's still sniffling, Elsa; but my mind is far away. I'm thinking of Tania and how she claws away at her adagio. I'm thinking of lots of things that are gone and buried. Thinking of a summer afternoon in Greenpoint when the Germans were romping over Belgium and we had not yet lost enough money to be concerned over the rape of a neutral country. A time when we were still innocent enough to listen to poets and to sit around a table in the twilight rapping for departed spirits. All that afternoon and evening the atmosphere is saturated with German music; the whole neighbourhood is German, more German even than Germany. We were brought up on Schumann and Hugo Wolf and sauerkraut and kümmel and potato dumplings. Towards evening we're sitting around a big table with the curtains drawn and some fool two-headed wench is rapping for Jesus Christ. We're holding hands under the table and the dame next to me has two fingers in my fly. And finally we lie on the floor, behind the piano, while someone sings a dreary song. The air is stifling and her breath is boozy. The pedal is moving up and down, stiffly, automatically, a crazy, futile movement, like a tower of dung that takes twenty-seven years to build but keeps perfect time. I pull her over me with the sounding board in my ears; the room is dark and the carpet is sticky with the kümmel that has been spilled about. Suddenly it seems as if the dawn were coming: it is like water purling over ice and the ice is blue with a rising mist, glaciers sunk in emerald green, chamois and antelope, golden groupers, sea cows mooching along and the amber jack leaping over the Arctic rim. . . .

Elsa is sitting in my lap. Her eyes are like little belly-buttons. I look at her large mouth, so wet and glistening, and I cover it. She is humming now. . . . *'Es wär' so schön gewesen. . . .'* Ah, Elsa, you don't know yet what that means to me, your *Trompeter von Säckingen*. German Singing Societies, Schwaben Hall, the Turnverein . . . *links um, rechts um* . . . and then a whack over the ass with the end of a rope.

Ah, the Germans! They take you all over like an omnibus. They give you indigestion. In the same night one cannot visit the morgue, the infirmary, the zoo, the signs of the zodiac, the limbos of philosophy, the caves of epistemology, the arcana of Freud and Stekel. . . . On the merry-go-round one doesn't get anywhere, whereas with the Germans one can go from Vega to Lope de Vega, all in one night, and come away as foolish as Parsifal.

As I say, the day began gloriously. It was only this morning that I became conscious again of this physical Paris of which I have been unaware for weeks. Perhaps it is because the book has begun to grow inside me. I am carrying it around with me everywhere. I walk through the streets big with child and the cops escort me across the street. Women get up to offer me their seats. Nobody pushes me rudely any more. I am pregnant. I waddle awkwardly, my big stomach pressed against the weight of the world.

It was this morning, on our way to the Post Office, that we gave the book its final imprimatur. We have evolved a new cosmogony of literature, Boris and I. It is to be a new Bible – The Last Book. All those who have anything to say will say it here – *anonymously*. We will exhaust the age. After us not another book – not for a generation, at least. Heretofore we had been digging in the dark, with nothing but instinct to guide us. Now we shall have a vessel in which to pour the vital fluid, a bomb which, when we throw it, will set off the world. We shall put into it enough to give the writers of tomorrow their plots, their dramas, their poems, their myths, their sciences. The world will be able to feed on it for a thousand years to come. It is colossal in its pretentiousness. The thought of it almost shatters us.

For a hundred years or more the world, *our* world, has been dying. And not one man, in these last hundred years or so, has been crazy enough to put a bomb up the asshole of creation and set it off. The world is rotting away, dying piecemeal. But it needs the *coup de grâce*, it needs to be blown to smithereens. Not one of us is intact, and yet we have in us all the continents and the seas between the continents and the birds of the air. We are going to put it down – the evolution of this world which has died but which has not been buried. We are swimming on the face of time and all else has drowned, is drowning, or will drown. It will be enormous, the Book. There will be oceans of space in which to move about, to perambulate, to sing, to dance, to climb, to bathe, to leap somersaults, to whine, to rape, to murder. A cathedral, a veritable cathedral, in the building of which everybody will assist who has lost his identity. There will be masses for the dead, prayers, confessions, hymns, a moaning and a chattering, a sort of murderous insouciance; there will be rose windows and gargoyles and acolytes and pallbearers. You can bring your horses in and gallop through the aisles. You can butt your head against the walls – they won't give. You can pray in any language you choose, or you can curl up outside and go to sleep. It will last a thousand years, at least, this cathedral, and there will be no replica, for the builders will be dead and the formula too.

186

We will have postcards made and organize tours. We will build a town around it and set up a free commune. We have no need for genius – genius is dead. We have need for strong hands, for spirits who are willing to give up the ghost and put on flesh. . . .

The day is moving along at a fine tempo. I am up on the balcony at Tania's place. The drama is going on down below in the drawing room. The dramatist is sick and from above his scalp looks more scabrous than ever. His hair is made of straw. His ideas are straw. His wife too is straw, though still a little damp. The whole house is made of straw. Here I am up on the balcony, waiting for Boris to arrive. My last problem – *breakfast* – is gone. I have simplified everything. If there are any new problems I can carry them in my rucksack, along with my dirty wash. I am throwing away all my sous. What need have I for money? I am a writing machine. The last screw has been added. The thing flows. Between me and the machine there is no estrangement. I am the machine. . . .

They have not told me yet what the new drama is about, but I can sense it. They are trying to get rid of me. Yet here I am for my dinner, even a little earlier than they expected. I have informed them where to sit, what to do. I ask them politely if I shall be disturbing them, but what I really mean, and they know it well, is – *will you be disturbing me?* No, you blissful cockroaches, you are not disturbing me. You are *nourishing* me. I see you sitting there close together and I know there is a chasm between you. Your nearness is the nearness of planets. I am the void between you. If I withdraw there will be no void for you to swim in.

Tania is in a hostile mood – I can feel it. She resents my being filled with anything but herself. She knows by the very calibre of my excitement that her value is reduced to zero. She knows that I did not come this evening to fertilize her. She knows there is something germinating inside me which will destroy her. She is slow to realize, but she is realizing it . . .

Sylvester looks more content. He will embrace her this evening at the dinner table. Even now he is reading my manuscript, preparing to inflame my ego, to set my ego against hers.

It will be a strange gathering this evening. The stage is being set. I hear the tinkle of the glasses. The wine is being brought out. There will be bumpers downed and Sylvester who is ill will come out of his illness.

It was only last night, at Cronstadt's, that we projected this setting.

It was ordained that the women must suffer, that off-stage there should be more terror and violence, more disasters, more suffering, more woe and misery.

It is no accident that propels people like us to Paris. Paris is simply an artificial stage, a revolving stage that permits the spectator to glimpse all phases of the conflict. Of itself Paris initiates no dramas. They are begun elsewhere. Paris is simply an obstetrical instrument that tears the living embryo from the womb and puts it in the incubator. Paris is the cradle of artificial births. Rocking here in the cradle each one slips back into his soil: one dreams back to Berlin, New York, Chicago, Vienna, Minsk. Vienna is never more Vienna than in Paris. Everything is raised to apotheosis. The cradle gives up its babes and new ones take their places. You can read here on the walls where Zola lived and Balzac and Dante and Strindberg and everybody who ever was anything. Everyone has lived here some time or other. Nobody *dies* here. . . .

They are talking downstairs. Their language is symbolic. The world 'struggle' enters into it. Sylvester, the sick dramatist, is saying: 'I am just reading the *Manifesto*.' And Tania says – '*Whose?*' Yes, Tania, I heard you. I am up here writing about you and you divine it well. *Speak more*, that I may record you. For when we go to table I shall not be able to make any notes. . . . Suddenly Tania remarks: 'There is no prominent hall in this place.' Now what does that mean, if anything?

They are putting up pictures now. That, too, is to impress me. See, they wish to say, we are at home here, living the conjugal life. Making the home attractive. We will even argue a little about the pictures, for *your* benefit. And Tania remarks again: 'How the eye deceives one!' Ah, Tania, what things you say! Go on, carry out this farce a little longer. I am here to get the dinner you promised me; I enjoy this comedy tremendously. And now Sylvester takes the lead. He is trying to explain one of Borowski's *gouaches*. 'Come here, do you see? One of them is playing the guitar; the other is holding a girl in his lap.' True, Sylvester. Very true. Borowski and his guitars! The girls in his lap! Only one never quite knows what it is he holds in his lap, or whether it is really a man playing the guitar. . . .

Soon Moldorf will be trotting in on all fours and Boris with that helpless little laugh of his. There will be a golden pheasant for dinner and Anjou and short fat cigars. And Cronstadt, when he gets the latest news, will live a little harder, a little brighter, for five minutes; and then he will subside again into the humus of his ideology and perhaps a poem will be born, a big golden bell of a poem without a tongue.

Had to knock off for an hour or so. Another customer to look at the apartment. Upstairs the bloody Englishman is practising his Bach. It is imperative now, when someone comes to look at the apartment, to run upstairs and ask the pianist to lay off for a while.

Elsa is telephoning the greengrocer. The plumber is putting a new seat on the toilet bowl. Whenever the doorbell rings Boris loses his equilibrium. In the excitement he has dropped his glasses; he is on his hands and knees, his frock coat is dragging the floor. It is a little like the Grand Guignol – the starving poet come to give the butcher's daughter lessons. Every time the phone rings the poet's mouth waters. Mallarmé sounds like a sirloin steak, Victor Hugo like *foie de veau*. Elsa is ordering a delicate little lunch for Boris – 'a nice juicy little pork chop', she says. I see a whole flock of pink hams lying cold on the marble, wonderful hams cushioned in white fat. I have a terrific hunger though we've only had breakfast a few minutes ago – it's the lunch that I'll have to skip. It's only Wednesdays that I eat lunch, thanks to Borowski. Elsa is still telephoning – she forgot to order a piece of bacon. 'Yes, a nice little piece of bacon, not too fatty,' she says . . . *Zut alors!* Throw in some sweetbreads, throw in some mountain oysters and some psst clams! Throw in some fried liverwurst while you're at it; I could gobble up the fifteen hundred plays of Lope de Vega in one sitting.

It is a beautiful woman who has come to look at the apartment. An American, of course. I stand at the window with my back to her watching a sparrow pecking at a fresh turd. Amazing how easily the sparrow is provided for. It is raining a bit and the drops are very big. I used to think a bird couldn't fly if its wings got wet. Amazing how these rich dames come to Paris and find all the swell studios. A little talent and a big purse. If it rains they have a chance to display their brand new slickers. Food is nothing: sometimes they're so busy gadding about that they haven't time for lunch. Just a little sandwich, a wafer, at the Café de la Paix or the Ritz Bar. 'For the daughters of gentlefolk only' – that's what it says at the old studio of Puvis de Chavannes. Happened to pass there the other day. Rich American cunts with paint boxes slung over their shoulders. A little talent and a fat purse.

The sparrow is hopping frantically from one cobblestone to another. Truly herculean efforts, if you stop to examine closely. Everywhere there is food lying about – in the gutter, I mean. The beautiful American woman is inquiring about the toilet. The toilet! Let me show you, you velvet-snooted gazelle! The toilet, you say: *Par ici, Madame. N'oubliez pas que les places numérotées sont réservées aux mutilés de la guerre.*

Boris is rubbing his hands – he is putting the finishing touches to the deal. The dogs are barking in the courtyard; they bark like wolves. Upstairs Mrs Melverness is moving the furniture around. She had nothing to do all day, she's bored; if she finds a crumb of dirt anywhere she cleans the whole house. There's a bunch of green grapes on the table and a bottle of wine – *vin de choix*, ten degrees. 'Yes,' says Boris. 'I could make a washstand for you, just come here, please. Yes, this is the toilet. There is one upstairs too, of course. Yes, a thousand francs a month. You don't care much for Utrillo, you say? No, this is it. It needs a new washer, that's all. . . .'

She's going in a minute now. Boris hasn't even introduced me this time. The son of a bitch! Whenever it's a rich cunt he forgets to introduce me. In a few minutes I'll be able to sit down again and type. Somehow I don't feel like it any more today. My spirit is dribbling away. She may come back in an hour or so and take the chair from under my ass. How the hell can a man write when he doesn't know where he's going to sit the next half-hour? If this rich bastard takes the place I won't even have a place to sleep. It's hard to know, when you're in such a jam, which is worse – not having a place to sleep or not having a place to work. One can sleep almost anywhere, but one must have a place to work. Even if it's not a masterpiece you're doing. Even a bad novel requires a chair to sit on and a bit of privacy. These rich cunts never think of a thing like that. Whenever they want to lower their soft behinds there's always a chair standing ready for them. . . .

Last night we left Sylvester and his God sitting together before the hearth. Sylvester in his pyjamas, Moldorf with a cigar between his lips. Sylvester is peeling an orange. He puts the peel on the couch cover. Moldorf draws closer to him. He asks permission to read again that brilliant parody, *The Gates of Heaven*. We are getting ready to go, Boris and I. We are too gay for this sickroom atmosphere. Tania is going with us. She is gay because she is going to escape. Boris is gay because the God in Moldorf is dead. I am gay because it is another act we are going to put on.

Moldorf's voice is reverent. 'Can I stay with you, Sylvester, until you go to bed?' He has been staying with him for the last six days, buying medicine, running errands for Tania, comforting, consoling, guarding the portals against malevolent intruders like Boris and his scalawags. He is like a savage who has discovered that his idol was mutilated during the night. There he sits, at the idol's feet, with breadfruit and grease and jabberwocky prayers. His voice goes out unctuously. His limbs are already paralysed.

To Tania he speaks as if she were a priestess who had broken her vows. 'You must make yourself worthy. Sylvester is your God.' And while Sylvester is upstairs suffering (he has a little wheeze in the chest) the priest and the priestess devour the food. 'You are polluting yourself,' he says, the gravy dripping from his lips. He has the capacity for eating and suffering at the same time. While he fends off the dangerous ones he puts out his fat little paw and strokes Tania's hair. 'I'm beginning to fall in love with you. You are like my Fanny.'

In other respects it has been a fine day for Moldorf. A letter arrived from America. Moe is getting As in everything. Murray is learning to ride the bicycle. The victrola was repaired. You can see from the expression on his face that there were other things in the letter besides report cards and velocipedes. You can be sure of it because this afternoon he bought 325 francs worth of jewellery for his Fanny. In addition he wrote her a twenty-page letter. The *garçon* brought him page after page, filled his fountain pen, served his coffee and cigars, fanned him a little when he perspired, brushed the crumbs from the table, lit his cigar when it went out, bought stamps for him, danced on him, pirouetted, salaamed . . . broke his spine damned near. The tip was fat. Bigger and fatter than a Corona Corona. Moldorf probably mentioned it in his diary. It was for Fanny's sake. The bracelet and the earrings, they were worth every sou he spent. Better to spend it on Fanny than waste it on little strumpets like Germaine and Odette. Yes, he told Tania so. He showed her his trunk. It is crammed with gifts – for Fanny, and for Moe and Murray.

'My Fanny is the most intelligent woman in the world. I have been searching and searching to find a flaw in her – but there's not one.

'She's perfect. I'll tell you what Fanny can do. She plays bridge like a shark; she's interested in Zionism; you give her an old hat, for instance, and see what she can do with it. A little twist here, a ribbon there, and *voilà quelque chose de beau!* Do you know what is perfect bliss? To sit beside Fanny, when Moe and Murray have gone to bed, and listen to the radio. She sits there so peacefully. I am rewarded for all my struggles and heartaches in just watching her. She listens intelligently. When I think of your stinking Montparnasse and then of my evenings in Bay Ridge with Fanny after a big meal, I tell you there is no comparison. A simple thing like food, the children, the soft lamps, and Fanny sitting there, a little tired, but cheerful, contented, heavy with bread . . . we just sit there for hours without saying a word. That's bliss!

'Today she writes me a letter – not one of those dull stock-report letters. She writes me from the heart, in language that even my little Murray could understand. She's delicate about everything, Fanny. She says that the children must continue their education but the expense worries her. It will cost a thousand bucks to send little Murray to school. Moe, of course, will get a scholarship. But little Murray, that little genius, Murray, what are we going to do about him? I wrote Fanny not to worry. Send Murray to school, I said. What's another thousand dollars? I'll make more money this year than ever before. I'll do it for little Murray – because he's a genius, that kid.'

I should like to be there when Fanny opens the trunk. 'See, Fanny, this is what I bought in Budapest from an old Jew. . . . This is what they wear in Bulgaria – it's pure wool. . . . This belonged to the Duke of something or other – no, you don't wind it, you put it in the sun. . . . This I want you to wear, Fanny, when we go to the Opera . . . wear it with that comb I showed you. . . . And this, Fanny, is something Tania picked up for me . . . she's a little bit on your type. . . .'

And Fanny is sitting there on the settee, just as she was in the oleograph, with Moe on one side of her and little Murray, Murray the genius, on the other. Her fat legs are a little too short to reach the floor. Her eyes have a dull permanganate glow. Breasts like ripe red cabbage; they bobble a little when she leans forward. But the sad thing about her is that the juice has been cut off. She sits there like a dead storage battery; her face is out of plumb – it needs a little animation, a sudden spurt of juice to bring it back into focus. Moldorf is jumping around in front of her like a fat toad. His flesh quivers. He slips and it is difficult for him to roll over again on his belly. She prods him with her thick toes. His eyes protrude a little further. 'Kick me again, Fanny, that was good.' She gives him a good prod this time – it leaves a permanent dent in his paunch. His face is close to the carpet; the wattles are joggling in the nap of the rug. He livens up a bit, flips around, springs from furniture to furniture. 'Fanny, you are marvellous!' He is sitting now on her shoulder. He bites a little piece from her ear, just a little tip from the lobe where it doesn't hurt. But she's still dead – all storage battery and no juice. He falls on her lap and lies there quivering like a toothache. He is all warm now and helpless. His belly glistens like a patent-leather shoe. In the sockets of his eyes a pair of fancy vest buttons. 'Unbutton my eyes, Fanny, I want to see you better!' Fanny carries him to bed and drops a little hot wax over his eyes. She puts rings around his navel and a thermometer up his ass. She places him and he quivers again. Suddenly he's dwindled, shrunk completely out of sight. She searches all over for him, in her intestines, everywhere. Something is tickling her – she doesn't know where exactly. The bed is full of toads and fancy vest buttons. 'Fanny, where are you?' Something is tickling her – she can't say where. The buttons are dropping off the bed. The toads are climbing the walls. A tickling and a tickling. 'Fanny, take the wax out of my eyes! I want to look at you!' But Fanny is laughing, squirming with laughter. There is something inside her, tickling and tickling. She'll die laughing if she doesn't find it. 'Fanny, the trunk is full of beautiful things. Fanny, do you hear me?' Fanny is laughing, laughing like a fat worm. Her belly is swollen with laughter. Her legs are getting blue. 'O God, Morris, there is something tickling me. . . . I can't help it!'

In America I had a number of Hindu friends, some good, some bad, some indifferent. Circumstances had placed me in a position where fortunately I could be of aid to them; I secured jobs for them, I harboured them, and I fed them when necessary. They were very grateful, I must say; so much so, in fact that they made my life miserable with their attentions. Two of them were saints, if I know what a saint is; particularly Gupte who was found one morning with his throat cut from ear to ear. In a little boarding house in Greenwich Village he was found one morning stretched out stark naked on the bed, his flute beside him, and his throat gashed, as I say, from ear to ear. It was never discovered whether he had been murdered or whether he had committed suicide. But that's neither here nor there. . . .

I'm thinking back to the chain of circumstances which has brought me finally to Nanantatee's place. Thinking how strange it is that I should have forgotten all about Nanantatee until the other day when lying in a shabby hotel room on the Rue Cels. I'm lying there on the iron bed thinking what a zero I have become, what a cipher, what a nullity, when bango! out pops the word: NONENTITY! That's what we called him in New York – Nonentity. *Mister* Nonentity.

I'm lying on the floor now in that gorgeous suite of rooms he boasted of when he was in New York. Nanantatee is playing the good

Samaritan; he has given me a pair of itchy blankets, horse blankets they are, in which I curl up on the dusty floor. There are little jobs to do every hour of the day – that is, if I am foolish enough to remain indoors. In the morning he wakes me rudely in order to have me prepare the vegetables for his lunch: onions, garlic, beans, etc. His friend, Kepi, warns me not to eat the food – he says it's bad. Bad or good what difference? *Food!* That's all that matters. For a little food I am quite willing to sweep his carpets with a broken broom, to wash his clothes and to scrape the crumbs off the floor as soon as he has finished eating. He's become absolutely immaculate since my arrival: everything has to be dusted now, the chairs must be arranged a certain way, the clock must ring, the toilet must flush properly. . . . A crazy Hindu if ever there was one! And parsimonious as a string bean. I'll have a great laugh over it when I get out of his clutches, but just now I'm a prisoner, a man without caste, an untouchable. . . .

If I fail to come back at night and roll up in the horse blankets he says to me on arriving: 'Oh, so you didn't die then? I thought you had died.' And though he knows I'm absolutely penniless he tells me every day about some cheap room he has just discovered in the neighbourhood. 'But I can't take a room yet, you know that,' I say. And then, blinking his eyes like a Chink, he answers smoothly: 'Oh, yes, I forgot that you had no money. I am always forgetting, Endree. . . . But when the cable comes . . . when Miss Mona sends you the money, then you will come with me to look for a room, eh?' And in the next breath he urges me to stay as long as I wish – 'six months . . . seven months, Endree . . . you are very good for me here.'

Nanantatee is one of the Hindus I never did anything for in America. He represented himself to me as a wealthy merchant, a pearl merchant, with a luxurious suite of rooms on the Rue Lafayette, Paris, a villa in Bombay, a bungalow in Darjeeling. I could see from first glance that he was a half-wit, but then half-wits sometimes have the genius to amass a fortune. I didn't know that he paid his hotel bill in New York by leaving a couple of fat pearls in the proprietor's hands. It seems amusing to me now that this little duck once swaggered about the lobby of that hotel in New York with an ebony cane, bossing the bellhops around, ordering luncheons for his guests, calling up the porter for theatre tickets, renting a taxi by the day, etc., etc., all without a sou in his pocket. Just a string of fat pearls around his neck which he cashed one by one as time wore on. And the fatuous way he used to pat me on the back, thank me for being so good to the Hindu boys – 'they are all very intelligent boys, Endree . . . very

194

intelligent!' Telling me that the good lord so-and-so would repay me for my kindness. That explains now why they used to giggle so, these intelligent Hindu boys, when I suggested that they touch Nanantatee for a five-spot.

Curious now how the good lord so-and-so is requiting me for my benevolence. I'm nothing but a slave to this fat little duck. I'm at his beck and call continually. He needs me here – he tells me so to my face. When he goes to the crap-can he shouts: 'Endree, bring me a pitcher of water, please. I must wipe myself.' He wouldn't think of using toilet paper, Nanantatee. Must be against his religion. No, he calls for a pitcher of water and a rag. He's *delicate*, the fat little duck. Sometimes when I'm drinking a cup of pale tea in which he has dropped a rose leaf he comes alongside of me and lets a loud fart, right in my face. He never says 'Excuse me!' The word must be missing from his Gujarati dictionary.

The day I arrived at Nanantatee's apartment he was in the act of performing his ablutions, that is to say, he was standing over a dirty bowl trying to work his crooked arm around toward the back of his neck. Beside the bowl was a brass goblet which he used to change the water. He requested me to be silent during the ceremony. I sat there silently, as I was bidden, and watched him as he sang and prayed and spat now and then into the washbowl. So this is the wonderful suite of rooms he talked about in New York! The Rue Lafayette! It sounded like an important street to me back there in New York. I thought only millionaires and pearl merchants inhabited the street. It sounds wonderful, the Rue Lafayette, when you're on the other side of the water. So does Fifth Avenue, when you're over here. One can't imagine what dumps there are on these swell streets. Anyway, here I am at last, sitting in the gorgeous suite of rooms on the Rue Lafayette. And this crazy duck with his crooked arm is going through the ritual of washing himself. The chair on which I'm sitting is broken, the bedstead is falling apart, the wallpaper is in tatters, there is an open valise under the bed crammed with dirty wash. From where I sit I can glance at the miserable courtyard down below where the aristocracy of the Rue Lafayette sit and smoke their clay pipes. I wonder now, as he chants the doxology, what that bungalow in Darjeeling looks like. It's interminable, his chanting and praying.

He explains to me that he is obliged to wash in a certain prescribed way – his religion demands it. But on Sundays he takes a bath in the tin tub – the Great I AM will wink at that, he says. When he's dressed he goes to the cupboard, kneels before a little idol on the third shelf, and repeats the mumbo jumbo. If you pray like that every day, he says, nothing will happen to you. The good lord what's his name never forgets an obedient servant. And then he shows me the crooked arm which he got in a taxi accident on a day doubtless when he had neglected to rehearse the complete song and dance. His arms looks like a broken compass; it's not an arm any more, but a knucklebone with a shank attached. Since the arm has been repaired he has developed a pair of swollen glands in the armpit – fat little glands, exactly like a dog's testicles. While bemoaning his plight he remembers suddenly that the doctor had recommended a more liberal diet. He begs me at once to sit down and make up a menu with plenty of fish and meat. 'And what about oysters, Endree – for *le petit frère*?' But all this is only to make an impression on me. He hasn't the slightest intention of buying himself oysters, or meat, or fish. Not as long as I am there, at least. For the time being we are going to nourish ourselves on lentils and rice and all the dry foods he has stored away in the attic. And the butter he bought last week, that won't go to waste either. When he commences to cure the butter the smell is unbearable. I used to run out at first, when he started frying the butter, but now I stick it out. He'd be only too delighted if he could make me vomit up my meal – that would be something else to put away in the cupboard along with the dry bread and the mouldy cheese and the little grease cakes that he makes himself out of the stale milk and the rancid butter.

For the last five years, so it seems, he hasn't done a stroke of work, hasn't turned over a penny. Business has gone to smash. He talks to me about pearls in the Indian Ocean – big fat ones on which you can live for a lifetime. The Arabs are ruining the business, he says. But meanwhile he prays to the lord so-and-so every day, and that sustains him. He's on a marvellous footing with the deity: knows just how to cajole him, how to wheedle a few sous out of him. It's a pure commercial relationship. In exchange for the flummery before the cabinet every day he gets his ration of beans and garlic, to say nothing of the swollen testicles under his arm. He is confident that everything will turn out well in the end. The pearls will sell again some day, maybe five years hence, maybe twenty – when the Lord Boomaroom wishes it. 'And when the business goes, Endree, you will get ten per cent – for writing the letters. But first Endree, you must write the letter to find out if we can get credit from India. It will take about six months for an answer, maybe seven months . . . the boats are not fast in India.' He has no conception of time at all, the little duck. When I ask him if he has slept well he will say: 'Ah, yes, Endree, I sleep very well . . . I sleep sometimes ninety-two hours in three days.'

Mornings he is usually too weak to do any work. His arm! That poor broken crutch of an arm! I wonder sometimes when I see him twisting it around the back of his neck how he will ever get it into place again. If it weren't for that little paunch he carries he'd remind me of one of those contortionists at the Cirque Médrano. All he needs is to break a leg. When he sees me sweeping the carpet, when he sees what a cloud of dust I raise, he begins to cluck like a pygmy. 'Good! Very good, Endree. And now I will pick up the knots.' That means that there are a few crumbs of dust which I have overlooked; it is a polite way he has of being sarcastic.

Afternoons there are always a few cronies from the pearl market dropping in to pay him a visit. They're all very suave, butter-tongued bastards with soft, doelike eyes; they sit around the table drinking the perfumed tea with a loud hissing noise while Nanantatee jumps up and down like a jack-in-the-box or points to a crumb on the floor and says in his smooth slippery voice – 'Will you please to pick that up, Endree.' When the guests arrive he goes unctuously to the cupboard and gets out the dry crusts of bread which he toasted maybe a week ago and which taste strongly now of the mouldy wood. Not a crumb is thrown away. If the bread gets too sour he takes it downstairs to the concierge who, so he says, has been very kind to him. According to him, the concierge is delighted to get the stale bread – she makes bread pudding with it.

One day my friend Anatole came to see me. Nanantatee was delighted. Insisted that Anatole stay for tea. Insisted that he try little grease cakes and the stale bread. 'You must come every day,' he says, 'and teach me Russian. Fine language, Russian . . . I want to speak it. How do you say that again, Endree – *borsht*? You will write that down for me, please, Endree. . . .' And I must write it on the typewriter, no less, so that he can observe my technique. He bought the typewriter, after he had collected on the bad arm, because the doctor recommended it as a good exercise. But he got tired of the typewriter shortly – it was an *English* typewriter.

When he learned that Anatole played the mandolin he said: 'Very good! You must come every day and teach me the music. I will buy a mandolin as soon as business is better. It is good for my arm.' The next day he borrows a phonograph from the concierge. 'You will please teach me to dance, Endree. My stomach is too big.' I am hoping that he will buy a porterhouse steak some day so that I can say to him: 'You will please bite it for me, *Mister* Nonentity. My teeth are not strong!'

As I said a moment ago, ever since my arrival he has become extraordinarily meticulous. 'Yesterday,' he says, 'you made three mistakes, Endree. First, you forgot to close the toilet door and so all night it makes boom-boom; second, you left the kitchen window open and so the window is cracked this morning. And you forgot to put out the milk bottle! Always you will put out the milk bottle please, before you go to bed, and in the morning you will please bring in the bread.'

Every day his friend Kepi drops in to see if any visitors have arrived from India. He waits for Nanantatee to go out and then he scurries to the cupboard and devours the sticks of bread that are hidden away in a glass jar. The food is no good, he insists, but he puts it away like a rat. Kepi is a scrounger, a sort of human tick who fastens himself to the hide of even the poorest compatriot. From Kepi's standpoint they are all nabobs. For a Manila cheroot and the price of a drink he will suck any Hindu's ass. A Hindu's, mind you, but not an Englishman's. He has the address of every whorehouse in Paris, and the rates. Even from the ten franc joints he gets his little commission. And he knows the shortest way to any place you want to go. He will ask you first if you want to go by taxi; if you say no, he will suggest the bus, and if that is too high then the streetcar or the metro. Or he will offer to walk you there and save a franc or two, knowing very well that it will be necessary to pass a *tabac* on the way and that you will please be so good as to buy me a little cheroot.

Kepi is interesting, in a way, because he has absolutely no ambition except to get a fuck every night. Every penny he makes, and they are damned few, he squanders in the dance halls. He has a wife and eight children in Bombay, but that does not prevent him from proposing marriage to any little *femme de chambre* who is stupid and credulous enough to be taken in by him. He has a little room on the Rue Condorcet for which he pays sixty francs a month. He papered it all himself. Very proud of it, too. He uses violet-coloured ink in his fountain pen because it lasts longer. He shines his own shoes, presses his own pants, does his own laundry. For a little cigar, a cheroot, if you please, he will escort you all over Paris. If you stop to look at a shirt or a collar button his eyes flash. 'Don't buy it here,' he will say. 'They ask too much. I will show you a cheaper place.' And before you have time to think about it he will whisk you away and deposit you before another show window where there are the same ties and shirts and collar buttons – maybe it's the very same store! but you don't know the difference. When Kepi hears that you want to buy something his soul becomes animated. He will ask you so many questions and drag you to so many places that you are bound to get thirsty and ask him to have a drink, whereupon you will discover to your amazement that you are again standing in a *tabac* – maybe the same *tabac*! – and Kepi is saying again in that small unctuous voice: 'Will you please be so good as to buy me a little cheroot?' No matter what you propose doing, even if it's only to walk around the corner, Kepi will economize for you. Kepi will show you the shortest way, the cheapest place, the biggest dish, because whatever you have to do you *must* pass a *tabac*, and whether there is a revolution or a lockout or a quarantine Kepi must be at the Moulin Rouge or the Olympia or the Ange Rouge when the music strikes up.

The other day he brought a book for me to read. It was about a famous suit between a holy man and the editor of an Indian paper. The editor, it seems had openly accused the holy man of leading a scandalous life; he went further, and accused the holy man of being diseased. Kepi says it must have been the great French pox, but Nanantatee avers that it was the Japanese clap. For Nanantatee everything has to be a little exaggerated. At any rate, says Nanantatee cheerily; 'You will please tell me what it says, Endree. I can't read the book – it hurts my arm.' Then, by way of encouraging me – 'it is a fine book about the fucking, Endree. Kepi has brought it for you. He thinks about nothing but the girls. So many girls he fucks – just like Krishna. We don't believe in that business, Endree. . . .'

A little later he takes me upstairs to the attic which is loaded down with tin cans and crap from India wrapped in burlap and firecracker paper. 'Here is where I bring the girls,' he says. And then rather wistfully: 'I am not a very good fucker, Endree. I don't screw the girls any more. I hold them in my arms and I say the words. I like only to say the words now.' It isn't necessary to listen any further: I know that he is going to tell me about his arm. I can see him lying there with that broken hinge dangling from the side of the bed. But to my surprise he adds: 'I am no good for the fucking, Endree. I never was a very good fucker. My brother, he is good! Three times a day, every day! And Kepi, he is good – just like Krishna.'

His mind is fixed now on the 'fucking business'. Downstairs, in the little room where he kneels before the open cabinet, he explains to me how it was when he was rich and his wife and the children were here. On holidays he would take his wife to the House of All Nations and hire a room for the night. Every room was appointed in a different style. His wife liked it there very much. 'A wonderful place for the fucking, Endree. I know all the rooms. . . .'

The walls of the little room in which we are sitting are crammed with photographs. Every branch of the family is represented, it is like a cross section of the Indian empire. For the most part the members of this genealogical tree look like withered leaves: the women are frail and they have a startled, frightened look in their eyes: the men have a keen, intelligent look, like educated chimpanzees. They are all there, about ninety of them, with their white bullocks, their dung cakes, their skinny legs, their old-fashioned spectacles; in the background, now and then, one catches a glimpse of the parched soil, of a crumbling pediment, of an idol with crooked arms, a sort of human centipede. There is something so fantastic, so incongruous about this gallery that one is reminded inevitably of the great spawn of temples which stretch from the Himalayas to the tip of Ceylon, a vast jumble of architecture, staggering in beauty and at the same time monstrous, hideously monstrous because the fecundity which seethes and ferments in the myriad ramifications of design seems to have exhausted the very soil of India itself. Looking at the seething hive of figures which swarm the facades of the temples one is overwhelmed by the potency of these dark, handsome peoples who mingled their mysterious streams in a sexual embrace that has lasted thirty centuries or more. These frail men and women with piercing eyes who stare out of the photographs seem like the emaciated shadows of those virile, massive figures who incarnated themselves in stone and fresco from one end of India to the other in order that the heroic myths of the races who here intermingled should remain forever entwined in the hearts of their countrymen. When I look at only a fragment of these spacious dreams of stone, these toppling, sluggish edifices studded with gems, coagulated with human sperm, I am overwhelmed by the dazzling splendour of those imaginative flights which enabled half a billion people of diverse origins to thus incarnate the most fugitive expressions of their longing.

It is a strange, inexplicable medley of feelings which assails me now as Nanantatee prattles on about the sister who died in childbirth. There she is on the wall, a frail, timid thing of twelve or thirteen clinging to the arm of a dotard. At ten years of age she was given in wedlock to this old roué who had already buried five wives. She had seven children, only one of whom survived her. She was given to the aged gorilla in order to keep the pearls in the family. As she was passing away, so Nanantatee puts it, she whispered to the doctor: 'I am tired of this fucking. . . . I don't want to fuck any more, doctor.' As he relates this to me he scratches his head solemnly with his withered arm. 'The fucking business is bad, Endree,' he says. 'But I will give you a word that will always make you lucky; you must say it every day, over and over, a million times you must say it. It is the best word there is, Endree . . . say it now . . . OOMAHARUMOOMA!'

'OOMARABOO. . . .'

'No, Endree . . . like this . . . OOMAHARUMOOMA!'

'OOMAMABOOMBA. . . .'

'No, Endree . . . like this. . . .'

. . . But what with the murky light, the botchy print, the tattered cover, the jigjagged page, the fumbling fingers, the fox-trotting fleas, the lie-a-bed lice, the scum on his tongue, the drop in his eye, the lump in his throat, the drink in his pottle, the itch in his palm, the wail of his wind, the grief from his breath, the fog of his brainfag, the tic of his conscience, the height of his rage, the gush of his fundament, the fire in his gorge, the tickle of his tail, the rats in his garret, the hullabaloo and the dust in his ears, since it took him a month to steal a march, he was hard-set to memorize more than a word a week.

I suppose I would never have gotten out of Nanantatee's clutches if fate hadn't intervened. One night, as luck would have it, Kepi asked me if I wouldn't take one of his clients to a whorehouse nearby. The young man had just come from India and he had not very much money to spend. He was one of Gandhi's men, one of that little band who made the historic march to the sea during the salt trouble. A very gay disciple of Gandhi's I must say, despite the vows of abstinence he had taken. Evidently he hadn't looked at a woman for ages. It was all I could do to get him as far as the Rue Laferrière; he was like a dog with his tongue hanging out. And a pompous, vain little devil to boot! He had decked himself out in a corduroy suit, a beret, a cane, a Windsor tie; he had bought himself two fountain pens, a Kodak, and some fancy underwear. The money he was spending was a gift from the merchants of Bombay; they were sending him to England to spread the gospel of Gandhi.

Once inside Miss Hamilton's joint he began to lose his *sang-froid*. When suddenly he found himself surrounded by a bevy of naked women he looked at me in consternation. 'Pick one out,' I said. 'You can have your choice.' He had become so rattled that he could scarcely look at them. 'You do it for me,' he murmured, blushing violently. I looked them over coolly and picked out a plump young wench who seemed full of feathers. We sat down in the reception room and waited for the drinks. The madam wanted to know why I didn't take a girl also. 'Yes, you take one too,' said the young Hindu. 'I don't want to be alone with her.' So the girls were brought in again and I chose one for myself, a rather tall, thin one with melancholy eyes. We were left alone, the four of us, in the reception room. After a few moments my young Gandhi leans over and whispers something in my ear. 'Sure, if you like her better, take her,' I said, and so, rather awkwardly and considerably embarrassed, I explained to the girls that we would like to switch. I saw at once that we had made a *faux pas*, but by now my young friend had become gay and lecherous and nothing would do but to get upstairs quickly and have it over with.

We took adjoining rooms with a connecting door between. I think my companion had in mind to make another switch once he had satisfied his sharp, gnawing hunger. At any rate, no sooner had the girls left the room to prepare themselves than I hear him knocking on the door. 'Where is the toilet, please?' he asks. Not thinking that it was anything serious I urge him to do in the *bidet*. The girls return with towels in their hands. I hear him giggling in the next room.

As I'm putting on my pants suddenly I hear a commotion in the next room. The girl is bawling him out, calling him a pig, a dirty little pig. I can't imagine what he has done to warrant such an outburst. I'm standing there with one foot in my trousers listening attentively. He's trying to explain to her in English, raising his voice louder and louder until it becomes a shriek.

I hear a door slam and in another moment the madam bursts into my room, her face as red as a beet, her arms gesticulating wildly. 'You ought to be ashamed of yourself,' she screams, 'bringing a man like that to my place! He's a barbarian . . . he's a pig . . . he's a . . . !' My companion is standing behind her, in the doorway, a look of utmost discomfiture on his face 'What did you do?' I ask.

'What did he do?' yells the madam. 'I'll show you. . . . Come here!' And grabbing me by the arm she drags me into the next room. 'There! There!' she screams, pointing to the *bidet*.

'Come on, let's get out,' says the Hindu boy.

'Wait a minute, you can't get out as easily as all that.'

The madam is standing by the *bidet*, fuming and spitting. The girls are standing there too, with towels in their hands. The five of us are

202

standing there looking at the *bidet*. There are two enormous turds floating in the water. The madam bends down and puts a towel over it. 'Frightful! Frightful!' she wails. 'Never have I seen anything like this! A pig! A dirty little pig!'

The Hindu boy looks at me reproachfully. 'You should have told me!' he says. 'I didn't know it wouldn't go down. I asked you where to go and you told me to use that.' He is almost in tears.

Finally the madam takes me to one side. She has become a little more reasonable now. After all, it was a mistake. Perhaps the gentlemen would like to come downstairs and order another drink – for the girls. It was a great shock to the girls. They are not used to such things. And if the good gentlemen will be so kind as to remember the *femme de chambre*. . . . It is not so pretty for the *femme de chambre* – that mess, that ugly mess. She shrugs her shoulders and winks her eye. A lamentable incident. But an accident. If the gentlemen will wait here a few moments the maid will bring the drinks. Would the gentlemen like to have some champagne? Yes?

'I'd like to get out of here,' says the Hindu boy weakly.

'Don't feel so badly about it,' says the madam. 'It is all over now. Mistakes will happen sometimes. Next time you will ask for the toilet.' She goes on about the toilet – one on every floor, it seems. And a bathroom too. 'I have lots of English clients,' she says. 'They are all gentlemen. The gentleman is a Hindu? Charming people, the Hindus. So intelligent. So handsome.'

When we get into the street the charming young gentleman is almost weeping. He is sorry now that he bought a corduroy suit and the cane and the fountain pens. He talks about the eight vows that he took, the control of the palate, etc. On the march to Dandi even a plate of ice cream it was forbidden to take. He tells me about the spinning wheel – how the little band of Satyagrahists imitated the devotion of their master. He relates with pride how he walked beside the master and conversed with him. I have the illusion of being in the presence of one of the twelve disciples.

During the next few days we see a good deal of each other; there are interviews to be arranged with the newspaper men and lectures to be given to the Hindus of Paris. It is amazing to see how these spineless devils order one another about; amazing also to see how ineffectual they are in all that concerns practical affairs. And the jealousy and the intrigues, the petty, sordid rivalries. Wherever there are ten Hindus together there is India with her sects and schisms, her racial, lingual, religious, political antagonisms. In the person of Gandhi they are experiencing for a brief moment the miracle of unity, but when he goes there will be a crash, an utter relapse into that strife and chaos so characteristic of the Indian people.

The young Hindu, of course, is optimistic. He has been to America and he has been contaminated by the cheap idealism of the Americans, contaminated by the ubiquitous bathtub, the five-and-ten-cent store bric-à-brac, the bustle, the efficiency, the machinery, the high wages, the free libraries, etc., etc. His ideal would be to Americanize India. He is not at all pleased with Gandhi's retrogressive mania. *Forward*, he says, just like a YMCA man. As I listen to his tales of America I see how absurd it is to expect of Gandhi that miracle which will deroute the trend of destiny. India's enemy is not England, but America. India's enemy is the time spirit, the hand which cannot be turned back. Nothing will avail to offset this virus which is poisoning the whole world. America is the very incarnation of doom. She will drag the whole world down to the bottomless pit.

He thinks the Americans are a very gullible people. He tells me about the credulous souls who succoured him there – the Quakers, the Unitarians, the Theosophists, the New Thoughters, the Seventh-day Adventists, etc. He knew where to sail his boat, this bright young man. He knew how to make the tears come to his eyes at the right moment; he knew how to take up a collection, how to appeal to the minister's wife, how to make love to the mother and daughter at the same time. To look at him you would think him a saint. And he is a saint, in the modern fashion; a contaminated saint who talks in one breath of love, brotherhood, bathtubs, sanitation, efficiency, etc.

The last night of his sojourn in Paris is given up to 'the fucking business'. He has had a full programme all day – conferences, cablegrams, interviews, photographs for the newspapers, affectionate farewells, advice to the faithful, etc., etc. At dinner time he decides to lay aside his troubles. He orders champagne with the meal, he snaps his fingers at the *garçon* and behaves in general like the boorish little peasant that he is. And since he has had a bellyful of all the good places he suggests now that I show him something more primitive. He would like to go to a very cheap place, order two or three girls at once. I steer him along the Boulevard de la Chapelle, warning him all the while to be careful of his pocketbook. Around Aubervilliers we duck into a cheap dive and immediately we've got a flock of them on our hands. In a few minutes he's dancing with a naked wench, a huge blonde with creases in her jowls. I can see her ass reflected a dozen times in the mirrors that line the room – and those dark, bony fingers of his clutching her tenaciously. The table is full of beer glasses, the mechanical piano is wheezing and gasping. The girls who are unoccupied are sitting placidly on the leather benches, scratching themselves peacefully just like a family of chimpanzees. There is a sort of subdued pandemonium in the air, a note of repressed violence, as if the awaited explosion required the advent of some utterly minute detail, something microscopic but thoroughly unpremeditated, completely unexpected. In that sort of half-reverie which permits one to participate in an event and yet remain quite aloof, the little detail which was lacking began obscurely but insistently to coagulate, to assume a freakish, crystalline form, like the frost which gathers on the windowpane. And like those frost patterns which seem so bizarre, so utterly free and fantastic in design, but which are nevertheless determined by the most rigid laws, so this sensation which commenced to take form inside me seemed also to be giving obedience to ineluctable laws. My whole being was responding to the dictates of an ambiance which it had never before experienced; that which I could call myself seemed to be contracting, condensing, shrinking from the stale, customary boundaries of the flesh whose perimeter knew only the modulations of the nerve ends.

And the more substantial, the more solid the core of me became, the more delicate and extravagant appeared the close, palpable reality out of which I was being squeezed. In the measure that I became more and more metallic, in the same measure the scene before my eyes became inflated. The state of tension was so finely drawn now that the introduction of a single foreign particle, even a microscopic particle, as I say, would have shattered everything. For the fraction of a second perhaps I experienced that utter clarity which the epileptic, it is said, is given to know. In that moment I lost completely the illusion of time and space: the world unfurled its drama simultaneously along a meridian which had no axis. In this sort of hair-trigger eternity I felt that everything was justified, supremely justified; I felt the wars inside me that had left behind this pulp and wrack; I felt the crimes that were seething here to emerge tomorrow in blatant screamers; I felt the misery that was grinding itself out with pestle and mortar, the long dull misery that dribbles away in dirty handkerchiefs. On the meridian of time there is no injustice: there is only the poetry of motion creating the illusion of truth and drama. If at any moment anywhere one comes face to face with the absolute, that great sympathy which makes men like Gautama and Jesus seem divine freezes away; the monstrous thing is not that men have created roses out of this dung heap, but that, for some reason or other, they should *want* roses. For some reason or other man looks for the miracle, and to accomplish it he will wade through blood. He will debauch himself with ideas, he will reduce himself to a shadow if for only one second of his life he can close his eyes to the hideousness of reality. Everything is endured – disgrace, humiliation, poverty, war, crime, *ennui* – in the belief that overnight something will occur, a miracle, which will render life tolerable. And all the while a meter is running inside and there is no hand that can reach in there and shut it off. All the while someone is eating the bread of life and drinking the wine, some dirty fat cockroach of a priest who hides away in the cellar guzzling it, while up above in the light of the street a phantom host touches the lips and the blood is pale as water. And out of the endless torment and misery no miracle comes forth, no microscopic vestige even of relief. Only ideas, pale, attenuated ideas which have to be fattened by slaughter; ideas which come forth like bile, like the guts of a pig when the carcass is ripped open.

And so I think what a miracle it would be if this miracle which man attends eternally should turn out to be nothing more than these two enormous turds which the faithful disciple dropped in the *bidet*. What if at the last moment, when the banquet table is set and the cymbals clash, there should appear suddenly, and wholly without warning, a silver platter on which even the blind could see that there is nothing more, and nothing less, than two enormous lumps of shit. That, I believe would be more miraculous than anything which man has looked forward to. It would be miraculous because it would be undreamed of. It would be more miraculous than even the wildest dream because *anybody* could imagine the possibility but nobody ever has, and probably nobody ever again will.

Somehow the realization that nothing was to be hoped for had a salutary effect upon me. For weeks and months, for years, in fact, all my life I had been looking forward to something happening, some extrinsic event that would alter my life, and now suddenly, inspired by the absolute hopelessness of everything, I felt relieved, felt as though a great burden had been lifted from my shoulders. At dawn I parted company with the young Hindu, after touching him for a few francs, enough for a room. Walking toward Montparnasse I decided to let myself drift with the tide, to make not the least resistance to fate, no matter in what form it presented itself. Nothing that had happened to me thus far had been sufficient to destroy me; nothing had been destroyed except my illusions. I myself was intact. The world was intact. Tomorrow there might be a revolution, a plague, an earth-quake; tomorrow there might not be left a single soul to whom one could turn for sympathy, for aid, for faith. It seemed to me that the great calamity had already manifested itself, that I could be no more truly alone than at this very moment. I made up my mind that I would hold on to nothing, that I would expect nothing, that henceforth I would live as an animal, a beast of prey, a rover, a plunderer. Even if war were declared, and it were my lot to go, I would grab the bayonet and plunge it, plunge it up to the hilt. And if rape were the order of the day then rape I would, and with a vengeance. At this very moment, in the quiet dawn of a new day, was not the earth giddy with crime and distress? Had one single element of man's nature been altered, vitally, fundamentally altered, by the incessant march of history? By what he calls the better part of his nature, man has been betrayed, that is all. At the extreme limits of his spiritual being man finds himself again naked as a savage. When he finds God, as it were, he has been picked clean: he is a skeleton. One must burrow into life again in order to put on flesh. The word must become flesh; the soul thirsts. On whatever crumb my eye fastens, I will pounce and devour. If to live is the paramount thing, then I will live, even if I must become a cannibal. Heretofore I have been trying to save my precious hide, trying to preserve the few pieces of meat that hid my bones. I am done with that. I have reached the limits of endurance. My back is to the wall; I can retreat no further. As far as history goes I am dead. If there is something beyond I shall have to bounce back. I have found God, but he is insufficient. I am only spiritually dead. Physically I am alive. Morally I am free. The world which I have departed is a menagerie. The dawn is breaking on a new world, a jungle world in which the lean spirits roam with sharp claws. If I am a hyena I am a lean and hungry one: I go forth to fatten myself.

Out of a clear sky there comes one day a letter from Boris whom I have not seen for months and months. It is a strange document and I don't pretend to understand it all clearly. 'What happened between us – at any rate, as far as I go – is that you touched me, touched my life, that is, at the one point where I am still alive: my death. By the emotional flow I went through another immersion. I lived again, alive. No longer by reminiscence, as I do with others, but alive.'

That's how it began. Not a word of greeting, no date, no address. Written in a thin, pompous scrawl on ruled paper torn out of a blank book. 'That is why, whether you like me or not – deep down I rather think you hate me – you are very close to me. By you I know how I died: I see myself dying again: I *am* dying. That is something. More than to be dead simply. That may be the reason why I am so afraid to see you: you may have played the trick on me, and died. Things happen so fast nowadays.'

I'm reading it over, line by line, standing by the stones. It sounds nutty to me, all this palaver about life and death and things happening so fast. Nothing is happening that I can see, except the usual calamities on the front page. He's been living all by himself for the last six months, tucked away in a cheap little room – probably holding telepathic communication with Cronstadt. He talks about the line falling back, the sector evacuated, and so on and so forth, as though he were dug into a trench and writing a report to headquarters. He probably had his frock coat on when he sat down to pen this missive, and he probably rubbed his hands a few times as he used to do when a customer was calling to rent the apartment. 'The reason I wanted you to commit suicide . . .' he begins again. At that I burst out laughing. He used to walk up and down with one hand stuck in the tail flap of his frock coat at the Villa Borghese, or at Cronstadt's – wherever there was deck space, as it were – and reel off this nonsense about living and dying to his heart's content. I never understood a word of it, I must confess, but it was a good show and, being a Gentile, I was naturally interested in what went on in that menagerie of a brainpan. Sometimes he would lie on his couch full length, exhausted by the surge of ideas that swept through his noodle. His feet just grazed the bookrack where he kept his Plato and Spinoza – he couldn't understand why I had no use for them. I must say he made them sound interesting, though what it was all about I hadn't the least idea. Sometimes I would glance at a volume furtively, to check up on these wild ideas which he imputed to them – but the connection was frail, tenuous. He had a language all his own, Boris, that is, when I had him alone; but when I listened to Cronstadt it seemed to me that Boris had plagiarized his wonderful ideas. They talked a sort of higher mathematics, these two. Nothing of flesh and blood ever crept in; it was weird, ghostly, ghoulishly abstract. When they got on to the dying business it sounded a little more concrete: after all, a cleaver or a meat axe has to have a handle. I enjoyed those sessions immensely. It was the first time in my life that death had ever seemed fascinating to me – all these abstract deaths which involved a bloodless sort of agony. Now and then they would compliment me on being alive, but in such a way that I felt embarrassed. They made me feel that I was alive in the nineteenth century, a sort of atavistic remnant, a romantic shred, a soulful Pithecanthropus erectus. Boris especially seemed to get a great kick out of touching me; he wanted me to be alive so that he could die to his heart's content. You would think that all those millions in the street were nothing but dead cows the way he looked at me and touched me. But the letter . . . I'm forgetting the letter. . . .

'The reason why I wanted you to commit suicide that evening at the Cronstadts', when Moldorf became God, was that I was very close to you then. Perhaps closer than I shall ever be. And I was afraid, terribly afraid, that some day you'd go back on me, die on my hands. And I would be left high and dry with my idea of you simply, and nothing to sustain it. I should never forgive you for that.'

Perhaps you can visualize him saying a thing like that! Myself it's not clear what his idea of me was, or at any rate, it's clear that I was just pure idea, an idea that kept itself alive without food. He never attached much importance, Boris, to the food problem. He tried to nourish me with ideas. Everything was idea. Just the same, when he had his heart set on renting the apartment, he wouldn't forget to put a new washer in the toilet. Anyway, he didn't want me to die on his hands. 'You must be life for me to the very end,' so he writes. 'That is the only way in which you can sustain my idea of you. Because you have gotten, as you see, tied up with something so vital to me, I do not think I shall ever shake you off. Nor do I wish to. I want you to live more vitally every day, as I am dead. That is why, when I speak of you to others, I am just a bit ashamed. It's hard to talk of one's self so intimately.'

You would imagine perhaps that he was anxious to see me, or that he would like to know what I was doing – but no, not a line about the concrete or the personal, except in this living-dying language, nothing but this little message from the trenches, this whiff of poison gas to apprise all and sundry that the war was still on. I sometimes ask myself how it happens that I attract nothing but crackbrained individuals, neurasthenics, neurotics, psychopaths – and Jews especially. There must be something in a healthy Gentile that excites the Jewish mind, like when he sees sour black bread. There was Moldorf, for example, who had made himself God, according to Boris and Cronstadt. He positively hated me, the little viper – yet he couldn't stay away from me. He came round regularly for his little dose of insults – it was like a tonic to him. In the beginning, it's true, I was lenient with him; after all, he was paying me to listen to him. And though I never displayed much sympathy I knew how to be silent when it involved a meal and a little pin money. After a while, however, seeing what a masochist he was, I permitted myself to laugh in his face now and then; that was like a whip for him, it made the grief and agony gush forth with renewed vigour. And perhaps everything would have gone smoothly between us if he had not felt it his duty to protect Tania. But Tania being a Jewess, that brought up a moral question. He wanted me to stick to Mlle. Claude for whom, I must admit, I had a genuine affection. He even gave me money occasionally to sleep with her. Until he realized that I was a hopeless lecher.

I mention Tania now because she's just got back from Russia – just a few days ago. Sylvester remained behind to worm his way into a job. He's given up literature entirely. He's dedicated himself to the new Utopia. Tania wants me to go back there with her, to the Crimea preferably, and start a new life. We had a fine drinking bout up in Carl's room the other day discussing the possibilities. I wanted to know what I could do for a living back there – if I could be a proofreader, for example. She said I didn't need to worry about what I would do – they would find a job for me as long as I was earnest and sincere. I tried to look earnest, but I only succeeded in looking pathetic. They don't want to see sad faces in Russia; they want you to be cheerful, enthusiastic, light-hearted, optimistic. It sounded very much like America to me. I wasn't born with this kind of enthusiasm. I didn't let on to her, of course, but secretly I was praying to be left alone, to go back to my little niche, and to stay there until the war breaks. All this hocus-pocus about Russia disturbed me a little. She got so excited about it, Tania, that we finished almost a half dozen bottles of *vin ordinaire*. Carl was jumping about like a cockroach. He has just enough Jew in him to lose his head over an idea like Russia. Nothing would do but to marry us off – immediately. 'Hitch up!' he says, 'You have nothing to lose!' And then he pretends to run a little errand so that we can pull off a fast one. And while she wanted it all right, Tania, still that Russia business had gotten so solidly planted in her skull that she pissed the interval away chewing my ear off, which made me somewhat grumpy and ill at ease. Anyway, we had to think about eating and getting to the office, so we piled into a taxi on the Boulevard Edgar-Quinet, just a stone's throw away from the cemetery, and off we whizzed. It was just a nice hour to spin through Paris in an open cab, and the wine rolling around in our tanks made it seem even more lovely than usual. Carl was sitting opposite us, on the *strapontin*, his face as red as a beet. He was happy, the poor bastard, thinking what a glorious new life he would lead on the other side of

Europe. And at the same time he felt a bit wistful, too – I could see that. He didn't really want to leave Paris, any more than I did. Paris hadn't been good to him, any more than it had to me, or to anybody, for that matter, but when you've suffered and endured things here it's then that Paris takes hold of you, grabs you by the balls, you might say, like some lovesick bitch who'd rather die than let you get out of her hands. That's how it looked to him, I could see that. Rolling over the Seine he had a big foolish grin on his face and he looked around at the buildings and the statues as though he were seeing them in a dream. To me it was like a dream too: I had my hand in Tania's bosom and I was squeezing her titties with all my might and I noticed the water under the bridges and the barges and Notre-Dame down below, just like the post cards show it, and I was thinking drunkenly to myself that's how one gets fucked, but I was sly about it too and I knew I wouldn't ever trade all this whirling about my head for Russia or heaven or anything on earth. It was a fine afternoon, I was thinking to myself, and soon we'd be pushing a feed down our bellies and what could we order as a special treat, some good heavy wine that would drown out all this Russia business. With a woman like Tania, full of sap and everything, they don't give a damn what happens to you once they get an idea in their heads. Let them go far enough and they'll pull the pants off you, right in the taxi. It was grand though, milling through the traffic, our faces all smudged with rouge and the wine gurgling like a sewer inside us, especially when we swung into the Rue Laffitte which is just wide enough to frame the little temple at the end of the street and above it the Sacré Coeur, a kind of exotic jumble of architecture, a lucid French idea that gouges right through your drunkenness and leaves you swimming helplessly in the past, in a fluid dream that makes you wide awake and yet doesn't jar your nerves.

With Tania back on the scene, a steady job, the drunken talk about Russia, the walks home at night, and Paris in full summer, life seems to lift its head a little higher. That's why perhaps, a letter such as Boris sent me seems absolutely cockeyed. Most every day I meet Tania around five o'clock, to have a Porto with her, as she calls it. I let her take me to places I've never seen before, the swell bars around the Champs-Elysées where the sound of jazz and baby voices crooning seems to soak right through the mahogany woodwork. Even when you go to the *lavabo* these pulpy, sappy strains pursue you, come floating into the cabinet through the ventilators and make life all soap and iridescent bubbles. And whether it's because Sylvester is away and she feels free now, or whatever it is, Tania certainly tries to behave like an angel. 'You treated me lousy just before I went away,' she says to me one day. 'Why did you want to act that way? I never did anything to hurt you, did I?' We were getting sentimental, what with the soft lights and that creamy, mahogany music seeping through the place. It was getting near time to go to work and we hadn't eaten yet. The stubs were lying there in front of us – six francs, four-fifty, seven francs, two-fifty – I was counting them up mechanically and wondering too at the same time if I would like it better being a bartender. Often like that, when she was talking to me, gushing about Russia, the future, love, and all that crap, I'd get to thinking about the most irrelevant things, about shining shoes or being a lavatory attendant, particularly I suppose because it was so cosy in these joints that she dragged me to and it never occurred to me that I'd be stone sober and perhaps old and bent . . . no, I imagined always that the future, however modest, would be in just this sort of ambiance, with the same tunes playing through my head and the glasses clinking and behind every shapely ass a trail of perfume a yard wide that would take the stink out of life, even downstairs in the *lavabo*.

The strange thing is it never spoiled me trotting around to the swell bars with her like that. It was hard to leave her, certainly. I used to lead her around to the porch of a church near the office and standing there in the dark we'd take a last embrace, she whispering to me 'Jesus, what am I going to do now?' She wanted me to quit the job so as I could make love night and day; she didn't even care about Russia any more, just so long we were together. But the moment I left her my head cleared. It was another kind of music, not so croony but good just the same, which greeted my ears when I pushed through the swinging door. And another kind of perfume, not just a yard wide, but omnipresent, a sort of sweat and patchouli that seemed to come from the machines. Coming in with a skinful, as I usually did, it was like dropping suddenly to a low altitude. Generally I made a beeline for the toilet – that braced me up rather. It was a little cooler there, or else the sound of water running made it seem so. It was always a cold douche, the toilet. It was real. Before you got inside you had to pass a line of Frenchmen peeling off their clothes. Ugh! but they stank, those devils! And they were well paid for it, too. But there they were, stripped down, some in long underwear, some with beards, most of them pale, skinny rats with lead in their veins. Inside the toilet you could take an inventory of their idle thoughts. The walls were crowded with sketches and epithets, all of them jocosely obscene, easy to understand, and on the whole rather jolly and sympathetic. It must have required a ladder to reach certain spots, but I suppose it was worth while doing it even looking at it from just the psychological viewpoint. Sometimes, as I stood there taking a leak, I wondered what an impression it would make on those swell dames whom I observed passing in and out of the beautiful lavatories on the Champs-Elysées. I wondered if they would carry their tails so high if they could see what was thought of an ass here. In their world, no doubt, everything was gauze and velvet – or they made you think so with the fine scents they gave out, swishing past you. Some of them hadn't always been such fine ladies either; some of them swished up and down like that just to advertise their trade. And maybe, when they were left alone with themselves, when they talked out loud in the privacy of their boudoirs, maybe some strange things fell out of their mouths too; because in that world, just as in every world, the greater part of what happens is just muck and filth, sordid as any garbage can, only they are lucky enough to be able to put covers over the can.

As I say, that afternoon life with Tania never had any bad effect upon me. Once in a while I'd get too much of a skinful and I'd have to stick my finger down my throat – because it's hard to read proof when you're not all there. It requires more concentration to detect a missing comma than to epitomize Nietzsche's philosophy. You can be brilliant sometimes, when you're drunk, but brilliance is out of place in the proofreading department. Dates, fractions, semicolons – these are the things that count. And these are the things that are most difficult to track down when your mind is all ablaze. Now and then I made some bad blunders, and if it weren't that I had learned how to kiss the boss's ass, I would have been fired, that's certain. I even got a letter one day from the big mogul upstairs, a guy I never even met, so high up he was, and between a few sarcastic phrases about my more than ordinary intelligence, he hinted pretty plainly that I'd better learn my place and toe the mark or there'd be what's what to pay. Frankly, that scared the shit out of me. After that I never used a polysyllabic word in conversation; in fact, I hardly ever opened my trap all night. I played the high-grade moron, which is what they wanted of us. Now and then, to sort of flatter the boss, I'd go up to him and ask politely what such and such a word might mean. He liked that. He was a sort of dictionary and timetable, that guy. No matter how much beer he guzzled during the break – and he made his own private breaks too, seeing as how he was running the show – you could never trip him up on a date or a definition. He was born to the job. My only regret was that I knew too much. It leaked out now and then, despite all the precautions I took. If I happened to come to work with a book under my arm this boss of ours would notice it, and if it were a good book it made him venomous. But I never did anything intentionally to displease him; I liked the job too well to put a noose around my neck. Just the same it's hard to talk to a man when you have nothing in common with him; you betray yourself, even if you use only monosyllabic words. He knew goddamn well, the boss, that I didn't take the least bit of interest in his yarns; and yet, explain it how you will, it gave him pleasure to wean me away from my dreams and fill me full of dates and historical events. It was his way of taking revenge, I suppose.

The result was that I developed a bit of a neurosis. As soon as I hit the air I became extravagant. It wouldn't matter what the subject of conversation happened to be, as we started back to Montparnasse in the early morning, I'd soon turn the fire hose on it, squelch it, in order to trot out my perverted dreams. I liked best talking about those things which none of us knew anything about. I had cultivated a mild sort of insanity, echolalia, I think it's called. All the tag ends of a night's proofing danced on the tip of my tongue. *Dalmatia* – I had held copy on an ad for that beautiful jewelled resort. All right, *Dalmatia*. You take a train and in the morning your pores are perspiring and the grapes are bursting their skins. I could reel it off about Dalmatia from the grand boulevard to Cardinal Mazarin's palace, further, if I chose to. I don't even know where it is on the map, and I don't want to know ever, but at three in the morning with all that lead in your veins and your clothes saturated with sweat and patchouli and the clink of bracelets passing through the wringer and those beer yarns that I was braced for, little things like geography, costume, speech, architecture don't mean a goddamn thing. Dalmatia belongs to a certain hour of the night when those high gongs are snuffed out and the court of the Louvre seems so wonderfully ridiculous that you feel like weeping for no reason at all, just because it's so beautifully silent, so empty, so totally unlike the front page and the guys upstairs rolling the dice. With that little piece of Dalmatia resting on my throbbing nerves like a cold knife blade I could experience the most wonderful sensations of voyage. And the funny thing is again that I could travel all around the globe but America would never enter my mind; it was even further lost than a lost continent, because with the lost continents I felt some mysterious attachment, whereas with America I felt nothing at all. Now and then, it's true, I did think of Mona, not as of a person in a definite aura of time and space, but separately, detached, as though she had blown up into a great cloudlike form that blotted out the past. I couldn't allow myself to think about her very long; if I had I would have jumped off the bridge. It's strange. I had become so reconciled to this life without her, and yet if I thought about her only for a minute it was enough to pierce the bone and marrow of my contentment and shove me back again into the agonizing gutter of my wretched past.

For seven years I went about, day and night, with only one thing on my mind – *her*. Were there a Christian so faithful to his God as I was to her we would all be Jesus Christs today. Day and night I thought of her, even when I was deceiving her. And now sometimes, in the very midst of things, sometimes when I feel that I am absolutely free of it all, suddenly, in rounding a corner perhaps, there will bob up a little square, a few trees and a bench, a deserted spot where we stood and had it out, where we drove each other crazy with bitter, jealous scenes. Always some deserted spot, like the Place de l'Estrapade, for example, or those dingy, mournful streets off the Mosque or along that open tomb of an Avenue de Breteuil which at ten o'clock in the evening is so silent, so dead, that it makes one think of murder or suicide, anything that might create a vestige of human drama. When I realize that she is gone, perhaps gone forever, a great void opens up and I feel that I am falling, falling, falling into deep, black space. And this is worse than tears, deeper than regret or pain or sorrow; it is the abyss into which Satan was plunged. There is no climbing back, no ray of light, no sound of human voice or human touch of hand.

How many thousand times, in walking through the streets at night, have I wondered if the day would ever come again when she would be at my side: all those yearning looks I bestowed on the buildings and statues, I had looked at them so hungrily, so desperately, that by now my thoughts must have become a part of the very buildings and statues, they must be saturated with my anguish. I could not help but reflect also that when we had walked side by side through these mournful, dingy streets now so saturated with my dream and longing, she had observed nothing, felt nothing: they were like any other streets to her, a little more sordid perhaps, and that is all. She wouldn't remember that at a certain corner I had stopped to pick up her hairpin, or that, when I bent down to tie her laces, I remarked the spot on which her foot had rested and that it would remain there for ever, even after the cathedrals had been demolished and the whole Latin civilization wiped out for ever and ever.

Walking down the Rue Lhomond one night in a fit of unusual

anguish and desolation, certain things were revealed to me with poignant clarity. Whether it was that I had so often walked this street in bitterness and despair or whether it was the remembrance of a phrase which she had dropped one night as we stood at the Place Lucien-Herr I do not know. 'Why don't you show me that Paris,' she said, 'that you have written about?' One thing I know, that at the recollection of these words I suddenly realized the impossibility of ever revealing to her that Paris which I had gotten to know, the Paris whose *arrondissements* are undefined, a Paris that has never existed except by virtue of my loneliness, my hunger for her. Such a huge Paris! It would take a lifetime to explore it again. This Paris, to which I alone had the key, hardly lends itself to a tour, even with the best of intentions; it is a Paris that has to be lived, that has to be experienced each day in a thousand different forms of torture, a Paris that grows inside you like a cancer, and grows and grows until you are eaten away by it.

Stumbling down the Rue Mouffetard, with these reflections stirring in my brain, I recalled another strange item out of the past, out of that guidebook whose leaves she had asked me to turn but which, because the covers were so heavy, I then found impossible to pry open. For no reason at all – because at the moment my thoughts were occupied with Salavin in whose sacred precincts I was now meandering – for no reason at all, I say, there came to mind the recollection of a day when, inspired by the plaque which I passed day in and day out, I impulsively entered the Pension Orfila and asked to see the room Strindberg had occupied. Up to that time nothing very terrible had befallen me, though I had already lost all my worldly possessions and had known what it was to walk the streets in hunger and in fear of the police. Up to then I had not found a single friend in Paris, a circumstance which was not so much depressing as bewildering, for wherever I have roamed in this world the easiest thing for me to discover has been a friend. But in reality, nothing very terrible had happened to me yet. One can live without friends, as one can live without love, or even without money, that supposed *sine qua non*. One can live in Paris – I discovered that! – on just grief and anguish. A bitter nourishment – perhaps the best there is for certain people. At any rate, I had not yet come to the end of my rope. I was only flirting with disaster. I had time and sentiment enough to spare to peep into other people's lives, to dally with the dead stuff of romance which, however morbid it may be, when it is wrapped between the covers of a book, seems deliciously remote and anonymous. As I was leaving the place I was conscious of an ironic smile hovering over my lips, as though I were saying to myself 'Not yet, the Pension Orfila!'

Since then, of course, I have learned what every madman in Paris discovers sooner or later; that there are no ready-made infernos for the tormented.

It seems to me I understand a little better now why she took such huge delight in reading Strindberg. I can see her looking up from her book after reading a *delicious* passage, and, with tears of laughter in her eyes, saying to me: 'You're just as mad as he was . . . you *want* to be punished!' What a delight that must be to the sadist when she discovers her own proper mashochist! When she bites herself, as it were, to test the sharpness of her teeth. In those days, when I first knew her, she was saturated with Strindberg. That wild carnival of maggots which he revelled in, that eternal duel of the sexes, that spiderish ferocity which had endeared him to the sodden oafs of the northland, it was that which had brought us together. We came together in a dance of death and so quickly was I sucked down into the vortex that when I came to the surface again I could not recognize the world. When I found myself loose the music had ceased; the carnival was over and I had been picked clean. . . .

After leaving the Pension Orfila that afternoon I went to the library and there, after bathing in the Ganges and pondering over the signs of the zodiac, I began to reflect on the meaning of that inferno which Strindberg had so mercilessly depicted. And, as I ruminated, it began to grow clear to me, the mystery of his pilgrimage, the flight which the poet makes over the face of the earth and then, as if he had been ordained to re-enact a lost drama, the heroic descent to the very bowels of the earth, the dark and fearsome sojourn in the belly of the whale, the bloody struggle to liberate himself, to emerge clean of the past, a bright, gory sun god cast up on an alien shore. It was no mystery to me any longer why he and others (Dante, Rabelais, Van Gogh, etc., etc.) had made their pilgrimage to Paris. I understood then why it is that Paris attracts the tortured, the hallucinated, the great maniacs of love. I understood why it is that here, at the very hub of the wheel, one can embrace the most fantastic, the most impossible theories, without finding them in the least strange; it is here that one reads again the books of his youth and the enigmas take on new meanings, one for every white hair. One walks the streets knowing that he is mad, possessed, because it is only too obvious that these cold, indifferent faces are the visages of one's keepers. Here all boundaries fade away and the world reveals itself for the mad slaughterhouse that it is. The treadmill stretches away to infinitude, the hatches are closed down tight, logic runs rampant, with bloody cleaver flashing. The air is chill and stagnant, the language apocalyptic. Not an exit sign anywhere; no issue save death. A blind alley at the end of which is a scaffold.

An eternal city, Paris! More eternal than Rome, more splendorous than Nineveh. The very navel of the world to which, like a blind and faltering idiot, one crawls back on hands and knees. And like a cork that has drifted to the dead centre of the ocean, one floats here in the scum and wrack of the seas, listless, hopeless, heedless even of a passing Columbus. The cradles of civilization are the putrid sinks of the world, the charnel house to which the stinking wombs confide their bloody packages of flesh and bone.

The streets were my refuge. And no man can understand the glamour of the streets until he is obliged to take refuge in them, until he has become a straw that is tossed here and there by every zephyr that blows. One passes along a street on a wintry day and, seeing a dog for sale, one is moved to tears. While across the way, cheerful as a cemetery, stands a miserable hut that calls itself 'Hôtel du Tombeau des Lapins'. That makes one laugh, laugh fit to die. Until one notices that there are hotels everywhere, for rabbits, dogs, lice, emperors, cabinet ministers, pawnbrokers, horse knackers, and so on. And almost every other one is an 'Hôtel de l'Avenir'. Which makes one more hysterical still. So many hotels of the future! No hotels in the past participle, no subjunctive modes, no conjunctivitis. Everything is hoary, grisly, bristling with merriment, swollen with the future, like a gumboil. Drunk with this lecherous eczema of the future, I stagger over to the Place Violet, the colours all mauve and slate, the doorways so low that only dwarfs and goblins could hobble in; over the dull cranium of Zola the chimneys are belching pure coke, while the Madonna of Sandwiches listens with cabbage ears to the bubbling of the gas tanks, those beautiful bloated toads which squat by the roadside.

Why do I suddenly recollect the Passage des Thermopyles? Because that day a woman addressed her puppy in the apocalyptic language of the slaughterhouse, and the little bitch, she understood what this greasy slut of a midwife was saying. How that depressed me! More even than the sight of those whimpering curs that were being sold on the Rue Brancion, because it was not the dogs which filled me so with pity, but the huge iron railing, those rusty spikes which seemed to stand between me and my rightful life. In the pleasant little lane near the Abattoir de Vaugirard (Abattoir Hippophagique), which is called the Rue des Périchaux, I had noticed here and there signs of blood. Just as Strindberg in his madness had recognized omens and portents in the very flagging of the Pension Orfila, so, as I wandered aimlessly through this muddy lane bespattered with blood, fragments of the past detached themselves and floated listlessly before my eyes, taunting me with the direst forebodings. I saw my own blood being spilled, the muddy road stained with it, as far back as I could remember, from the very beginning doubtless. One is ejected into the world like a dirty little mummy; the roads are slippery with blood and no one knows why it should be so. Each one is travelling his own way and, though the earth be rotting with good things, there is no time to pluck the fruits; the procession scrambles toward the exit sign, and such a panic is there, such a sweat to escape, that the weak and the helpless are trampled into the mud and their cries are unheard.

My world of human beings had perished; I was utterly alone in the world and for friends I had the streets, and the streets spoke to me in that sad, bitter language compounded of human misery, yearning, regret, failure, wasted effort. Passing under the viaduct along the Rue Broca, one night after I had been informed that Mona was ill and starving, I suddenly recalled that it was here in the squalor and gloom of this sunken street, terrorized perhaps by a premonition of the future, that Mona clung to me and with a quivering voice begged me to promise that I would never leave her, never, no matter what happened. And, only a few days later, I stood on the platform of the Gare St Lazare and I watched the train pull out, the train that was bearing her away; she was leaning out of the window, just as she had leaned out of the window when I left her in New York, and there was that same, sad, inscrutable smile on her face, that last-minute look which is intended to convey so much, but which is only a mask that is twisted by a vacant smile. Only a few days before, she had clung to me desperately and then something happened, something which is not even clear to me now, and of her own volition she boarded the train and she was looking at me again with that sad, enigmatic smile which baffles me, which is unjust, unnatural, which I distrust with all my soul. And now it is I, standing in the shadow of the viaduct, who reach out for her, who cling to her desperately and there is that same inexplicable smile on my lips, the mask that I have clamped down over my grief. I can stand here and smile vacantly, and no matter how fervid my prayers, no matter how desperate my longing, there is an ocean between us; there she will stay and starve, and here I shall walk from one street to the next, the hot tears scalding my face.

It is that sort of cruelty which is embedded in the streets; it is *that* which stares out from the walls and terrifies us when suddenly we respond to a nameless fear, when suddenly our souls are invaded by a sickening panic. It is *that* which gives the lampposts their ghoulish twists, which makes them beckon to us and lure us to their strangling grip; it is *that* which makes certain houses appear like the guardians of secret crimes and their blind windows like the empty sockets of eyes that have seen too much. It is that sort of thing, written into the human physiognomy of the streets which makes me flee when over-head I suddenly see inscribed 'Impasse Satan'. That which makes me shudder when at the very entrance to the Mosque I observe that it is written: 'Mondays and Thursdays *tuberculosis*; Wednesdays and Fridays *syphilis*.' In every Metro station there are grinning skulls that greet you with *'Défendez-vous contre la syphilis!'* Wherever there are walls, there are posters with bright venomous crabs heralding the approach of cancer. No matter where you go, no matter what you touch, there is cancer and syphilis. It is written in the sky; it flames and dances, like an evil portent. It has eaten into our souls and we are nothing but a dead thing like the moon.

I think it was the Fourth of July when they took the chair from under my ass again. Not a word of warning. One of the big muck-a-mucks from the other side of the water had decided to make economies; cutting down on proofreaders and helpless little *dactylos* enabled him to pay the expenses of his trips back and forth and the palatial quarters he occupied at the Ritz. After paying what little debts I had accumulated among the linotype operators and a goodwill token at the *bistro* across the way, in order to preserve my credit, there was scarcely anything left out of my final pay. I had to notify the *patron* of the hotel that I would be leaving; I didn't tell him why because he'd have worried about his measly two hundred francs.

'What'll you do if you lose your job?' That was the phrase that rang in my ears continually. *Ça y est maintenant! Ausgespielt!* Nothing to do but to get down into the street again, walk, hang around, sit on benches, kill time. By now, of course, my face was familiar in Montparnasse; for a while I could pretend that I was still working on the paper. That would make it a little easier to bum a breakfast or a dinner. It was summertime and the tourists were pouring in. I had schemes up my sleeve for mulcting them. 'What'll you do. . . ?' Well, I wouldn't starve, that's one thing. If I should do nothing else but

220

concentrate on food that would prevent me from falling to pieces. For a week or two I could still go to Monsieur Paul's and have a square meal every evening; he wouldn't know whether I was working or not. The main thing is to eat. Trust to Providence for the rest!

Naturally, I kept my ears open for anything that sounded like a little dough. And I cultivated a whole new set of acquaintances – bores whom I had sedulously avoided heretofore, drunks whom I loathed, artists who had a little money, Guggenheim-prize men, etc. It's not hard to make friends when you squat on a *terrasse* twelve hours a day. You get to know every sot in Montparnasse. They cling to you like lice, even if you have nothing to offer them but your ears.

Now that I had lost my job Carl and Van Norden had a new phrase for me: 'What if your wife should arrive now?' Well, what of it? Two mouths to feed, instead of one. I'd have a companion in misery. And, if she hadn't lost her good looks, I'd probably do better in double harness than alone: the world never permits a good-looking woman to starve. Tania I couldn't depend on to do much for me; she was sending money to Sylvester. I had thought at first that she might let me share her room, but she was afraid of compromising herself; besides, she had to be nice to her boss.

The first people to turn to when you're down and out are the Jews. I had three of them on my hands almost at once. Sympathetic souls. One of them was a retired fur merchant who had an itch to see his name in the papers; he proposed that I write a series of articles under his name for a Jewish daily in New York. I had to scout around the Dôme and the Coupole searching for prominent Jews. The first man I picked on was a celebrated mathematician; he couldn't speak a word of English. I had to write about the theory of shock from the diagrams he left on the paper napkins; I had to describe the movements of the astral bodies and demolish the Einsteinian conception at the same time. All for twenty-five francs. When I saw my articles in the newspaper I couldn't read them; but they looked impressive, just the same, especially with the pseudonym of the fur merchant attached.

I did a lot of pseudonymous writing during this period. When the big new whorehouse opened up on the Boulevard Edgar-Quinet, I got a little rake-off, for writing the pamphlets. That is to say, a bottle of champagne and a free fuck in one of the Egyptian rooms. If I succeeded in bringing a client I was to get my commission, just like Kepi got his in the old days. One night I brought Van Norden; he was going to let me earn a little money by enjoying himself upstairs. But when the *madame* learned that he was a newspaperman she wouldn't hear of

221

taking money from him; it was a bottle of champagne again and a free fuck. I got nothing out of it. As a matter of fact, I had to write the story for him because he couldn't think how to get round the subject without mentioning the kind of place it was. One thing after another like that. I was getting fucked good and proper.

The worst job of all was a thesis I undertook to write for a deaf and dumb psychologist. A treatise on the care of crippled children. My head was full of diseases and braces and workbenches and fresh air theories; it took about six weeks off and on, and then, to rub it in, I had to proofread the goddamned thing. It was in French, such a French as I've never in my life seen or heard. But it brought me in a good breakfast every day, an American breakfast, with orange juice, oatmeal, cream, coffee, now and then ham and eggs for a change. It was the only period of my Paris days that I ever indulged in a decent breakfast, thanks to the crippled children of Rockaway Beach, the East Side, and all the coves and inlets bordering on these sore points.

Then one day I fell in with a photographer; he was making a collection of the slimy joints of Paris for some degenerate in Munich. He wanted to know if I would pose for him with my pants down, and in other ways. I thought of those skinny little runts, who look like bell-hops and messenger boys, that one sees on pornographic post cards in little bookshop windows occasionally, the mysterious phantoms who inhabit the Rue de la Lune and other malodorous quarters of the city. I didn't like very much the idea of advertising my physiog in the company of these élite. But, since I was assured that the photographs were for a strictly private collection, and since it was destined for Munich, I gave my consent. When you're not in your home town you can permit yourself little liberties, particularly for such a worthy motive as earning your daily bread. After all, I hadn't been so squeamish, come to think of it, even in New York. There were nights when I was so damned desperate, back there, that I had to go out right in my own neighbourhood and panhandle.

We didn't go to the show places familiar to the tourists, but to the little joints where the atmosphere was more congenial, where we could play a game of cards in the afternoon before getting down to work. He was a good companion, the photographer. He knew the city inside out, the walls particularly; he talked to me about Goethe often, and the days of the Hohenstaufen, and the massacre of the Jews during the reign of the Black Death. Interesting subjects, and always related in some obscure way to the things he was doing. He had ideas for scenarios too, astounding ideas, but nobody had the courage to execute them. The sight of a horse, split open like a saloon door, would inspire him to talk of Dante or Leonardo da Vinci or Rembrandt; from the slaughterhouse at Villette he would jump into a cab and rush me to the Trocadéro Museum, in order to point out a skull or a mummy that had fascinated him. We explored the 5th, the 13th, the 19th and the 20th *arrondissements* thoroughly. Our favourite resting places were lugubrious little spots such as the Place Nationale, Place des Peupliers, Place de la Contrescarpe, Place Paul-Verlaine. Many of these places were already familiar to me, but all of them I now saw in a different light owing to the rare flavour of his conversation. If today I should happen to stroll down the Rue du Château-des-Rentiers, for example, inhaling the fetid stench of the hospital beds with which the 13th *arrondissement* reeks, my nostrils would undoubtedly expand with pleasure, because, compounded with that odour of stale piss and formaldehyde, there would be the odours of our imaginative voyages through the charnel house of Europe which the Black Death had created.

Through him I got to know a spiritual-minded individual named Kruger, who was a sculptor and painter. Kruger took a shine to me for some reason or other; it was impossible to get away from him once he discovered that I was willing to listen to his 'esoteric' ideas. There are people in this world for whom the word 'esoteric' seems to act as a divine ichor. Like 'settled' for Herr Peeperkorn of the *Magic Mountain*. Kruger was one of those saints who have gone wrong, a masochist, an anal type whose law is scrupulousness, rectitude and conscientiousness, who on an off day would knock a man's teeth down his throat without a qualm. He seemed to think I was ripe to move on to another plane, 'a *higher* plane', as he put it. I was ready to move on to any plane he designated, provided that one didn't eat less or drink less. He chewed my head off about the 'threadsoul', the 'causal body', 'ablation', the Upanishads, Plotinus, Krishnamurti, 'the Karmic vestiture of the soul', 'the nirvanic consciousness', all that flapdoodle which blows out of the East like a breath from the plague. Sometimes he would go into a trance and talk about his previous incarnations, how he imagined them to be, at least. Or he would relate his dreams which, so far as I could see, were thoroughly insipid, prosaic, hardly worth even the attention of a Freudian, but, for him, there were vast esoteric marvels hidden in their depths which I had to aid him to decipher. He had turned himself inside out, like a coat whose nap is worn off.

Little by little, as I gained his confidence, I wormed my way into his heart. I had him at such a point that he would come running after me, in the street, to inquire if he could lend me a few francs. He wanted to hold me together in order to survive the transition to a higher plane. I acted like a pear that is ripening on the tree. Now and then I had relapses and I would confess my need for more earthly nourishment – a visit to the Sphinx or the Rue St Apolline where I knew he repaired in weak moments when the demands of the flesh had become too vehement.

As a painter he was nil; as a sculptor less than nil. He was a good housekeeper, that I'll say for him. And an economical one to boot. Nothing went to waste, not even the paper that the meat was wrapped in. Friday nights he threw open his studio to his fellow artists; there was always plenty to drink and good sandwiches, and if by chance there was anything left over I would come round the next day to polish it off.

Back of the Bal Bullier was another studio I got into the habit of frequenting – the studio of Mark Swift. If he was not a genius he was certainly an eccentric, this caustic Irishman. He had for a model a Jewess whom he had been living with for years; he was now tired of her and was searching for a pretext to get rid of her. But as he had eaten up the dowry which she had originally brought with her, he was puzzled as to how to disembarrass himself of her without making restitution. The simplest thing was to so antagonize her that she would choose starvation rather than support his cruelties.

She was rather a fine person, his mistress; the worst that one could say against her was that she had lost her shape, *and* her ability to support him any longer. She was a painter herself and, among those who professed to know, it was said that she had far more talent than he. But no matter how miserable he made life for her she was just; she would never allow anyone to say that he was not a great painter. It was because he really has genius, she said, that he was such a rotten individual. One never saw her canvases on the wall – only his. Her things were stuck away in the kitchen. Once it happened, in my presence, that someone insisted on seeing her work. The result was painful. 'You see this figure,' said Swift, pointing to one of her canvases with his big foot. 'The man standing in the doorway there is just about to go for a leak. He won't be able to find his way back because his head is on wrong. . . . Now take that nude over there. . . It was all right until she started to paint the cunt. I don't know what she was thinking about, but she made it so big that her brush slipped and she couldn't get it out again.'

By way of showing us what a nude ought to be like he hauls out a huge canvas which he had recently completed. It was a picture of *her*, a splendid piece of vengeance inspired by a guilty conscience. The work of a madman – vicious, petty, malign, brilliant. You had the feeling that he had spied on her through the keyhole, that he had caught her in an off moment, when she was picking her nose absent-mindedly, or scratching her ass. She sat there on the horsehair sofa, in a room without ventilation, an enormous room without a window; it might as well have been the anterior lobe of the pineal gland. Back of her ran the zigzag stairs leading to the balcony; they were covered with a bilious-green carpet, such a green as could only emanate from a universe that had been pooped out. The most prominent thing was her buttocks, which were lopsided and full of scabs; she seemed to have slightly raised her ass from the sofa, as if to let a loud fart. Her face he had idealized: it looked sweet and virginal, pure as a cough drop. But her bosom was distended, swollen with sewer gas; she seemed to be swimming in a menstrual sea, an enlarged foetus with the dull, syrupy look of an angel.

Nevertheless one couldn't help but like him. He was an indefatigable worker, a man who hadn't a single thought in his head but paint. And cunning as a lynx withal. It was he who put it into my head to cultivate the friendship of Fillmore, a young man in the diplomatic service who had found his way into the little group that surrounded Kruger and Swift. 'Let him help you,' he said. 'He doesn't know what to do with his money.'

When one spends what he has on himself, when one has a thoroughly good time with his own money, people are apt to say 'he doesn't know what to do with his money'. For my part, I don't see any better use to which one can put money. About such individuals one can't say that they're generous or stingy. They put money into circulation – that's the principal thing. Fillmore knew that his days in France were limited; he was determined to enjoy them. And as one always enjoys himself better in the company of a friend it was only natural that he should turn to one like myself, who had plenty of time on his hands, for that companionship which he needed. People said he was a bore, and so he was, I suppose, but when you're in need of food you can put up with worse things than being bored. After all, despite the fact that he talked incessantly, and usually about himself or the authors whom he admired slavishly – such birds as Anatole France and Joseph Conrad – he nevertheless made my nights interesting in other ways. He liked to dance, he liked good wines, and he liked women. That he liked Byron also, and Victor Hugo, one could forgive; he was only a few years out of college and he had plenty of time ahead of him to be cured of such tastes. What he had that I liked was a sense of adventure.

Paris is like a whore. From a distance she seems ravishing, you can't wait until you have her in your arms. And five minutes later you feel empty, disgusted with yourself. You feel tricked.

I returned to Paris with money in my pocket – a few hundred francs, which Collins had shoved in my pocket just as I was boarding the train. It was enough to pay for a room and at least a week's good rations. It was more than I had had in my hands at one time for several years. I felt elated, as though perhaps a new life was opening before me. I wanted to conserve it too, so I looked up a cheap hotel over a bakery on the Rue du Château, just off the Rue de Vanves, a place that Eugene had pointed out to me once. A few yards away was the bridge that spans the Montparnasse tracks. A familiar quarter.

I could have had a room for a hundred francs a month, a room without any conveniences to be sure – without even a window – and perhaps I would have taken it, just to be sure of a place to flop for a while, had it not been for the fact that in order to reach this room I would have been obliged to first pass through the room of a blind man. The thought of passing his bed every night had a most depressing effect upon me. I decided to look elsewhere. I went over to the Rue Cels, just behind the cemetery, and I looked at a sort of rat trap there with balconies running around the courtyard. There were birdcages suspended from the balcony too, all along the lower tier. A cheerful sight perhaps, but to me it seemed like the public ward in a hospital. The proprietor didn't seem to have all his wits either. I decided to wait for the night, to have a good look around, and then choose some attractive little joint in a quiet side street.

At dinnertime I spent fifteen francs for a meal, just about twice the amount I had planned to allot myself. That made me so wretched that I wouldn't allow myself to sit down for a coffee, even despite the fact that it had begun to drizzle. No, I would walk about a bit and then go quietly to bed, at a reasonable hour. I was already miserable, trying to husband my resources this way. I had never in my life done it; it wasn't in my nature.

Finally it began to come down in bucketsful. I was glad. That would give me the excuse I needed to duck somewhere and stretch my legs out. It was still too early to go to bed. I began to quicken my pace, heading back toward the Boulevard Raspail. Suddenly a woman comes up to me and stops me, right in the pouring rain. She wants to know what time it is. I told her I didn't have a watch. And then she bursts out, just like this: 'Oh, my good sir, do you speak English by chance?' I nod my head. It's coming down in torrents now. 'Perhaps, my dear good man, you would be so kind as to take me to a café. It is raining so and I haven't the money to sit down anywhere. You will excuse me, my dear sir, but you have such a kind face . . . I knew you were English right away.' And with this she smiles at me, a strange, half-demented smile. 'Perhaps you could give me a little advice, dear sir. I am all alone in the world . . . my God, it is terrible to have no money. . .'

This 'dear sir' and 'kind sir' and 'my good man', etc., had me on the verge of hysteria. I felt sorry for her and yet I had to laugh. I did laugh. I laughed right in her face. And then she laughed too, a weird, high-pitched laugh, off key, an altogether unexpected piece of cachinnation. I caught her by the arm and we made a bolt for it to the nearest café. She was still giggling when we entered the *bistro*. 'My dear good sir,' she began again, 'perhaps you think I am not telling you the truth. I am a good girl . . . I come of a good family. Only' – and here she gave me that wan, broken smile again – 'only I am so misfortunate as not to have a place to sit down.' At this I began to laugh again. I couldn't help it – the phrases she used, the strange accent, the crazy hat she had on, that demented smile. . . .

'Listen,' I interrupted, 'what nationality are you?'

'I'm English,' she replied. 'That is, I was born in Poland, but my father is Irish.'

'So that makes you English?'

'Yes,' she said, and she began to giggle again, sheepishly, and with a pretence of being coy.

'I suppose you know a nice little hotel where you could take me?' I said this, not because I had any intention of going with her, but just to spare her the usual preliminaries.

'Oh, my dear sir,' she said, as though I had made the most grievous error, 'I'm sure you don't mean that! I'm not that kind of girl. You were joking with me, I can see that. You're so good . . . you have such a kind face. I would not dare to speak to a Frenchman as I did to you. They insult you right away. . .'

She went on in this vein for some time. I wanted to break away from her. But she didn't want to be left alone. She was afraid – her papers were not in order. Wouldn't I be good enough to walk her to her hotel?

Perhaps I could 'lend' her fifteen or twenty francs, to quiet the *patron*? I walked her to the hotel where she said she was stopping and I put a fifty franc bill in her hand. Either she was very clever, or very innocent – it's hard to tell sometimes – but, at any rate, she wanted me to wait until she ran to the *bistro* for change. I told her not to bother. And with that she seized my hand impulsively and raised it to her lips. I was flabbergasted. I felt like giving her every damned thing I had. That touched me, that crazy little gesture. I thought to myself, it's good to be rich once in a while, just to get a new thrill like that. Just the same, I didn't lose my head. Fifty francs! That was quite enough to squander on a rainy night. As I walked off she waved to me with that crazy little bonnet which she didn't know how to wear. It was as though we were old playmates. I felt foolish and giddy. 'My dear kind sir . . . you have such a gentle face . . . you are so good, etc.' I felt like a saint.

When you feel all puffed up inside it isn't so easy to go to bed right away. You feel as though you ought to atone for such unexpected bursts of goodness. Passing the 'Jungle' I caught a glimpse of the dance floor; women with bare backs and ropes of pearls choking them – or so it looked – were wiggling their beautiful bottoms at me. Walked right up to the bar and ordered a *coupe* of champagne. When the music stopped, a beautiful blonde – she looked like a Norwegian – took a seat right beside me. The place wasn't as crowded or as gay as it had appeared from outside. There were only a half dozen couples in the place – they must have all been dancing at once. I ordered another *coupe* of champagne in order not to let my courage dribble away.

When I got up to dance with the blonde there was no one on the floor but us. Any other time I would have been self-conscious, but the champagne and the way she clung to me, the dimmed lights and the solid feeling of security which the few hundred francs gave me, well . . . We had another dance together, a sort of private exhibition, and then we fell into conversation. She had begun to weep – that was how it started. I thought possibly she had had too much to drink, so I pretended not to be concerned. And meanwhile I was looking around to see if there was any other timber available. But the place was thoroughly deserted.

The thing to do when you're trapped is to breeze – at once. If you don't, you're lost. What retained me, oddly enough, was the thought of paying for a hat check a second time. One always lets himself in for it because of a trifle.

The reason she was weeping, I discovered soon enough, was

because she had just buried her child. She wasn't Norwegian either, but French, and a midwife to boot. A chic midwife, I must say, even with the tears running down her face. I asked her if a little drink would help to console her, whereupon she very promptly ordered a whisky and tossed it off in the wink of an eye. 'Would you like another?' I suggested gently. She thought she would, she felt so rotten, so terribly dejected. She thought she would like a package of Camels too. 'No, wait a minute,' she said, 'I think I'd rather have *les* Pall Mall.' Have what you like, I thought, but stop weeping, for Christ's sake, it gives me the willies. I jerked her to her feet for another dance. On her feet she seemed to be another person. Maybe grief makes one more lecherous, I don't know. I murmured something about breaking away. 'Where to?' she said eagerly. 'Oh, anywhere. Some quiet place where we can talk.'

I went to the toilet and counted the money over again. I hid the hundred franc notes in my fob pocket and kept a fifty franc note and the loose change in my trousers pocket. I went back to the bar determined to talk turkey.

She made it easier for me because she herself introduced the subject. She was in difficulties. It was not only that she had just lost her child, but her mother was home, ill, very ill, and there was the doctor to pay and medicine to be bought, and so on and so forth. I didn't believe a word of it, of course. And since I had to find a hotel for myself, I suggested that she come along with me and stay the night. A little economy there, I thought to myself. But she wouldn't do that. She insisted on going home, said she had an apartment to herself – and besides she had to look after her mother. On reflection I decided that it would be still cheaper sleeping at her place, so I said yes and let's go immediately. Before going, however, I decided it was best to let her know just how I stood, so that there wouldn't be any squawking at the last minute. I thought she was going to faint when I told her how much I had in my pocket. 'The likes of it!' she said. Highly insulted she was. I thought there would be a scene. . . . Undaunted, however, I stood my ground. 'Very well, then, I'll leave you,' I said quietly. 'Perhaps I've made a mistake.'

'I should say you have!' she exclaimed, but clutching me by the sleeve at the same time. '*Ecoute, chéri . . . sois raisonnable!*' When I heard that all my confidence was restored. I knew that it would be merely a question of promising her a little extra and everything would be OK. 'All right,' I said wearily, 'I'll be nice to you, you'll see.'

'You were lying to me, then?' she said.

'Yes,' I smiled, 'I was just lying. . . .'

Before I had even put my hat on she had hailed a cab. I heard her give the Boulevard de Clichy for an address. That was more than the price of a room, I thought to myself. Oh well, there was time yet . . . we'd see. I don't know how it started any more but soon she was raving to me about Henry Bordeaux. I have yet to meet a whore who doesn't know of Henry Bordeaux! But this one was genuinely inspired; her language was beautiful now, so tender, so discerning, that I was debating how much to give her. It seemed to me that I had heard her say – *'quand il n'y aura plus de temps'*. It sounded like that, anyway. In the state I was in, a phrase like that was worth a hundred francs. I wondered if it was her own or if she had pulled it from Henry Bordeaux. Little matter. It was just the right phrase with which to roll up to the foot of Montmartre. 'Good evening, mother,' I was saying to myself, 'daughter and I will look after you – *quand il n'y aura plus de temps!*' She was going to show me her diploma, too, I remembered that.

She was all aflutter, once the door had closed behind us. Distracted. Wringing her hands and striking Sarah Bernhardt poses, half undressed too, and pausing between times to urge me to hurry, to get undressed, to do this and do that. Finally, when she had stripped down and was poking about with a chemise in her hand, searching for her kimono, I caught hold of her and gave her a good squeeze. She had a look of anguish on her face when I released her. 'My God! My God! I must go downstairs and have a look at mother!' she exclaimed. 'You can take a bath if you like, *chéri*. There! I'll be back in a few minutes.' At the door I embraced her again. I was in my underclothes and I had a tremendous erection. Somehow all this anguish and excitement, all the grief and histrionics, only whetted my appetite. Perhaps she was just going downstairs to quiet her *maquereau*. I had a feeling that something unusual was happening, some sort of drama which I would read about in the morning paper. I gave the place a quick inspection. There were two rooms and a bath, not badly furnished. Rather coquettish. There was her diploma on the wall – 'first class', as they all read. And there was the photograph of a child, a little girl with beautiful locks, on the dresser. I put the water on for a bath, and then I changed my mind. If something were to happen and I were found in the tub . . . I didn't like the idea. I paced back and forth, getting more and more uneasy as the minutes rolled by.

When she returned she was even more upset than before. 'She's going to die . . . she's going to die!' she kept wailing. For a moment I was almost on the point of leaving. How the hell can you climb over a woman when her mother's dying downstairs, perhaps right beneath you? I put my arms around her, half in sympathy and half determined to get what I had come for. As we stood thus she murmured, as if in real distress, her need for the money I had promised her. It was for '*maman*'. Shit, I didn't have the heart to haggle about a few francs at the moment. I walked over to the chair where my clothes were lying and I wiggled a hundred franc note out of my fob pocket, carefully keeping my back turned to her just the same. And, as a further precaution, I placed my pants on the side of the bed where I knew I was going to flop. The hundred francs wasn't altogether satisfactory to her, but I could see from the feeble way that she protested that it was quite enough. Then, with an energy that astonished me, she flung off her kimono and jumped into bed. As soon as I had put my arms around her and pulled her to me she reached for the switch and out went the lights. She embraced me passionately, and she groaned as all French cunts do when they get you in bed. She was getting me frightfully roused with her carrying on; that business of turning out the lights was a new one to me . . . it seemed like the real thing. But I was suspicious too, and as soon as I could manage conveniently I put my hands out to feel if my trousers were still there on the chair.

I thought we were settled for the night. The bed felt very comfortable, softer than the average hotel bed – and the sheets were clean, I had noticed that. If only she wouldn't squirm so! You would think she hadn't slept with a man for a month. I wanted to stretch it out. I wanted full value for my hundred francs. But she was mumbling all sorts of things in that crazy bed language which goes to your blood even more rapidly when it's in the dark. I was putting up a stiff fight, but it was impossible with her groaning and gasping going on, and her muttering: '*Vite chéri! Vite chéri! Oh, c'est bon! Oh, oh! Vite, vite, chéri!*' and this time she gave such a gasping shudder that bango! I heard the stars chiming and there was my hundred francs gone and the fifty that I had forgotten all about and the lights were on again and with the same alacrity that she had bounced into bed she was bouncing out again and grunting and squealing like an old sow. I lay back and puffed a cigarette, gazing ruefully at my pants the while; they were terribly wrinkled. In a moment she was back again, wrapping the kimono around her, and telling me in that agitated way which was getting on my nerves that I should make myself at home. 'I'm going downstairs to see mother,' she said. '*Mais faites comme chez vous, chéri. Je reviens tout de suite.*'

After a quarter of an hour had passed I began to feel thoroughly restless. I went inside and I read through a letter that was lying on the table. It was nothing of any account – a love letter. In the bathroom I examined all the bottles on the shelf; she had everything a woman requires to make herself smell beautiful. I was still hoping that she would come back and give me another fifty francs' worth. But time dragged on and there was no sign of her. I began to grow alarmed. Perhaps there *was* someone dying downstairs. Absent-mindedly, out of a sense of self-preservation, I suppose, I began to put my things on. As I was buckling my belt it came to me like a flash how she had stuffed the hundred franc note into her purse. In the excitement of the moment she had thrust the purse in the wardrobe, on the upper shelf. I remembered the gesture she made – standing on her tiptoes and reaching for the shelf. It didn't take me a minute to open the wardrobe and feel around for the purse. It was still there. I opened it hurriedly and saw my hundred franc note lying snugly between the silk coverlets. I put the purse back just as it was, slipped into my coat and shoes, and then I went to the landing and listened intently. I couldn't hear a sound. Where she had gone to, Christ only knows. In a jiffy I was back at the wardrobe and fumbling with her purse. I pocketed the hundred francs and all the loose change besides. Then, closing the door silently, I tiptoed down the stairs and when once I had hit the street I walked just as fast as my legs would carry me. At the Café Boudon I stopped for a bite. The whores were having a gay time pelting a fat man who had fallen asleep over his meal. He was sound asleep; snoring, in fact, and yet his jaws were working away mechanically. The place was in an uproar. There were shouts of 'All aboard!' and then a concerted banging of knives and forks. He opened his eyes for a moment, blinked stupidly, and then his head rolled forward again on his chest. I put the hundred franc bill carefully away in my fob pocket and counted the change. The din around me was increasing and I had difficulty to recall exactly whether I had seen 'first-class' on her diploma or not. It bothered me. About her mother I didn't give a damn. I hoped she had croaked by now. It would be strange if what she had said were true. Too good to believe. *Vite chéri . . . vite, vite!* And the other half-wit with her 'my good sir' and 'you have such a kind face'! I wondered if she had really taken a room in that hotel we stopped by.

*Henry Miller took a job for a while teaching English in a French boarding school, an experience he found more interesting than enjoyable, especially*

*as he was cold and underfed most of the time. But it helped to stave him over*
*a bad financial period. At the first opportunity he left without giving notice.*

It was spring before I managed to escape from the penitentiary, and then only by a stroke of fortune. A telegram from Carl informed me one day that there was a vacancy 'upstairs'; he said he would send me the fare back if I decided to accept. I telegraphed back at once and as soon as the dough arrived I beat it to the station. Not a word to M. le Proviseur or anyone. French leave, as they say.

I went immediately to the hotel at 1 *bis*, where Carl was staying. He came to the door stark naked. It was his night off and there was a cunt in the bed as usual. 'Don't mind her,' he says, 'she's asleep. If you need a lay you can take her on. She's not bad.' He pulls the covers back to show me what she looks like. However, I wasn't thinking about a lay right away. I was too excited. I was like a man who has just escaped from gaol. I just wanted to see and hear things. Coming from the station it was like a long dream. I felt as though I had been away for years.

It was not until I had sat down and taken a good look at the room that I realized I was back again in Paris. It was Carl's room and no mistake about it. Like a squirrel cage and shithouse combined. There was hardly room on the table for the portable machine he used. It was always like that, whether he had a cunt with him or not. Always a dictionary lying open on a gilt-edged volume of *Faust*, always a tobacco pouch, a beret, a bottle of *vin rouge*, letters, manuscripts, old newspapers, water colours, teapot, dirty socks, toothpicks, Kruschen Salts, condoms, etc. In the *bidet* were orange peels and the remnants of a ham sandwich.

'There's some food in the closet,' he said. 'Help yourself! I was just going to give myself an injection.'

I found the sandwich he was talking about and a piece of cheese that he had nibbled at beside it. While he sat on the edge of the bed, dosing himself with his argyrol, I put away the sandwich and cheese with the aid of a little wine.

'I liked that letter you sent me about Goethe,' he said, wiping his prick with a dirty pair of drawers.

'I'll show you the answer to it in a minute – I'm putting it in my book. The trouble with you is that you're not a German. You have to be German to understand Goethe. Shit, I'm not going to explain it to you now. I've put it all in the book. . . . By the way, I've got a new cunt now – not this one – this one's a half-wit. At least, I had her until a few days ago. I'm not sure whether she'll come back or not. She was living with me all the time you were away. The other day her parents came and took her away. They said she was only fifteen. Can you beat that? They scared the shit out of me too. . . .'

I began to laugh. It was like Carl to get himself into a mess like that.

'What are you laughing for?' he said. 'I may go to prison for it. Luckily, I didn't knock her up. And that's funny, too, because she never took care of herself properly. But do you know what saved me? So I think, at least. It was *Faust*. Yeah! Her old man happened to see it lying on the table. He asked me if I understood German. One thing led to another and before I knew it he was looking through my books. Fortunately I happened to have the Shakespeare open too. That impressed him like hell. He said I was evidently a very serious guy.'

'What about the girl – what did *she* have to say?'

'She was frightened to death. You see, she had a little watch with her when she came; in the excitement we couldn't find the watch, and her mother insisted that the watch be found or she'd call the police. You see how things are here. I turned the whole place upside down – but I couldn't find the goddamned watch. The mother was furious. I liked her too, in spite of everything. She was even better-looking than the daughter. Here – I'll show you a letter I started to write her. I'm in love with her. . . .'

'With the *mother*?'

'Sure. Why not? If I had seen the mother first I'd never have looked at the daughter. How did I know she was only fifteen? You don't ask a cunt how old she is before you lay her, do you?'

'Joe, there's something funny about this. You're not shitting me, are you?'

'Am I shitting you? Here – look at this!' And he shows me the watercolours the girl had made – cute little things – a knife and a loaf of bread, the table and teapot, everything running uphill. 'She was in love with me,' he said. 'She was just like a child. I had to tell her when to brush her teeth and how to put her hat on. Here – look at the lollipops! I used to buy her a few lollipops every day – she liked them.'

'Well, what did she do when her parents came to take her away? Didn't she put up a row?'

'She cried a little, that's all. What *could* she do? She's under age. . . . I had to promise never to see her again, never to write her either. That's what I'm waiting to see now – whether she'll stay away or not. She was a virgin when she came here. The thing is, how long will she be able to go without a lay? She couldn't get enough of it when she was here. She almost wore me out.'

234

By this time the one in bed had come to and was rubbing her eyes. She looked pretty young to me, too. Not bad looking, but dumb as hell. Wanted to know right away what we were talking about.

'She lives here in the hotel,' said Carl. 'On the third floor. Do you want to go to her room? I'll fix it up for you.'

I didn't know whether I wanted to or not, but when I saw Carl mushing it up with her again I decided I did want to. I asked her first if she was too tired. Useless question. A whore is never too tired to open her legs. Some of them can fall asleep while you diddle them. Anyway, it was decided we would go down to her room. Like that I wouldn't have to pay the *patron* for the night.

In the morning I rented a room overlooking the little park down below where the sandwich-board men always came to eat their lunch. At noon I called for Carl to have breakfast with him. He and Van Norden had developed a new habit in my absence – they went to the Coupole for breakfast every day. 'Why the Coupole?' I asked. 'Why the Coupole?' says Carl. 'Because the Coupole serves porridge at all hours and porridge makes you shit.' – 'I see,' said I.

So it's just like it used to be again. The three of us walking back and forth to work. Petty dissensions, petty rivalries. Van Norden still bellyaching about his cunts and about washing the dirt out of his belly. Only now he's found a new diversion. He's found that it's less annoying to masturbate. I was amazed when he broke the news to me. I didn't think it possible for a guy like that to find any pleasure in jerking himself off. I was still more amazed when he explained to me how he goes about it. He had 'invented' a new stunt, so he put it. 'You take an apple,' he says, 'and you bore out the core. Then you rub some cold cream on the inside so as it doesn't melt too fast. Try it some time! It'll drive you crazy at first. Anyway, it's cheap and you don't have to waste much time.

'By the way,' he says, switching the subject, 'that friend of yours, Fillmore, he's in the hospital. I think he's nuts. Anyway, that's what his girl told me. He took on a French girl, you know, while you were away. They used to fight like hell. She's a big, healthy bitch – wild like. I wouldn't mind giving her a tumble, but I'm afraid she'd claw the eyes out of me. He was always going around with his face and hands scratched up. She looks bunged up too once in a while – or she used to. You know how these French cunts are – when they love they lose their minds.'

Evidently things had happened while I was away. I was sorry to hear about Fillmore. He had been damned good to me. When I left Van Norden I jumped a bus and went straight to the hospital.

They hadn't decided yet whether he was completely off his base or not, I suppose, for I found him upstairs in a private room, enjoying all the liberties of the regular patients. He had just come from the bath when I arrived. When he caught sight of me he burst into tears. 'It's all over,' he says immediately. 'They say I'm crazy – and I may have syphilis too. They say I have delusions of grandeur.' He fell over on to the bed and wept quietly. After he had wept a while he lifted his head up and smiled – just like a bird coming out of a snooze. 'Why do they put me in such an expensive room?' he said. 'Why don't they put me in the ward – or in the bughouse? I can't afford to pay for this. I'm down to my last five hundred dollars.'

'That's why they're keeping you here,' I said. 'They'll transfer you quickly enough when your money runs out. Don't worry.'

My words must have impressed him, for I had no sooner finished than he handed me his watch and chain, his wallet, his fraternity pin, etc. 'Hold on to them,' he said. 'These bastards'll rob me of everything I've got.' And then suddenly he began to laugh, one of those weird, mirthless laughs which makes you believe a guy's goofy whether he is or not. 'I know you'll think I'm crazy,' he said, 'but I want to atone for what I did. I want to get married. You see, I didn't know I had the clap. I gave her the clap and then I knocked her up. I told the doctor I don't care what happens to me, but I want him to let me get married first. He keeps telling me to wait until I get better – but I know I'm never going to get better. This is the end.'

I couldn't help laughing myself, hearing him talk that way. I couldn't understand what had come over him. Anyway, I had to promise him to see the girl and explain things to her. He wanted me to stick by her, comfort her. Said he could trust me, etc. I said yes to everything in order to soothe him. He didn't seem exactly nuts to me – just caved-in like. Typical Anglo-Saxon crisis. An eruption of morals. I was rather curious to see the girl, to get the lowdown on the whole thing.

The next day I looked her up. She was living in the Latin Quarter. As soon as she realized who I was she became exceedingly cordial. Ginette she called herself. Rather big, rawboned, healthy, peasant type with a front tooth half eaten away. Full of vitality and a kind of crazy fire in her eyes. The first thing she did was to weep. Then, seeing that I was an old friend of her Jo-Jo – that was how she called him – she ran downstairs and brought back a couple of bottles of white wine. I was to stay and have dinner with her – she insisted on it. As she drank she became by turns gay and maudlin. I didn't have to ask her any questions – she went on like a self-winding machine. The thing that worried her principally was – would he get his job back when he was released from the hospital? She said her parents were well off, but they were displeased with her. They didn't approve of her wild ways. They didn't approve of him particularly – he had no manners, and he was an American. She begged me to assure her that he would get his job back, which I did without hesitancy. And then she begged me to know if she could believe what he said – that he was going to marry her. Because now, with a child under her belt, and a dose of clap besides, she was in no position to strike a match – with a Frenchman anyway. That was clear, wasn't it? Of course, I assured her. It was all clear as hell to me – except how in Christ's name Fillmore had ever fallen for her. However, one thing at a time. It was my duty now to comfort her, and so I just filled her up with a lot of baloney, told her everything would turn out all right and that I would stand godfather to the child, etc. Then suddenly it struck me as strange that she should have the child at all – especially as it was likely to be born blind. I told her that as tactfully as I could. 'It doesn't make any difference,' she said, 'I want a child by him.'

'Even if it's blind?' I asked.

'*Mon Dieu, ne dites pas ça!*' she groaned. '*Ne dites pas ça!*'

Just the same, I felt it was my duty to say it. She got hysterical and began to weep like a walrus, poured out more wine. In a few moments she was laughing boisterously. She was laughing to think how they used to fight when they got in bed. 'He liked me to fight with him,' she said. 'He was a brute.'

As we sat down to eat, a friend of hers walked in – a little tart who lived at the end of the hall. Ginette immediately sent me down to get some more wine. When I came back they had evidently had a good talk. Her friend, Yvette, worked in the police department. A sort of stool pigeon, as far as I could gather. At least that was what she was trying to make me believe. It was fairly obvious that she was just a little whore. But she had an obsession about the police and their doings. Throughout the meal they were urging me to accompany them to a *bal musette*. They wanted to have a gay time – it was so lonely for Ginette with Jo-Jo in the hospital. I told them I had to work, but that on my night off I'd come back and take them out. I made it clear too that I had no dough to spend on them. Ginette, who was really thunderstruck to hear this, pretended that that didn't matter in the least. In fact, just to show what a good sport the was, she insisted on driving me to work in a cab. She was doing it because I was a friend of

Jo-Jo's. And therefore I was a friend of hers. 'And also,' thought I to myself, 'if anything goes wrong with your Jo-Jo you'll come to me on the double-quick. Then you'll see what a friend I can be!' I was as nice as pie to her. In fact, when we got out of the cab in front of the office, I permitted them to persuade me into having a final Pernod together. Yvette wanted to know if she couldn't call for me after work. She had a lot of things to tell me in confidence, she said. But I managed to refuse without hurting her feelings. Unfortunately I did unbend sufficiently to give her my address.

*Unfortunately*, I say. As a matter of fact, I'm rather glad of it when I think back on it. Because the very next day things began to happen. The very next day, before I had even gotten out of bed, the two of them called on me. Jo-Jo had been removed from the hospital – they had incarcerated him in a little château in the country, just a few miles out of Paris. The *château*, they called it. A polite way of saying 'the bughouse'. They wanted me to get dressed immediately and go with them. They were in a panic.

Perhaps I might have gone alone – but I just couldn't make up my mind to go with these two. I asked them to wait for me downstairs while I got dressed, thinking that it would give me time to invent some excuse for not going. But they wouldn't leave the room. They sat there and watched me wash and dress, just as if it were an everyday affair. In the midst of it, Carl popped in. I gave him the situation briefly, in English, and then we hatched up an excuse that I had some important work to do. However, to smooth things over, we got some wine in and we began to amuse them by showing them a book of dirty drawings. Yvette had already lost all desire to go to the château. She and Carl were getting along famously. When it came time to go Carl decided to accompany them to the château. He thought it would be funny to see Fillmore walking around with a lot of nuts. He wanted to see what it was like in the nuthouse. So off they went, somewhat pickled, and in the best of humour.

All the time that Fillmore was at the château I never once went to see him. It wasn't necessary, because Ginette visited him regularly and gave me all the news. They had hopes of bringing him around in a few months, so she said. They thought it was alcoholic poisoning – nothing more. Of course, he had a dose – but that wasn't difficult to remedy. So far as they could see, he didn't have syphilis. That was something. So, to begin with, they used the stomach pump on him. They cleaned his system out thoroughly. He was so weak for a while that he couldn't get out of bed. He was depressed, too. He said he didn't want to be cured – he wanted to die. And he kept repeating this nonsense so insistently that finally they grew alarmed. I suppose it wouldn't have been a very good recommendation if he had committed suicide. Anyway, they began to give him mental treatment. And in between times they pulled out his teeth, more and more of them, until he didn't have a tooth left in his head. He was supposed to feel fine after that, yet strangely he didn't. He became more despondent than ever. And then his hair began to fall out. Finally he developed a paranoid streak – began to accuse them of all sorts of things, demanded to know by what right he was being detained, what he had done to warrant being locked up, etc. After a terrible fit of despondency he would suddenly become energetic and threaten to blow up the place if they didn't release him. And to make it worse, as far as Ginette was concerned, he had gotten all over his notion of marrying her. He told her straight up and down that he had no intention of marrying her, and that if she was crazy enough to go and have a child then she could support it herself.

The doctors interpreted all this as a good sign. They said he was coming round. Ginette, of course, thought he was crazier than ever, but she was praying for him to be released so that she could take him to the country where it would be quiet and peaceful and where he would come to his right senses. Meanwhile her parents had come to Paris on a visit and had even gone so far as to visit the future son-in-law at the château. In their canny way they had probably figured it out that it would be better for their daughter to have a crazy husband than no husband at all. The father thought he could find something for Fillmore to do on the farm. He said that Fillmore wasn't such a bad chap at all. When he learned from Ginette that Fillmore's parents had money he became even more indulgent, more understanding.

The thing was working itself out nicely all round. Ginette returned to the provinces for a while with her parents. Yvette was coming regularly to the hotel to see Carl. She thought he was the editor of the paper. And little by little she became more confidential. When she got good and tight one day, she informed us that Ginette had never been anything but a whore, that Ginette was a bloodsucker, that Ginette never had been pregnant and was not pregnant now. About the other accusations we hadn't much doubt, Carl and I, but about not being pregnant, that we weren't so sure of.

'How did she get such a big stomach, then?' asked Carl.

Yvette laughed. 'Maybe she uses a bicycle pump,' she said. 'No, seriously,' she added, 'the stomach comes from drink. She drinks like a fish, Ginette. When she comes back from the country, you will see, she will be blown up still more. Her father is a drunkard. Ginette is a drunkard. Maybe she had the clap, yes – but she is not pregnant.'

'But why does she want to marry him? Is she really in love with him?'

'*Love*? Pfooh! She has no heart, Ginette. She wants someone to look after her. No Frenchman would ever marry her – she has a police record. No, she wants him because he's too stupid to find out about her. Her parents don't want her any more – she's a disgrace to them. But if she can get married to a rich American, then everything will be all right . . . You think maybe she loves him a little, eh? You don't know her. When they were living together at the hotel, she had men coming to her room while he was at work. She said he didn't give her enough spending money. He was stingy. That fur she wore – she told him her parents had given it to her, didn't she? Innocent fool! Why, I've seen her bring a man back to the hotel right while he was there. She brought the man to the floor below. I saw it with my own eyes. And what a man! An old derelict. He couldn't get an erection!'

If Fillmore, when he was released from the château, had returned to Paris, perhaps I might have tipped him off about his Ginette. While he was still under observation I didn't think it well to upset him by poisoning his mind with Yvette's slanders. As things turned out, he went directly from the château to the home of Ginette's parents. There, despite himself, he was inveigled into making public his engagement. The banns were published in the local papers and a reception was given to the friends of the family. Fillmore took advantage of the situation to indulge in all sorts of escapades. Though he knew quite well what he was doing he pretended to be still a little daffy. He would borrow his father-in-law's car, for example, and tear about the countryside all by himself; if he saw a town that he liked he would plank himself down and have a good time until Ginette came searching for him. Sometimes the father-in-law and he would go off together – on a fishing trip, presumably – and nothing would be heard of them for days. He became exasperatingly capricious and exacting. I suppose he figured he might as well get what he could out of it.

When he returned to Paris with Ginette he had a complete new wardrobe and a pocketful of dough. He looked cheerful and healthy, and had a fine coat of tan. He looked sound as a berry to me. But as soon as we had gotten away from Ginette he opened up. His job was gone and his money had all run out. In a month or so they were to be married. Meanwhile the parents were supplying the dough. 'Once

240

they've got me properly in their clutches,' he said, 'I'll be nothing but a slave to them. The father thinks he's going to open up a stationery store for me. Ginette will handle the customers, take in the money, etc., while I sit in the back of the store and write – or something. Can you picture me sitting in the back of a stationery store for the rest of my life? Ginette thinks it's an excellent idea. She likes to handle money. I'd rather go back to the château than submit to such a scheme.'

For the time being, of course, he was pretending that everything was hunky-dory. I tried to persuade him to go back to America but he wouldn't hear of that. He said he wasn't going to be driven out of France by a lot of ignorant peasants. He had an idea that he would slip out of sight for a while and then take up quarters in some outlying section of the city where he'd not be likely to stumble upon her. But we soon decided that that was impossible: you can't hide away in France as you can in America.

'You could go to Belgium for a while,' I suggested.

'But what'll I do for money?' he said promptly. 'You can't get a job in these goddamned countries.'

'Why don't you marry her and get a divorce, then?' I asked.

'And meanwhile she'll be dropping a kid. Who's going to take care of the kid, eh?'

'How do you know she's going to have a kid?' I said, determined now that the moment had come to spill the beans.

'How do I know?' he said. He didn't quite seem to know what I was insinuating.

I gave him an inkling of what Yvette had said. He listened to me in complete bewilderment. Finally he interrupted me. 'It's no use going on with that,' he said. 'I know she's going to have a kid, all right. I've felt it kicking around inside. Yvette's a dirty little slut. You see, I didn't want to tell you, but up until the time I went to the hospital I was shelling out for Yvette too. Then when the crash came I couldn't do any more for her. I figured out that I had done enough for the both of them . . . I made up my mind to look after myself first. That made Yvette sore. She told Ginette that she was going to get even with me . . . No, I wish it were true, what she said. Then I could get out of this thing more easily. Now I'm in a trap. I've promised to marry her and I'll have to go through with it. After that I don't know what'll happen to me. They've got me by the balls now.'

Since he had taken a room in the same hotel with me I was obliged to see them frequently, whether I wanted to or not. Almost every evening I had dinner with them, preceded, of course, by a few Pernods. All through the meal they quarrelled noisily. It was embarrassing because I had sometimes to take one side and sometimes the other. One Sunday afternoon, for example, after we had had lunch together, we repaired to a café on the corner of the Boulevard Edgar-Quinet. Things had gone unusually well this time. We were sitting inside at a little table, one alongside the other, our backs to a mirror. Ginette must have been passionate or something for she had suddenly gotten into a sentimental mood and was fondling him and kissing him in front of everybody, as the French do so naturally. They had just come out of a long embrace when Fillmore said something about her parents which she interpreted as an insult. Immediately her cheeks flushed with anger. We tried to mollify her by telling her that she had misunderstood the remark and then, under his breath, Fillmore said something to me in English – something about giving her a little soft soap. That was enough to set her completely off the handle. She said we were making fun of her. I said something sharp to her which angered her still more and then Fillmore tried to put in a word. 'You're too quick-tempered,' he said, and he tried to pat her on the cheek. But she, thinking that he had raised his hand to slap her face, she gave him a sound crack in the jaw with that big peasant hand of hers. For a moment he was stunned. He hadn't expected a wallop like that, and it stung. I saw his face go white and the next moment he raised himself from the bench and with the palm of his hand he gave her such a crack that she almost fell off her seat. 'There! that'll teach you how to behave!' he said – in his broken French. For a moment there was a dead silence. Then, like a storm breaking, she picked up the cognac glass in front of her and hurled it at him with all her might. It smashed against the mirror behind us. Fillmore had already grabbed her by the arm, but with her free hand she grabbed the coffee glass and smashed it on the floor. She was squirming around like a maniac. It was all we could do to hold her. Meanwhile, of course, the *patron* had come running in and ordered us to beat it. 'Loafers!' he called us. 'Yes, loafers; that's it!' screamed Ginette. 'Dirty foreigners! Thugs! Gangsters! Striking a pregnant woman!' We were getting black looks all around. A poor Frenchwoman with two American toughs. Gangsters. I was wondering how the hell we'd ever get out of the place without a fight. Fillmore, by this time, was as silent as a clam. Ginette was bolting it through the door, leaving us to face the music. As she sailed out she turned back with fist upraised and shouted: 'I'll pay you back for this, you brute! You'll see! No foreigner can treat a decent Frenchwoman like that! Ah, no! Not like that!'

Hearing this the *patron*, who had now been paid for his drinks and his broken glasses, felt it incumbent to show his gallantry toward a splendid representative of French motherhood such as Ginette, and so, without more ado, he spat at our feet and shoved us out of the door. 'Shit on you, you dirty loafers!' he said, or some such pleasantry.

Once in the street and nobody throwing things after us, I began to see the funny side of it. It would be an excellent idea, I thought to myself, if the whole thing were properly aired in court. *The whole thing!* With Yvette's little stories as a side dish. After all, the French have a sense of humour. Perhaps the judge, when he heard Fillmore's side of the story, would absolve him from marriage.

Meanwhile Ginette was standing across the street brandishing her fist and yelling at the top of her lungs. People were stopping to listen in, to take sides, as they do in street brawls. Fillmore didn't know what to do – whether to walk away from her, or to go over to her and try to pacify her. He was standing in the middle of the street with his arms outstretched, trying to get a word in edgewise. And Ginette still yelling: '*Gangster! Brute! Tu verras, salaud!*' and other complimentary things. Finally Fillmore made a move toward her and she, probably thinking that he was going to give her another good cuff, took it on a trot down the street. Fillmore came back to where I was standing and said: 'Come on, let's follow her quietly.' We started off with a thin crowd of stragglers behind us. Every once in a while she turned back toward us and brandished her fist. We made no attempt to catch up with her, just followed her leisurely down the street to see what she would do. Finally she slowed up her pace and we crossed over to the other side of the street. She was quiet now. We kept walking behind her, getting closer and closer. There were only about a dozen people behind us now – the others had lost interest. When we got near the corner she suddenly stopped and waited for us to approach. 'Let me do the talking,' said Fillmore, 'I know how to handle her.'

The tears were streaming down her face as we came up to her. Myself, I didn't know what to expect of her. I was somewhat surprised therefore when Fillmore walked up to her and said in an aggrieved voice: 'Was that a nice thing to do? Why did you act that way?' Whereupon she threw her arms around his neck and began to weep like a child, calling him her little this and her little that. Then she turned to me imploringly. 'You saw how he struck me,' she said. 'Is that the way to behave towards a woman?' I was on the point of saying yes when Fillmore took her by the arm and started leading her off. 'No more of that,' he said. 'If you start again I'll crack you right here in the street.'

I thought it was going to start up all over again. She had fire in her eyes. But evidently she was a bit cowed, too, for it subsided quickly. However, as she sat down at the café she said quietly and grimly that he needn't think it was going to be forgotten so quickly; he'd hear more about it later on . . . perhaps tonight.

And sure enough she kept her word. When I met him the next day his face and hands were all scratched up. Seems she had waited until he got to bed and then, without a word, she had gone to the wardrobe and, dumping all his things out on the floor, she took them one by one and tore them to ribbons. As this had happened a number of times before, and as she had always sewn them up afterward, he hadn't protested very much. And that made her angrier than ever. What she wanted was to get her nails into him, and she did, to the best of her ability. Being pregnant she had a certain advantage over him.

Poor Fillmore! It was no laughing matter. She had him terrorized. If he threatened to run away she retorted by a threat to kill him. And she said it as if she meant it. 'If you go to America,' she said, 'I'll follow you! You won't get away from me. A French girl always knows how to get vengeance.' And the next moment she would be coaxing him to be 'reasonable', to be '*sage*', etc. Life would be so nice once they had the stationery store. He wouldn't have to do a stroke of work. She would do everything. He could stay in back of the store and write – or whatever he wanted to do.

It went on like this, back and forth, a seesaw, for a few weeks or so. I was avoiding them as much as possible, sick of the affair and disgusted with the both of them. Then one fine summer's day, just as I was passing the Credit Lyonnais, who comes marching down the steps but Fillmore. I greeted him warmly, feeling rather guilty because I had dodged him for so long. I asked him, with more than ordinary curiosity, how things were going. He answered me rather vaguely and with a note of despair in his voice.

'I've just gotten permission to go to the bank,' he said, in a peculiar, broken, abject sort of way. 'I've got about half an hour, no more. She keeps tabs on me.' And he grasped my arm as if to hurry me away from the spot.

We were walking down toward the Rue de Rivoli. It was a beautiful day, warm, clear, sunny – one of those days when Paris is at its best. A mild pleasant breeze blowing, just enough to take that stagnant odour out of your nostrils. Fillmore was without a hat. Outwardly he looked the picture of health – like the average American tourist who slouches along with money jingling in his pockets.

'I don't know what to do any more,' he said quietly. 'You've got to do something for me. I'm helpless. I can't get a grip on myself. If I could only get away from her for a little while perhaps I'd come round all right. But she won't let me out of her sight. I just got permission to run to the bank – I had to draw some money. I'll walk around with you a bit and then I must hurry back – she'll have lunch waiting for me.'

I listened to him quietly, thinking to myself that he certainly did need someone to pull him out of the hole he was in. He had completely caved in, there wasn't a speck of courage left in him. He was just like a child – like a child who is beaten every day and doesn't know any more how to behave, except to cower and cringe. As we turned under the colonnade of the Rue de Rivoli he burst into a long diatribe against France. He was fed up with the French. 'I used to rave about them,' he said, 'but that was all literature. I know them now. . . . I know what they're really like. They're cruel and mercenary. At first it seems wonderful, because you have a feeling of being free. After a while it palls on you. Underneath it's all dead; there's no feeling, no sympathy, no friendship. They're selfish to the core. The most selfish people on earth! They think of nothing but money, money, money. And so goddamned respectable, so bourgeois! That's what drives me nuts. When I see her mending my shirts I could club her. Always mending, mending. Saving, saving. *Faut faire des économies*! That's all I hear her say all day long. You hear it everywhere. *Sois raisonnable, mon chéri! Sois raisonnable*! I don't want to be reasonable and logical. I hate it! I want to bust loose, I want to enjoy myself. I want to *do* something. I don't want to sit in a café and talk all day long. Jesus, we've got our faults – but we've got enthusiasm. It's better to make mistakes than not do anything. I'd rather be a bum in America than to be sitting pretty here. Maybe it's because I'm a Yankee. I was born in New England and I belong there, I guess. You can't become a European overnight. There's something in your blood that makes you different. It's the climate – and everything. We see things with different eyes. We can't make ourselves over, however much we admire the French. We're Americans and we've got to remain Americans. Sure, I hate those puritanical buggers back home – I hate 'em with all my guts. But I'm one of them myself. I don't belong here. I'm sick of it.'

All along the arcade he went on like this. I wasn't saying a word. I let him spill it all out – it was good for him to get it off his chest. Just the same, I was thinking how strange it was that this same guy, had it been a year ago, would have been beating his chest like a gorilla and saying: 'What a marvellous day! What a country! What a people!' And if an American had happened along and said one word against France Fillmore would have flattened his nose. He would have died for France – a year ago. I never saw a man who was so infatuated with a country, who was so happy under a foreign sky. It wasn't natural. When he said *France* it meant wine, women, money in the pocket, easy come, easy go. It meant being a bad boy, being on a holiday. And then, when he had had his fling, when the tent top blew off and he had a good look at the sky, he saw that it wasn't just a circus, but an arena, just like everywhere. And a damned grim one. I often used to think, when I heard him rave about glorious France, about liberty and all that crap, what it would have sounded like to a French workman, could he have understood Fillmore's words. No wonder they think we're all crazy. We *are* crazy to them. We're just a pack of children. Senile idiots. What we call life is a five-and-ten-cent store romance. That enthusiasm underneath – what is it? That cheap optimism which turns the stomach of any ordinary European? It's illusion. No, illusion's too good a word for it. Illusion means something. No, it's not that – it's *delusion*. It's sheer delusion, that's what. We're like a herd of wild horses with blinders over our eyes. On the rampage. Stampede. Over the precipice. Bango! Anything that nourishes violence and confusion. On! On! No matter where. And foaming at the lips all the while. Shouting Hallelujah! *Hallelujah*! Why? God knows. It's in the blood. It's the climate. It's a lot of things. It's the end, too. We're pulling the whole world down about our ears. We don't know why. It's our destiny. The rest is plain shit. . . .

At the Palais Royal I suggested that we stop and have a drink. He hesitated a moment. I saw that he was worrying about her, about the lunch, about the bawling out he'd get.

'For Christ's sake,' I said, 'forget about her for a while. I'm going to order something to drink and I want you to drink it. Don't worry, I'm going to get you out of this fucking mess.' I ordered two stiff whiskies.

When he saw the whiskies coming he smiled at me just like a child again.

'Down it!' I said, 'and let's have another. This is going to do you good. I don't care what the doctor says – this time it'll be all right. Come on, down with it!'

He put it down all right and while the *garçon* disappeared to fetch another round he looked at me with brimming eyes, as though I were the last friend in the world. His lips were twitching a bit, too. There was something he wanted to say to me and he didn't quite know how to begin. I looked at him easily, as though ignoring the appeal, and, shoving the saucers aside, I leaned over on my elbow and I said to him earnestly; 'Look here, Fillmore, what is it you'd *really* like to do? Tell me!'

With that the tears gushed up and he blurted out: 'I'd like to be home with my people. I'd like to hear English spoken.' The tears were streaming down his face. He made no effort to brush them away. He just let everything gush forth. Jesus, I thought to myself, that's fine to have a release like that. Fine to be a complete coward at least once in your life. To let go that way. Great! Great! It did me so much good to see him break down that way that I felt as though I could solve any problem. I felt courageous and resolute. I had a thousand ideas in my head at once.

'Listen,' I said, bending still closer to him, 'if you mean what you said why don't you do it . . . why don't you go? Do you know what I would do, if I were in your shoes? I'd go today. Yes, by Jesus, I mean it . . . I'd go right away, without even saying goodbye to her. As a matter of fact that's the only way you can go – she'd never let you say goodbye. You know that.'

The *garçon* came with the whiskies. I saw him reach forward with a desperate eagerness and raise the glass to his lips. I saw a glint of hope in his eyes – far-off, wild, desperate. He probably saw himself swimming across the Atlantic. To me it looked easy, simple as rolling off a log. The whole thing was working itself out rapidly in my mind. I knew just what each step would be. Clear as a bell, I was.

'Whose money is that in the bank?' I asked. 'Is it her father's or is it yours?'

'It's mine!' he exclaimed. 'My mother sent it to me. I don't want any of her goddamned money.'

'That's swell!' I said. 'Listen, suppose we hop a cab and go back there. Draw out every cent. Then we'll go to the British Consulate and get a visa. You're going to hop the train this afternoon for London. From London you'll take the first boat to America. I'm saying that because then you won't be worried about her trailing you. She'll never suspect that you went via London. If she goes searching for you she'll naturally go to Le Havre first, or Cherbourg. . . . And here's another thing – you're not going back to get your things. You're going to leave everything here. Let her keep them. With that French mind of hers she'll never dream that you scooted off without bag or baggage. It's incredible. A Frenchman would never dream of doing a thing like that . . . unless he was as cracked as you are.'

'You're right!' he exclaimed. 'I never thought of that. Besides, you might send them to me later on – if she'll surrender them! But that doesn't matter now. Jesus, though, I haven't even got a hat!'

'What do you need a hat for? When you get to London you can buy everything you need. All you need now is to hurry. We've got to find out when the train leaves.'

'Listen,' he said, reaching for his wallet, 'I'm going to leave everything to you. Here, take this and do whatever's necessary. I'm too weak. . . . I'm dizzy.'

I took the wallet and emptied it of the bills he had just drawn from the bank. A cab was standing at the kerb. We hopped in. There was a train leaving the Gare du Nord at four o'clock, or thereabouts. I was figuring it out – the bank, the Consulate, the American Express, the station. Fine! Just about make it.

'Now buck up!' I said, 'and keep your shirt on! Shit, in a few hours you'll be crossing the Channel. Tonight you'll be walking around in London and you'll get a good bellyful of English. Tomorrow you'll be on the open sea – and then, by Jesus, you're a free man and you needn't give a fuck what happens. By the time you get to New York this'll be nothing more than a bad dream.'

This got him so excited that his feet were moving convulsively, as if he were trying to run inside the cab. At the bank his hand was trembling so that he could hardly sign his name. That was one thing I couldn't do for him – sign his name. But I think, had it been necessary, I could have sat him on the toilet and wiped his ass. I was determined to ship him off, even if I had to fold him up and put him in a valise.

It was lunch hour when we got to the British Consulate, and the place was closed. That meant waiting until two o'clock. I couldn't think of anything better to do, by way of killing time, than to eat. Fillmore, of course, wasn't hungry. He was for eating a sandwich. 'Fuck that!' I said. 'You're going to blow me to a good lunch. It's the last square meal you're going to have over here – maybe for a long while.' I steered him to a cosy little restaurant and ordered a good spread. I ordered the best wine on the menu, regardless of price or taste. I had all his money in my pocket – oodles of it, it seemed to me. Certainly never before had I had so much in my fist at one time. It was a treat to break a thousand franc note. I held it up to the light first to look at the beautiful watermark. Beautiful money! One of the few things the French make on a grand scale. Artistically done, too, as if they cherished a deep affection even for the symbol.

The meal over, we went to a café. I ordered Chartreuse with the coffee. Why not? And I broke another bill – a five-hundred franc note this time. It was a clean, new, crisp bill. A pleasure to handle such money. The waiter handed me back a lot of dirty old bills that had been patched up with strips of gummed paper; I had a stack of five and ten franc notes and a bagful of chicken feed. Chinese money, with holes in it. I didn't know in which pocket to stuff the money any more. My trousers were bursting with coins and bills. It made me slightly uncomfortable also, hauling all that dough out in public. I was afraid we might be taken for a couple of crooks.

When we got to the American Express there wasn't a devil of a lot of time left. The British, in their usual fumbling farting way, had kept us on pins and needles. Here everybody was sliding around on castors. They were so speedy that everything had to be done twice. After all the cheques were signed and clipped in a neat little holder, it was discovered that he had signed in the wrong place. Nothing to do but start all over again. I stood over him, with one eye on the clock, and watched every stroke of the pen. It hurt to hand over the dough. Not all of it, thank God – but a good part of it. I had roughly about 2,500 francs in my pocket. Roughly, I say. I wasn't counting by francs any more. A hundred, or two hundred, more or less – it didn't mean a goddamned thing to me. As for him, he was going through the whole transaction in a daze. He didn't know how much money he had. All he knew was that he had to keep something aside for Ginette. He wasn't certain yet how much – we were going to figure that out on the way to the station.

In the excitement we had forgotten to change all the money. We were already in the cab, however, and there wasn't any time to be lost. The thing was to find out how we stood. We emptied our pockets quickly and began to whack it up. Some of it was lying on the floor, some of it was on the seat. It was bewildering. There was French, American and English money. And all that chicken feed besides. I felt like picking up the coins and chucking them out of the window – just to simplify matters. Finally we sifted it all out; he held on to the English and American money, and I held on to the French money.

We had to decide quickly now what to do about Ginette – how much

249

to give her, what to tell her, etc. He was trying to fix up a yarn for me to hand her – didn't want her to break her heart and so forth. I had to cut him short.

'Never mind what to tell her,' I said. 'Leave that to me. How much are you going to *give* her, that's the thing? Why give her anything?'

That was like setting a bomb under his ass. He burst into tears. Such tears! It was worse than before. I thought he was going to collapse on my hands. Without stopping to think, I said: 'All right, let's give her all this French money. That ought to last her for a while.'

'How much is it?' he asked feebly.

'I don't know – about 2,000 francs or so. More than she deserves anyway.'

'Christ! Don't say that!' he begged. 'After all, it's a rotten break I'm giving her. Her folks'll never take her back now. No, give it to her. Give her the whole damned business. . . . I don't care what it is.'

He pulled a handkerchief out to wipe the tears away. 'I can't help it,' he said. 'It's too much for me.' I said nothing. Suddenly he sprawled himself out full length – I thought he was taking a fit or something – and he said: 'Jesus, I think I ought to go back. I ought to go back and face the music. If anything should happen to her I'd never forgive myself.'

That was a rude jolt for me. 'Christ!' I shouted, 'you can't do that! Not now. It's too late. You're going to take the train and I'm going to tend to her myself. I'll go see her just as soon as I leave you. Why, you poor boob, if she ever thought you had tried to run away from her she'd murder you, don't you realize that? You can't go back any more. It's settled.'

Anyway, what *could* go wrong? I asked myself. Kill herself? *Tant mieux.*

When we rolled up to the station we had still about twelve minutes to kill. I didn't dare to say goodbye to him yet. At the last minute, rattled as he was, I could see him jumping off the train and scooting back to her. Anything might swerve him. A straw. So I dragged him across the street to a bar and I said: 'Now you're going to have a Pernod – your *last* Pernod and I'm going to pay for it . . . with *your* dough.'

Something about this remark made him look at me uneasily. He took a big gulp of the Pernod and then, turning to me like an injured dog, he said: 'I know I oughtn't to trust you with all that money, but . . . but. . . . Oh, well, do what you think best. I don't want her to kill herself, that's all.'

'*Kill herself?*' I said. 'Not her! You must think a hell of a lot of yourself if you can believe a thing like that. As for the money, though I hate to give it to her, I promise you I'll go straight to the post office and telegraph it to her. I wouldn't trust myself with it a minute longer than is necessary.' As I said this I spied a bunch of postcards in a revolving rack. I grabbed one off – a picture of the Eiffel Tower it was – and made him write a few words. 'Tell her you're sailing now. Tell her you love her and that you'll send for her as soon as you arrive. . . . I'll send it by *pneumatique* when I go to the post office. And tonight I'll see her. Everything'll be Jake, you'll see.'

With that we walked across the street to the station. Only two minutes to go. I felt it was safe now. At the gate I gave him a slap on the back and pointed to the train. I didn't shake hands with him – he would have slobbered all over me. I just said: 'Hurry! She's going in a minute.' And with that I turned on my heel and marched off. I didn't even look round to see if he was boarding the train. I was afraid to.

I hadn't thought, all the while I was bundling him off, what I'd do once I was free of him. I had promised a lot of things – but that was only to keep him quiet. As for facing Ginette, I had about as little courage for it as he had. I was getting panicky myself. Everything had happened so quickly that it was impossible to grasp the nature of the situation in full. I walked away from the station in a kind of delicious stupor – with the postcard in my hand. I stood against a lamppost and read it over. It sounded preposterous. I read it again, to make sure that I wasn't dreaming, and then I tore it up and threw it in the gutter.

I looked around uneasily, half expecting to see Ginette coming after me with a tomahawk. Nobody was following me. I started walking leisurely toward the Place Lafayette. It was a beautiful day, as I had observed earlier. Light, puffy clouds above, sailing with the wind. The awnings flapping. Paris had never looked so good to me; I almost felt sorry that I had shipped the poor bugger off. At the Place Lafayette I sat down facing the church and stared at the clock tower; it's not such a wonderful piece of architecture, but that blue in the dial face always fascinated me. It was bluer than ever today. I couldn't take my eyes off it.

Unless he were crazy enough to write her a letter, explaining everything, Ginette need never know what had happened. And even if she did learn that he had left her 2,500 francs or so she couldn't prove it. I could always say that he imagined it. A guy who was crazy enough to walk off without even a hat was crazy enough to invent the 2,500 francs, or whatever it was. How much was it, anyhow? I wondered. My pockets were sagging with the weight of it. I hauled it all out and counted it carefully. There was exactly 2,875 francs and 35 centimes. More than I had thought. The 75 francs and 35 centimes had to be gotten rid of. I wanted an even sum – a clean 2,800 francs. Just then I saw a cab pulling up to the kerb. A woman stepped out with a white poodle dog in her hands; the dog was peeing over her silk dress. The idea of taking a dog for a ride got me sore. I'm as good as her dog, I said to myself, and with that I gave the driver a sign and told him to drive me through the Bois. He wanted to know where exactly. 'Anywhere,' I said. 'Go through the Bois, go all around it – and take your time, I'm in no hurry.' I sank back and let the houses whizz by, the jagged roofs, the chimney pots, the coloured walls, the urinals, the dizzy *carrefours*. Passing the Rond-Point I thought I'd go downstairs and take a leak. No telling what might happen down there. I told the driver to wait. It was the first time in my life I had let a cab wait while I took a leak. How much can you waste that way? Not very much. With what I had in my pocket I could afford to have two taxis waiting for me.

I took a good look around but I didn't see anything worth while. What I wanted was something fresh and unused – something from Alaska or the Virgin Islands. A clean fresh pelt with a natural fragrance to it. Needless to say, there wasn't anything like that walking about. I wasn't terribly disappointed. I didn't give a fuck whether I found anything or not. The thing is, never to be too anxious. Everything comes in due time.

We drove on past the Arc de Triomphe. A few sightseers were loitering around the remains of the Unknown Soldier. Going through the Bois I looked at all the rich cunts promenading in their limousines. They were whizzing by as if they had some destination. Do that, no doubt, to look important – to show the world how smooth run their Rolls Royces and their Hispano Suizas. Inside me things were running smoother than any Rolls Royce ever ran. It was just like velvet inside. Velvet cortex and velvet vertebrae. And velvet axle grease, what! It's a wonderful thing, for half an hour, to have money in your pocket and piss it away like a drunken sailor. You feel as though the world is yours. And the best part of it is, you don't know what to do with it. You can sit back and let the meter run wild, you can let the wind blow through your hair, you can stop and have a drink, you can give a big tip, and you can swagger off as though it were an everyday occurrence. But you can't create a revolution. You can't wash *all* the dirt out of your belly.

When we got to the Porte d'Auteuil I made him head for the Seine.

At the Pont de Sèvres I got out and started walking along the river, toward the Auteuil Viaduct. It's about the size of a creek along here and the trees come right down to the river's bank. The water was green and glassy, especially near the other side. Now and then a scow chugged by. Bathers in tights were standing in the grass sunning themselves. Everything was close and palpitant, and vibrant with the strong light.

Passing a beer garden I saw a group of cyclists sitting at a table. I took a seat nearby and ordered a *demi*. Hearing them jabber away I thought for a moment of Ginette. I saw her stamping up and down the room, tearing her hair, and sobbing and bleating, in that beastlike way of hers. I saw his hat on the rack. I wondered if his clothes would fit me. He had a raglan that I particularly liked. Well, by now he was on his way. In a little while the boat would be rocking under him. English! He wanted to hear English spoken. What an idea!

Suddenly it occurred to me that if I wanted I could go to America myself. It was the first time the opportunity had ever presented itself. I asked myself – 'do you want to go?' There was no answer. My thoughts drifted out, towards the sea, toward the other side where, taking a last look back, I had seen the skyscrapers fading out in a flurry of snowflakes. I saw them looking up again, in that same ghostly way as when I left. Saw the lights creeping through their ribs. I saw the whole city spread out, from Harlem to the Battery, the streets choked with ants, the elevated rushing by, the theatre emptying. I wondered in a vague way what had ever happened to my wife.

After everything had quietly sifted through my head a great peace came over me. Here, where the river gently winds through the girdle of hills, lies a soil so saturated with the past that however far back the mind roams one can never detach it from its human background. Christ, before my eyes there shimmered such a golden peace that only a neurotic could dream of turning his head away. So quietly flows the Seine that one hardly notices its presence. It is always there, quiet and unobtrusive, like a great artery running through the human body. In the wonderful peace that fell over me it seemed as if I had climbed to the top of a high mountain; for a little while I would be able to look around me, to take in the meaning of the landscape.

Human beings make a strange fauna and flora. From a distance they appear negligible; close up they are apt to appear ugly and malicious. More than anything they need to be surrounded with sufficient space – space even more than time.

The sun is setting. I feel this river flowing through me – its past, its ancient soil, the changing climate. The hills gently girdle it about: its course is fixed.

# Via Dieppe-Newhaven

The thing was that I wanted to be among English-speaking people again, for a little while at least. I had nothing against the French; on the contrary, I had at last made a bit of a home for myself in Clichy and everything would have been swell if it hadn't been for the fact that I had just gone through a crisis with my wife. She was living in Montparnasse and I was living with my friend Fred, who had taken an apartment, in Clichy just outside the Porte. We had agreed to separate; she was going back to America as soon as the money arrived for the boat fare.

So far so good. I had said goodbye to her and I thought everything was finished. Then one day when I walked into the grocer's the old woman informed me that my wife had just been in with a young man and that they had taken away a good supply of groceries which they had charged up to my account. The old woman seemed a bit perplexed and a little worried too. I told her it was OK. And it was OK too, because I knew my wife didn't have any money, and after all a wife has to eat just like any other person. About the young man, that was OK too: he was just a fairy who felt sorry for her and I supposed he had put her up for the time being in his apartment. In fact, everything was OK except that she was still in Paris, and when in Christ's name was she going to beat it, that's what I was wondering about.

A few more days passed and then she dropped in one late afternoon to have dinner with us. Why not? We could always scrape up a bit of food whereas in Montparnasse among the riff-raff she was obliged to hang out where food was almost unobtainable. After the dinner she got hysterical: she said she was suffering from dysentery ever since she had left me and that it was my fault, that I had tried to poison her. I walked her to the Metro station at the Porte without saying a word. I was sore as hell, so goddamned sore that I couldn't talk. She was sore too, sore because I refused to argue the matter with her. I thought to myself, walking back, well this is the last straw, she surely won't come back again. I poisoned her. Good, if she wants to think that way let her! That ought to settle the issue.

A few days later I had a letter from her asking for a little cash with which to meet the rent. Seems she wasn't living with the fairy at all, but in a cheap hotel back of the Gare Montparnasse. I couldn't give her the money immediately as I didn't have any myself so I let a few days intervene before going to her hotel and settling the bill. While I was trotting round to her hotel a pneumatique had come for me saying that she simply must have the money or she'd be kicked out. If I had had a little money I wouldn't have put her to all these humiliations, but the point is I didn't have any. However, she didn't believe me. And even if it were true, she said, I could at least have borrowed it for her. Which was also true. But I was never good on borrowing large sums; all my life I had been used to asking for hand-outs, for chicken feed, and feeling damned grateful when I got that. She seemed to have forgotten that. It was natural enough that she should because she was bitter and her pride had been wounded. And to do her justice I must add that had the situation been reversed the money would have been forthcoming; she always knew how to raise money for me but never for herself. That I've got to admit.

I was getting pretty wrought up about the whole thing. I felt like a louse. And the worse I felt the less I was able to do. I even suggested that she come back and stay with us until the money which she was expecting for the boat trip should come. But this she wouldn't hear of, naturally. Or was it natural? I was so damned perplexed and humiliated and confused that I didn't know any more what was natural and what wasn't. Money. Money. All my life it had been a question of money. I would never be able to solve the problem and I didn't hope to.

After turning round and round like a rat in a trap I got the brilliant idea of beating it myself. Just walk out on the problem, that's always the easiest way. I don't know how the idea came to me but suddenly I had decided that I would go to London. If you had offered me a château in Touraine I would have said no. For some reason or other I had made up my mind that it must be London and no other place. The reason I gave myself was that she'd never think of looking for me in London. She knew I hated the place. But the real reason, as I soon discovered, was that I wanted to be among English-speaking people; I wanted to hear English spoken twenty-four hours of the day, and nothing but English. In my weak condition that was like falling back on the bosom of the Lord. Talking and listening to English meant just that less strain. God knows, when you're in a jam to talk a foreign language, or even just to listen to it – because you can't shut your ears even if you try to – is a subtle form of torture. I had absolutely nothing against the French, nor against the language they spoke. Up until she arrived on the scene I had been living in a sort of Paradise. Suddenly everything had gone sour. I found myself muttering things against the French, and against the language particularly, which I would never have dreamed of thinking in my sober senses. I knew it was my own fault, but that only made it worse. Well, London then. A little vacation and perhaps by the time I returned she would have left. That's all there was to it.

I rustled up the dough for a visa and a return trip ticket. I bought a visa for a year thinking that if by any chance I should change my mind about the English I might go back a second or a third time to England. It was getting on towards Christmas and I began to think what a jolly old place London might be during the holidays. Perhaps I would find a different sort of London than the one I knew, a Dickensian London such as tourists always dream of. I had the visa and the ticket in my pocket and just about enough dough to last me for ten days. I was feeling almost jubilant about the trip.

When I got back to Clichy it was almost dinner time. I walked into the kitchen and there was my wife helping Fred with the dinner. They were laughing and joking as I walked in. I knew that Fred wouldn't say anything to her about my going to London and so I sat down to the table and laughed and joked a bit myself. It was a jolly meal, I must say, and everything would have gone off splendidly if Fred hadn't been obliged to go to the newspaper office after dinner. I had been canned a few weeks ago but he was still working, though expecting the same fate any day. The reason I was canned was that, even though I was an American, I had no right to be working on an American newspaper as a proofreader. According to French theory the job could just as well have been held by a Frenchman who knew English. That griped me a bit and no doubt contributed to my feeling sour towards the French the last few weeks. Anyway, that was over and done with and I was a free man again and I would soon be in London talking English all day long and far into the night if I wanted to. Besides, my book was coming out very soon and that might change everything. All in all things weren't half as black as they had seemed a few days back. Thinking how nicely I was going to duck the whole thing I got a bit careless and ran out, in a moment of exuberation, to buy a bottle of Chartreuse which I knew she liked better than anything. That was a fatal mistake. The Chartreuse made her mellow and then hysterical and then reproving. We sat there at the table, the two of us, and I guess we rehearsed a lot of things that should have been forgotten. Finally I got to such a point of guilt and tenderness that I blurted out the whole thing – about the trip to London, the money I had borrowed, and so on and so forth. I forked the whole thing out and laid it on the table. There it was, I don't know how many pounds and shillings, all in bright new English money. I told her I was sorry and to hell with the trip and tomorrow I would try to get a refund on the tickets and give that to her too.

And here again I must render her justice. She really didn't want to take the money. It made her wince, I could see that, but finally she accepted it reluctantly and stuffed it away in her bag. As she was leaving she forgot the bag and I was obliged to run down the stairs after her and hand it to her. As she took the bag she said goodbye again and this time I felt that it was the last goodbye. She said goodbye and she stood there on the stairs looking up at me with a strange sorrowful smile. If I had made the least gesture I know she would have thrown the money out of the window and rushed back into my arms and stayed with me for ever. I took a long look at her, walked slowly back to the door, and closed it. I went back to the kitchen table, sat there a few minutes looking at the empty glasses, and then I broke down and sobbed like a child.

It was about three in the morning when Fred came back from work. He saw right away that something had gone wrong. I told him what had happened and then we sat down and ate, and after we had eaten we drank some good Algerian wine and then some Chartreuse and after that a little cognac. It was a damned shame, in Fred's opinion, and I was a fool to have forked up all the money. I agreed, but I felt good about it just the same.

'And what about London? Do you mean to tell me you're not going to London?' he says.

'No,' I said, 'I've given up the idea. Besides, I couldn't go now even if I wanted to. Where's the dough to come from?'

Fred didn't seem to think the lack of dough was any grave obstacle. He thought he could borrow a couple of hundred francs at the office and on pay-day, which was only a few days off, he would wire me more. We sat there discussing the thing until dawn, and of course drinking a bit too. When I hit the hay I could hear the Westminster chimes – and a few rusty sleigh bells too. I saw a beautiful blanket of snow lying over dirty London and everybody greeting me with a hearty 'Merry Christmas!' – *in English*, to be sure.

I made the Channel crossing at night. It was a miserable night and we stayed indoors shivering with the cold. I had a hundred franc note and some change – that was all. The idea was that as soon as I found a hotel I was to cable and Fred would cable back some more dough. I sat at the long table in the salon listening to the conversation going on around me. The thought uppermost in my mind was how to make the hundred francs stretch as far as possible, because the more I thought about it the less sure I was that Fred would raise the dough immediately. The scraps of conversation I picked up also had to do with money. Money. Money. The same thing everywhere and all the time. It seems that England had just that day paid her debt to America, much against her will. She had kept her word, as they were saying all about me. England always kept her word. And more of that and more, until I felt like strangling them for their bloody honesty.

I hadn't intended to break the hundred franc note until absolutely necessary, but with this silly conversation going on about England keeping her word and knowing that they had spotted me as an American I finally got so jumpy that I ordered a beer and a ham sandwich. That brought me directly into contact with the steward. He wanted to know what I thought about the situation. I could see that he thought it was a bloody crime what we had done to England. I felt sore that he should make me responsible for the situation just because I happened to be born an American. So I told him I didn't know anything about the situation, that it was none of my affair, and furthermore that it was a matter of absolute indifference to me whether England paid her debts or didn't pay her debts. He didn't relish this very much. A man ought to have an interest in the affairs of his country, even if his country is in the wrong, that's what he thought. I told him I didn't give a damn about America or Americans. I told him I didn't have an ounce of patriotism in me. At that moment a man who had been pacing up and down beside the table stopped to listen to me. I had a feeling that he was a spy or a detective. I piped down almost at once and turned to the young man beside me who had also called for a beer and a sandwich.

Apparently he had been listening to me with some interest. He wanted to know where I came from and what I was going to do in England. I told him I was taking a little vacation, and then, impulsively, I asked him if he could recommend a very cheap hotel. He said he had been away from England quite a long while and that he didn't know London very well anyhow. Said he had been living in Australia the last few years. Just then the steward happened along and the young man interrupted himself to ask the steward if he knew of any good cheap little hotel in London. The steward called the waiter over and asked him the same question, and just as he put the question to the waiter the man who looked like a spy came along and paused a moment to listen in. From the serious way in which the subject was discussed I could see at once that I had made a mistake. One shouldn't ask questions like that of a steward or a waiter. I felt that they were looking me over suspiciously, that they were giving my pocket-book the X-ray. I tossed off the beer at one gulp and, as though to prove that money was the least of my worries I called for another and then, turning to the young man at my elbow, I asked him if he wouldn't let me buy him a drink too. When the steward came back with the drinks we were deep in the wilds of Australia. He started to say something about a hotel but I told him immediately to forget about it. It was just an idle question, I added. That seemed to stump him. He stood there a few moments not knowing what to do, then suddenly, moved by some friendly impulse, he blurted out that he would be glad to put me up in his own home at Newhaven if I cared to spend the night there. I thanked him warmly and told him not to worry about it any more, that I would go on to London just the same. It really isn't important, I added. And the moment I said it I knew that that too was a mistake, because somehow, despite myself, I had made the thing seem quite important to everybody.

There was still a bit of time to kill and so I listened to the young Englishman who had had a strange time of it in Australia. He was telling me of his life as a sheep herder, how they castrated I don't know how many thousands of sheep in a day. One had to work fast. So fast, in fact, that the most expedient thing to do was to grab the testicles with your teeth and then a quick slit with the knife and spit them out. He was trying to estimate how many thousand pair of testicles he had bitten off in his hand to mouth operation during his sojourn in Australia. And as he was going through his mental calculations he wiped his mouth with the back of his hand.

'You must have had a strange taste in your mouth,' I said, instinctively wiping my own mouth.

'It wasn't as bad as you might imagine,' he answered calmly. 'You get used to everything – in time. No, it wasn't a bad taste at all . . . the idea is worse than the actual thing. Just the same, I never thought when I left my comfortable home in England that I would be spitting out those things for a living. A man can get used to doing most anything when he's really up against it.'

I was thinking the same thing. I was thinking of the time I burned brush in an orange grove in Chula Vista. Ten hours a day in the broiling sun running from one fire to another and the flies biting like mad. And for what? To prove to myself that I was a man, I suppose, that I could take it on the chin. And another time working as a gravedigger: to show that I wasn't afraid of tackling anything. The gravedigger! With a volume of Nietzsche under his arm, and trying to memorize the last part of Faust to and from work. Well, as the steward says, '*the English never twist you!*' The boat is coming to a stop. Another swig of beer to drown the taste of sheep's nuts and a handsome little tip for the waiter just to prove that Americans pay their debts too sometimes. In the excitement I find myself quite alone, standing behind a bulky Englishman with a chequered cap and a big ulster. Landing in any other country the chequered cap would look ridiculous, but as it's his own country he can do as he pleases, and what's more I almost admire him for it, it makes him seem so big and independent. I'm beginning to think that they're not such a bad race after all.

On deck it's dark and drizzly. The last time I pulled into England, that was coming up the Thames, it was also dark and drizzly and the faces were ashen grey and the uniforms were black and the houses were grim and grimy. And up High Holborn Street every morning I remember there passed me the most respectable, lamentable, dilapidated paupers God ever made. Grey, watery paupers with bowlers and cutaways and that absurd air of respectability which only the English can muster in adversity. And now the language is coming to me a little stronger and I must say I don't like it at all: it sounds oily, slimy, servile, unctuous. I feel the class line cutting through the accents. The man with the chequered cap and the ulster has suddenly become a pompous ass; he seems to be talking Choctaw to the porters. I hear Sir all the time. Can I do this, *Sir*? Which way, *Sir*? Yes, *Sir*, No, *Sir*. Bugger me if it doesn't make me a bit creepy, all this yes sir and no sir. *Sir my ass*, I say under my breath.

At the Immigration Office. Waiting my turn on the line. The rich bastards go first, as usual. We move up inch by inch. Those who've passed through are having their baggage inspected on the quay. The porters are bustling about loaded down like donkeys. Only two people ahead of me now. I have my passport in my hand and my train ticket and my baggage checks. Now I'm standing square in front of him, offering him my passport. He looks at the big white sheet beside him, finds my name and checks it off.

'How long do you intend to stay in England, Mr Miller?' he says, holding the passport in his hand as though ready to give it back to me.

'A week or two,' I answer.

'You're going to London, are you?'

'Yes.'

'What hotel are you stopping at, Mr Miller?'

I have to smile at this. 'Why, I don't know,' I respond, still smiling. 'Perhaps you can recommend me a hotel.'

'Have you any friends in London, Mr Miller?'

'No.'

'Just what are you going to do in London, if I may ask?'

'Why, I'm going to take a little vacation.' Still smiling.

'I suppose you have enough money for your stay in England?'

'I think so,' says I, still nonchalant, still smiling. And thinking to myself what a cinch it is to bluff it through with questions like that.

'Do you mind showing me your money, Mr Miller?'

'Of course not,' and reaching into my jeans I haul out the remains of the hundred franc note. The people next to me are laughing. I try to laugh too, but I'm not very successful. As for my inquisitor, he gives a feeble little chuckle and looking me square in the eye he says with all the sarcasm he can put into it: 'You didn't expect to stay very long in London on that, did you, Mr Miller?'

Always this *Mr Miller* tacked on to every phrase! I'm beginning to dislike the son-of-a-bitch. What's more it's beginning to get uncomfortable.

'Look here,' I say, still amiable and still outwardly nonchalant, 'I don't intend to have a vacation on that. As soon as I get a hotel I expect to wire for money. I left Paris in a great hurry and . . .'

He cuts me short. Can I give him the name of my bank in Paris, he wants to know.

'I haven't got a bank account,' I'm obliged to answer. That makes a very bad impression I realize at once. I can feel the hostility growing up all about me. People who were holding their bags are putting them down now, as though they knew they were in for a long siege. The passport which he had been holding in his hands like a little testament he puts on the counter before him and holds it there, like a damaging piece of evidence, with outstretched fingertips.

'Where were you going to get the money from, Mr Miller?' he asks more blandly than ever.

'Why, from a friend of mine, the man who lives with me in Paris.'

'Has he a bank account?'

'No, but he's got a job. He works on the *Chicago Tribune*.'

'And you think he will send you the money for your vacation?'

'I don't think so, I *know* so,' I answered tartly. 'I'm not trying to give you a cock and bull story. I told you I left in a hurry. I left with the understanding that he'd send me the money as soon as I arrived in London. Besides, it's *my* money, not his.'

'You left your money with him rather than put it in a bank, is that it, Mr Miller?'

'Well,' I said, beginning to lose my temper, 'it isn't a hell of a lot of money and besides, I don't see the point of all this. If you don't believe me I'll stay right here and you can send a cable and find out for yourself.'

'Just a minute, Mr Miller. You say the two of you live together . . . do you live in a hotel or in an apartment?'

'An apartment.'

'And the apartment is in your name?'

'No, in his. That is, it belongs to the both of us, but it's in his name because he's a Frenchman and it makes it easier.'

'And he keeps your money for you?'

'No, not usually. You see, I left under rather unusual circumstances. I . . .'

'Just a minute, Mr Miller,' and he motions to me to step back from the ranks a bit. At the same time he calls one of his assistants over and hands him my passport. The latter takes the passport and goes behind a screen some distance off. I stand there watching the others go through.

'You might go and have your baggage inspected meanwhile,' I hear him say as if in a trance. I move off to the shed and open my luggage. The train is waiting for us. It looks like a team of Eskimo dogs straining at the leash. The locomotive is puffing and steaming. Finally I walk back and take my stand in front of my interlocutor. The last few passengers are being hustled through the examination.

Now the tall thin man from behind the screen comes forward with the passport in his hand. He seems determined in advance that I'm a malefactor.

'You're an American citizen, Mr Miller?'

'Obviously,' I answer. With this guy I know there's going to be no mercy. He hasn't a speck of humour in him.

'How long have you been in France?'

'Two or three years, I guess. You can see the date there for your-

263

self . . . *Why*? What's that got to do with it?'

'You were thinking of spending several months in England, were you?'

'No, I wasn't. I was thinking of spending a week or ten days there, that's all. But now . . .'

'So you bought a visa for a year, thinking to spend a week.'

'I bought a return trip ticket too, if that interests you.'

'One could always throw the return ticket away,' he says with a malicious twist of the mouth.

'One could if he were an idiot. I don't get the point. And anyway, look here, I'm tired of all this nonsense. I'm going to stay in New-haven overnight and take the next boat back. I don't have to spend my vacation in England.'

'Not so fast, Mr Miller. I think we ought to look into this a little more closely.'

As he said this I heard the whistle blow. The passengers were all aboard and the train was just starting. I thought of my trunk which I had checked through to London. Nearly all my manuscripts were in it, and my typewriter too. A nice mess, I thought to myself. All because of that chicken feed I slapped down on the counter.

The little fat fellow with the bland imperturbable mask now joined us. He seemed to be expecting a treat.

Hearing the train roll out of the station I resigned myself to the inquisition. Thinks I to myself, now that they've fucked me, let's see how far they can prolong the agony. First of all, however, I demanded my passport back. If they wanted to grill me a little more OK. There was nothing to do at that hour of the night and before turning in at Newhaven I thought I'd go through with the song and dance.

To my amazement the tall thin fellow refused to return my passport. That made me furious. I demanded to know if there was an American Consul on hand. 'Listen,' I said, 'you may think what you like, but that passport belongs to me and I want it back.'

'There's no need to get excited, Mr Miller. You'll have your passport before you leave. But first there are a few questions I'd like to put to you . . . I see that you are a married man. Is your wife living with you – and your friend? Or is she in America?'

'I don't see that that's any of your business,' I said. 'But since you brought the subject up I'm going to tell you something now. The reason I came away with so little money is because I gave the money for my trip to my wife before leaving. We're separating and she's

264

going back to America in a few days. I gave her the money because she was broke.'

'How much money did you give her, if I may ask?'

'You're asking so damned many questions that you have no right to ask I don't see why you shouldn't ask that too. If you want to know, I gave her about sixty pounds. Let's see. I may still have the exchange slip in my wallet . . .' And I made a gesture as if to reach for my wallet and look for the slip.

'Wasn't that rather foolish to give your wife all that money and come to England penniless, or almost so?'

I gave him a sour smile. 'My dear man, I've tried to explain to you that I'm not coming to England as a pauper. If you had let me go to London and wire for the money everything would have been all right. I suppose it's a waste of time to say a thing like this to you but try to understand me, will you? *I'm a writer*. I do things impulsively. I don't have bank accounts and I don't plan things years in advance. When I want to do something I do it. For some reason or other you seem to think that I want to come to England to . . . frankly, I don't know what the hell's in your mind. I just wanted to come to England to hear English, if you can believe it – and partly too to escape my wife. Does that make sense to you?'

'I should say it does,' says the tall thin fellow. 'You want to run away from your wife and let her become a public charge. How do you know she won't follow you to England? And how will you take care of her in England – without money?'

I felt as though I were talking to a stone wall. What was the use of rehearsing the whole thing again? 'Listen,' I said, 'as far as I'm concerned I don't care what happens to her. If she becomes a public charge that's her affair, not mine.'

'You're working for the *Chicago Tribune*, you say?'

'I never said anything of the kind. I said my friend, the man who was to send me the money, *he's* working on the *Chicago Tribune*.'

'You never worked for the newspaper then?'

'Yes, I used to work for them, but I don't now. They fired me a few weeks ago.'

He snapped me up immediately. 'Oh, then you *did* work for the newspaper in Paris?'

'Didn't I just say so? Why? Why do you ask?'

'Mr Miller, could I see your carte d'identité . . . I suppose you *have* a carte d'identité, living in Paris, as you say.'

I fished it out for him. The two of them looked it over together.

'You have a non-worker's card – yet you worked for the *Chicago Tribune* as a proofreader. How do you explain that, Mr Miller?'

'No, I suppose I can't explain that to you. I suppose it's useless to explain to you that I'm an American citizen and that the *Chicago Tribune* is an American newspaper and that therefore . . .'

'Excuse me, but why were you dismissed from the newspaper?'

'That's just what I was coming to. You see, the French officials, those who have to do with the red tape, seem to take the same attitude as you do. Perhaps I could have remained on the *Tribune* if I hadn't also been a bad proofreader. That's the real reason why I was fired, if you want to know.'

'You seem rather proud of the fact.'

'I am. I think it's a mark of intelligence.'

'And so, not having a job on the *Tribune* any more you thought you'd come to England for a little vacation. And you provided yourself with a visa for a year and a return trip ticket.'

'Also to hear English and to escape my wife,' I added.

Here the little round-faced fellow spoke up. The tall fellow seemed ready to relinquish the tussle.

'You're a writer, Mr Miller?'

'Yes.'

'You mean you write books and stories?'

'Yes.'

'Do you write for the magazines in America?'

'Yes.'

'Which ones . . . can you name a few?'

'Certainly. The *American Mercury, Harper's, Atlantic Monthly, Scribner's*, the *Virginia Quarterly*, the *Yale Review* . . . '

'Just a minute.' He walked back to the counter and bending down he pulled out a big fat directory. '*American Mercury . . . American Mercury . . .*' he kept mumbling as he thumbed the pages. 'Henry V. Miller, isn't it? Henry V. Miller . . . Henry V. Miller . . . Was it this year or last year, Mr Miller?'

'It may be three years ago – for the *Mercury*,' I said blandly.

Apparently he had no book on hand that went back that far. Couldn't I give him the name of a magazine I had written for in the last year or two? I said no, I had been too busy writing a book the last year or so.

Had the book been published? What was the name of the American publisher?

I said it had been published by an Englishman.

What was the name of the publisher?

'The Obelisk Press.'

He scratched his head. 'An *English* publisher?' He couldn't seem to remember any English house by that name. He called his sidekick who had disappeared behind the screen with my passport. 'Ever hear of the Obelisk Press?' he yelled.

At this point I thought it timely to tell him that my English publisher published from Paris. That seemed to make him hopping mad. An English publisher in Paris! It was a violation of the rules of nature. Well, anyway, what were the names of the books?

'There's only one,' I said. 'It's called *Tropic of Cancer.*'

At this I thought he would throw a fit. I didn't know what had come over him for the moment. Finally he seemed to bring himself under partial control and, in the suavest, the most sarcastic voice imaginable, he said: 'Come, Mr Miller, you don't mean to tell me that you write *medical* books too?'

It was my turn to be flabbergasted. The two of them were standing there boring me through with their mean gimlet-like eyes.

'The *Tropic of Cancer*,' I said slowly and solemnly, 'is *not* a medical book.'

'Well, what is it then?' they asked simultaneously.

'The title,' I answered, 'is a symbolic title. The Tropic of Cancer is a name given in textbooks to a temperate zone lying above the Equator. Below the Equator you have the Tropic of Capricorn, which is the south temperate zone. The book, of course, has nothing to do with climatic conditions either, unless it be a sort of mental climate. Cancer is a name which has always intrigued me: you'll find it in zodiacal lore too. Etymologically it comes from chancre, meaning crab. In Chinese symbolism it is a sign of great importance. The crab is the only living creature which can walk backwards and forwards and sideways with equal facility. Of course my book doesn't treat of all this explicitly. It's a novel, or rather an autobiographical document. If my trunk were here I might have shown you a copy. I think you'd be interested in it. By the way, the reason it was published in Paris is because it's too obscene for England or America. Too much cancer in it, if you know what I mean . . .'

This brought the discussion to a close. The tall slim fellow packed his brief case, put on his hat and coat and waited impatiently for the little fellow to get ready. I asked for my passport again. The tall slim fellow went behind the screen and got it for me. I opened it and I saw that he had drawn a big black X through my visa. That infuriated me. It was like a black mark against my good name. 'Where's a place to put up for the night in this burg?' I asked, putting as much snot and venom in it as I could muster.

'The constable here will take care of that,' says the big fellow, giving me a wry smile and turning on his heel. And with that I see a very tall man dressed in black with a big helmet and a cadaverous face coming towards me out of the gloom of the far corner.

'What do you mean?' I yelled. 'Do you mean that I'm under arrest?'

'No, I wouldn't say *that*, Mr Miller. The constable will put you up for the night and in the morning he'll put you on the boat for Dieppe.' And he started to walk away again.

'OK,' I said. 'But you're going to see me back here, maybe next week.'

By this time the constable was at my side and had me by the arm. I was white with rage, but that firm grasp of the arm told me it was useless to say anything more. It was like the hand of death itself.

As we walked towards the door I explained very calmly to the constable that my trunk had gone on to London and that it contained all my manuscripts as well as other things.

'We can take care of that, Mr Miller,' he says in a quiet, low, steady voice. 'Just step this way with me,' and he made for the telegraph office. I gave him the necessary dope and he assured me in his quiet, easy voice that I'd have my things in the morning, the first thing in the morning. I knew from the way he spoke that he was a man of his word. Somehow I had an instant respect for him. I did wish, however, that he'd let go my arm. Shit, I wasn't a criminal, and even if I did want to make a break for it where would I go? I couldn't jump in the sea, could I? However, it was no use starting things with him. He was a man who obeyed orders and it was enough just to take one look at him to know that he had been trained like a dog. He escorted me gently and firmly to the hoosegow. We had to pass through a number of vacant, dimlit rooms or halls to get to the joint. Each time we opened a door he paused and, taking out a bunch of keys, locked the door behind us. It was impressive. I began to get a bit of a thrill out of it. It was ridiculous and awesome at the same time. Christ knows what he would have done if I had been a really dangerous criminal. I suppose he'd have manacled me first. Anyway, finally we got to the hoosegow, which was a sort of big gloomy waiting room very dimly lit. There wasn't a soul in the place, nothing but a few long empty benches, as far as I could make out.

'Here's where we spend the night,' said the constable in the same quiet, steady voice. Really a gentle voice it was. I was beginning to take a liking to him. 'There's a washroom in there,' he added, pointing to a door just in back of me.

'I don't need to wash up,' I said. 'What I'd really like to do is to take a crap.'

'You'll find the place in there,' he answered, and opening the door he turned on the light for me.

I went in, took my coat off and sat down. Suddenly, as I was sitting there I looked up and to my amazement there was the constable sitting by the doorway on a little stool. I wouldn't say he was watching me, but certainly he had one eye on me, as they say. At once my bowels were paralyzed. *That*, I thought to myself, that beats everything! And then and there I made a mental note to write about the incident.

As I was buttoning up I expressed a little of my amazement. He took what I said in good part, replying very simply that it was part of his duty. 'I've got to keep you under observation until I hand you over to the captain in the morning,' he said. 'Those are the orders.'

'Do people try to run away sometimes?' I asked.

'Not very often,' he said. 'But things are very bad now, you know, and lots of people are trying to get into England who don't belong here. People who are looking for work, you know.'

'Yes, I know,' I said. 'Things are in a mess.'

I was pacing slowly up and down in the big waiting room. Suddenly I felt rather chilly. I went over to the big bench where my overcoat was lying and flung it around my shoulders.

'Would you like me to build you a fire, sir?' the constable suddenly asked.

I thought it was damned considerate of him to ask a question like that and so I said, 'Why, I don't know. How about you? Do you want a fire too?'

'It isn't that, sir,' he said. 'You see the law entitles you to a fire, if you wish it.'

'The hell with that!' I said. 'The question is, would it be a bother to make one? Perhaps I can help you.'

'No, it's my duty to make you a fire if you wish it. I have nothing to do but look after you.'

'Well, if that's the case, let's have a fire,' I said. I sat down on the bench and watched him getting it started. Pretty decent, I thought to myself. So the law entitles you to a fire. Well, I'll be goddamned!

When the fire was made the constable suggested that I stretch out on the bench and make myself comfortable. He dug up a cushion from somewhere and a blanket. I lay there looking at the fire and thinking what a strange world it is after all. I mean how on the one hand they manhandle you and on the other hand they nurse you like a baby. All written down in the same book, like debit and credit columns in a ledger. The government is the invisible bookkeeper who makes the entries, and the constable is just a sort of human blotter who dries the ink. If you happen to get a kick in the ass or a couple of teeth pushed down your throat that's gratis and no record is made of it.

The constable was sitting on the little stool by the fireside reading the evening paper. He said he would just sit there and read a bit until I fell asleep. He said it in a neighourly way, without the slightest malice or sarcasm. A different species entirely from the other two bastards whom I had just left.

I watched him reading the paper for a while and then I started to talk to him, in a human way, what I mean, not like he was the constable and me the prisoner. He was not an unintelligent man, nor did he lack sensibility. He struck me, in fact, very much like a fine greyhound, something anyway with blood and breeding. Whereas those other two farts, who were also doing their duty by the government, impressed me as a couple of sadistic jakes, as mean, low, cringing bastards who enjoyed doing their dirty work for the government. I'm sure if the constable were to kill a man in the line of duty you could forgive him for it. But those other pimps! Bah! I spat into the fire with disgust.

I was curious to know if the constable ever did any serious reading. To my surprise he told me that he had read Shaw and Belloc and Chesterton – and some of Somerset Maugham's work. *Of Human Bondage* was a great book, he thought. I thought so too and I scored another strike for the constable on my mental blackboard.

'And you're a writer too?' he said, very gently, almost timidly, I thought.

'A bit of a one,' I said diffidently. And then impulsively, faltering, stutteringly, I launched into an account of *Tropic of Cancer*. I told him about the streets and the cafes. I told him how I had tried to put it all in the book and whether I had succeeded or not I didn't know. 'But it's a *human* book,' I said, getting up from the bench and moving very close to him. 'And I tell you one thing, constable, you impress me as being very human too. I've enjoyed this evening with you and I want you to know that I have a respect and admiration for you. And if you don't think it's immodest of me why I'd like to send you a copy of my book when I get back to Paris.'

He wrote his name and address in my notebook and told me he would read the book with great pleasure. 'You're a very interesting man,' he said, 'and I'm sorry we had to meet under such painful circumstances.'

'Well, let's not talk about that,' I said. 'What do you say we do a wink of sleep now? Eh?'

'Why yes,' he said, 'you can make yourself comfortable on the bench there. I'll just sit here and doze a bit. By the way,' he added, 'would you like me to order breakfast for you in the morning?'

I thought to myself well that's a pretty swell guy, about as decent as they make 'em. And with that I closed my eyes and dozed off.

In the morning the constable took me aboard the boat and handed me over to the captain. There were no passengers aboard yet. I waved goodbye to the constable and then I stood at the prow of the boat and took a good look at England. It was one of those quiet, peaceful mornings with a clear sky overhead and the gulls flying. Always, looking at England from the sea, I am impressed by the gentle, peaceful, somnolent quality of the landscape. England comes so gently down to the sea, it's almost touching. Everything seems so still, so civilized. I stood there looking at Newhaven with tears in my eyes. I wondered where the steward lived and whether he was up and eating his breakfast or pottering around the garden. In England every man *ought* to own a garden: it's meant to be that way, you feel it immediately. As I say, it couldn't have been a better day and England couldn't have looked lovelier, more inviting, than she looked at this moment. I thought of the constable again and how he fitted into the landscape. I want him to know, if he ever reads this, how much I regret the fact, seeing how gentle and sensitive he was, that I had to take a crap in front of him. If I had ever dreamed that he was going to sit there and keep an eye on me I would have held it in until we got to sea. I want him to know that. As for the other two bastards, I want to warn them here and now that if ever I encounter them again in this life I am going to spit in their eye. And may the curse of Job be on them for the rest of their lives. May they die in agony in a foreign land!

One of the most beautiful mornings I have ever known. The little village of Newhaven nestling in the white chalk cliffs. The end of the land, where civilization slips quietly into the sea. I stood there in a reverie for a long while, and a profound peace came over me. In such moments it seems that everything that happens to you happens for the best. Standing there quiet and peaceful like that I got to thinking of our own New Haven (Connecticut), where I had gone once to visit a man in gaol. He was a man who had worked for me as a messenger and we had become friends. And then one day in a fit of jealousy he had shot his wife and then himself. Fortunately both of them recovered. After they had transferred him from the hospital to the prison I went to see him one day; we had a long talk through a steel mesh. When I left the prison I suddenly remarked how beautiful it was outdoors and, acting on the impulse, I went to a beach nearby and took a dip. It was one of the strangest days I ever spent at the ocean. When I dove off the springboard I had a feeling that I was taking leave of the earth for ever. I didn't try to drown myself, but I didn't care a hoot if I were to drown. It felt marvellous to dive off the earth, to leave behind me all that man-made muck which we glorify with the word civilization. Anyway, as I came up and swam around I seemed to be looking at the world with new eyes. Nothing was like it had been before. People looked curiously separate and detached; they were sitting around like seals drying themselves in the sun. What I'm trying to say is that they seemed absolutely devoid of significance. They were just part of the landscape, like the rocks and the trees and the cows in the meadows. How they had ever assumed such a colossal importance on this earth was a mystery to me. I saw them plainly and distinctly as natural objects, as animals or plants. I felt that day that I could commit the most dastardly crime with a clear conscience. A crime without reason. Yes, it was that that I felt strongly: to kill some innocent person without reason.

As soon as the boat turned its nose towards Dieppe my thoughts began to take a different turn. I had never been out of France before and here I was returning in disgrace with that black mark against my visa. What would the French think? Perhaps they would begin to cross-examine me too. What was I doing in France? How did I make my living? Was I taking bread out of the mouths of French workers? Was I apt to become a public charge?

Suddenly I got into a panic. Supposing they refused to let me return to Paris? Supposing they transferred me to another boat and shipped me back to America? I got into a terrible funk. America! To be shipped back to New York and dumped there like a load of rotten apples! No, if they were going to try that stunt I'd jump overboard. I couldn't bear the thought of returning to America. It was Paris I wanted to see again. Never again would I grumble over my lot. It wouldn't matter if I had to live the rest of my life in Paris as a beggar. Better a beggar in Paris than a millionaire in New York!

I rehearsed a marvellous speech, in French, which I intended to make to the officials. It was such an elaborate, melodramatic speech that the crossing of the Channel passed like a dream. I was trying to conjugate a verb in the subjunctive when suddenly I saw the land popping up and the passengers flocking to the rail. Now it's coming, I thought. Brace up, me bucko, and unloose the subjunctives!

I stood apart from the others instinctively, as though not to contaminate them. I didn't know just what the procedure would be in stepping off – whether there'd be an *agent* to meet me or whether somebody would just pounce on me with the grappling hooks as I hit the gangplank. It was all much more simple than my anxiety led me to anticipate. As the boat pulled into the wharf the captain came forward, and grasping me by the arm just as the constable had done, he led me to the rail where I was in plain view of the men ashore. When he had caught the eye of the man on the quay whom he was seeking he raised his left hand aloft with the index finger pointing heavenward and then motioned to me. It was like saying *One!* One head of cabbage today! One head of cattle! I was more amazed than ashamed. It was so direct and logical, too, that you could hardly quarrel about it. After all, I was on a boat and the boat was pulling in and I was the man they were looking for and why send a cablegram or telephone when all you need to do is raise your arm and point like that? What could be simpler, less expensive?

When I observed the man whom I was being delivered to my heart sank. He was a big brute of a fellow with black handlebars for moustache and an enormous derby which half crushed his big appetizing ears. Even at long range his hands looked like big hams. And he too was dressed all in black. Clearly things were against me.

Walking down the gangplank I was struggling desperately to recall fragments of the speech which I had rehearsed only a few moments ago. I couldn't remember a blooming phrase. All I kept saying to myself was – 'Oui, monsieur, je suis un Américain – mais je ne suis pas un mendiant. Je vous jure, monsieur, je ne suis pas un mendiant.'

'Votre passeport, s'il vous plaît!'

'Oui, monsieur!'

I knew I was destined to say 'Oui, monsieur' over and over again. Each time it came out of me I cursed myself for saying it. But what are you going to do? That's the first thing that's drummed into you when you come to France. *Oui, monsieur! Non, monsieur!* You feel like a cockroach at first. And then you get used to it and you say it unconsciously, and if the other fellow doesn't say it you notice it and you hold it against him. And when you're in trouble that's the first thing that pops out of your mouth. *'Oui, monsieur!'* You say it like an old billy-goat.

Anyway, I had only said it once or twice, because like the constable this chap was also a silent man. His duty consisted, as I happily discovered, in nothing more than escorting me to the office of another official who again demanded my passport and my carte d'identité. Here I was politely asked to sit down. I did so with a great feeling of relief and at the same time, taking a last look at the big brute who had dismissed me, I asked myself – where have I seen that man before?

After the grilling of the night before one great difference made itself felt immediately: *Respect for one's individuality*! I think now that even if he had put me on a boat for America I would have accepted my fate tranquilly. There was an inner order to the language, for one thing. He said nothing capricious, nothing insolent, nothing mean or foul or vindictive. He was talking the language of his people and there was form in it, an inner form which had come out of a deep experience of life. It was all the more striking, this clarity, in comparison with the external chaos in which he moved. In fact, it was almost ridiculous, this disorder which enveloped him. It was not altogether ridiculous because what inspired it was human, human foibles, human fallibilities. It was a disorder in which you feel at home, which is a purely French disorder. He had, after a few entirely perfunctory questions, left me undisturbed. I still had no idea what my fate was to be, but I knew definitely that whatever his verdict it would not be capricious or malevolent. I sat there in silence observing the way he went about his work. Nothing seemed to work just right, neither the pen, nor the blotter, nor the ink, nor the ruler. It was as though he had just opened the office and I was his first client. But he had had other offices before, thousands of them, and so he was not greatly perturbed if things didn't go smoothly all at once. The important thing, as he had learned, was to get it all down correctly in the proper books. And to have the necessary stamps and seals which were to give the case its legal, orthodox aspect. *Who was I? What had I done? Ça ne me regarde pas!* I could almost hear him saying it to himself. All he had asked me was – where were you born? Where do you live in Paris? When did you come to France? With those three facts in his hand he was constructing a beautiful little dossier in my name to which he would finally sign his name with the proper flourish and then affix the stamps with the proper seal. That was his job and he understood it thoroughly.

It took him quite a little while to go about this task, I must admit. But time now was all in my favour. I would have sat there until the next morning quietly watching him if it had been necessary. I felt that he was working in my interest and in the interest of the French people

274

and that our interests were one because clearly we were both intelligent and reasonable and why would either of us want to cause any one any trouble? I suppose he was a man whom the French would call a *quelconque*, which is not quite the same as a nobody in English, because Mr Anybody or Everybody in France is quite another species from Mr Nobody in America or England. A *quelconque* is not a nobody in France. He is a man like any other man, but he has a history and a tradition and a race behind him which often makes him more than the so-called Somebodies in other countries. Like this patient little man working on my dossier these men are often shabbily dressed: they look ragged about the edges and sometimes, be it said, they are not very clean either. But they know how to mind their own business, which is a very great deal.

As I say, it took him a little while to transcribe this data from one record to another. There were carbons to be adjusted, receipts to be detached, little labels to be pasted on, and so forth. Meanwhile the pencil had to be sharpened, a new stub had to be inserted in the penholder, the scissors had to be found, and they were found finally in the waste basket, the ink had to be changed, a new blotter dug up . . . there were lots of things to be done. And to complicate matters he discovered at the last minute that my French visa had expired. Perhaps it was out of delicacy that he merely suggested that it would be a good thing if I were to renew my visa – in case I intended to travel out of France again, he said. I was only too delighted to fall in line with the suggestion, feeling at the same time, however, that it would be a long time before I would ever think of leaving France again. I gave my consent more out of politeness and consideration for his valiant efforts on my behalf.

When everything had been put in order and my passport and carte d'identité were safely in my pocket again I very respectfully suggested that we have a little drink together at the bar across the way. He very graciously accepted the invitation and together we sauntered leisurely out to the *bistrot* opposite the station. He asked me if I liked living in Paris. A little more exciting than this hole, eh? he added. We didn't have time for much of a conversation as the train was due to leave in a few minutes. I thought perhaps at the end he would say – 'How did you ever come to get into such a mess?' – but no, not the slightest allusion to the subject.

We walked back to the quay and as the whistle blew we shook hands cordially and he wished me a bon voyage. As I took my seat he was still standing there. He waved his hand and again he said: 'Au revoir,

Monsieur Miller, et bon voyage!' This time the *Monsieur Miller* sounded good to my ears, and perfectly natural. In fact it sounded so good and natural that it brought tears to my eyes. Yes, as the train rolled out of the station I distinctly remembered two big tears rolling down my cheeks and falling on to my hands. I felt safe again and among human beings. The 'bon voyage' was ringing in my ears. *Bon voyage! Bon voyage!*

A light drizzle was falling over Picardy. It made the thatched roofs look invitingly black and the grass a little greener. Now and then a patch of ocean veered into sight, to be swallowed up immediately by rolling sand dunes, then farms and meadows and brooks. A silent, peaceful countryside where each man minds his own business.

Suddenly I felt so goddamned happy I wanted to stand up and shout or sing. But all I could think of was '*bon voyage!*' What a phrase that! All our lives we're knocking about here and there mumbling that phrase which the French have given us, but do we ever take the *bon voyage*? Do we realize that even when we walk to the *bistrot*, or to the corner grocer, that it's a voyage from which we may never return? If we keenly felt that, that each time we sailed out of the house we were embarking on a voyage, would it make our lives a little different? While we make the little trip to the corner, or to Dieppe, or to Newhaven, or wherever it may be, the earth too is making her little trip, where nobody knows, not even the astronomers. But all of us, whether we move from here to the corner or from here to China, are making a voyage with our mother the earth, and the earth is moving with the sun and with the sun the other planets too are moving . . . Mars, Mercury, Venus, Neptune, Jupiter, Saturn, Uranus. The whole firmament is moving and with it, if you listen closely, you will hear '*Bon Voyage!*' '*Bon Voyage!*' And if you get still as a needle and don't ask a lot of foolish questions you will realize that to make a voyage is only an idea, that there is nothing in life but voyage, voyage within voyage, and that death is not the last voyage but the beginning of a new voyage and nobody knows why or whither, but *bon voyage* just the same! I wanted to stand up and sing that in the key of Ut-Mineur. I saw the whole universe like a network of tracks, some deep and invisible like the planetary grooves, and in this vast misty slithering to and fro, in the ghost-like passage from one realm to another, I saw all things animate and inanimate waving to one another, the cockroaches to the cockroaches, the stars to the stars, man to man, and God to God. All aboard for the big trek to nowhere, but *Bon Voyage* just the same! From osmosis to cataclysm, all a vast, silent, and perpetual movement. To stand still within the big crazy movement, to move with the earth however she wobbles, to join up with the cockroaches and the stars and the gods and men, that's voyaging! And out there in space where we are moving, where we leave our invisible tracks, out there is it possible that I hear a faint, sarcastic echo, a slimy, anaemic little English voice asking incredulously – 'Come, Mr Miller, you don't mean to say that you write *medical* books too?' Yes, by Jesus, now I can say it with a clean conscience. Yes, Mr Nobody from Newhaven, I *do* write medical books too, marvellous medical books which cure all the ills of time and space. In fact, I am writing now, this very minute, the one great purgative of the human consciousness: *the sense of voyage*!

And just as I imagined I saw the idiot from Newhaven cocking his ear to hear me better a big shadow loomed in front of him and blotted him out. Just as I was about to say to myself – 'Where have I seen this face before?' – it dawned on me like a flash. The man with the moustache at Dieppe, that face I had seen somewhere before, I recognized it now: it was the face of Mack Swain! He was The Big Bad Wolf and Charlie was Samson Agonistes. That's all. I just wanted to straighten it out in my mind. *Et bon voyage. Bon voyage a tout le monde*!

# Part IV

# America Rediscovered

# Glittering Pie

It's wonderful to come back to America as a foreigner. Better still if one had never heard or read about America. You get it at one crack, just walking down the street. The newspapers may lie, the magazines may gloss it over, the politicians may falsify, but the streets howl with truth. I walk the streets and I see men and women talking, but there is no talk. I see wine and beer advertised everywhere, but there is no wine or beer anywhere. On every table I see the same glass of ice water, in every window the same glittering baubles, in every face the same empty story. The sameness of everything is appalling. It's like the proliferation of a cancer germ. The disease spreads, it eats and eats away until there is nothing left but the thing itself – cancer.

Every day, every hour, every minute America becomes more American. It's as though the influx of immigrants, the great tidal waves of alien blood which bathed the great American organism, had proved ineffective against the disease. Now there is no new blood coming; the heart has stopped pumping. It's a race between the quick and the dead. Now the germs have a clear field of it: the disease must run its course. And the disease *is* running its course. The whole world is rapidly becoming inoculated with the virus of it. It's impossible to escape, no matter where you go. Even the Chinese are infected. The whole world must be infected before there can be a let-up – if ever there will be a let-up.

It's no use dreaming about economic salvation: the fight is not between the inherited and the disinherited, but between America and the rest of the world. The question is – will America destroy the world or will America itself be destroyed? That a cure is found for cancer, for instance, does not imply that cancer will be eradicated. On the contrary, it may flourish more luxuriantly than ever. We may lose our fear of it, that's all. And whether we live in fear of cancer or not, what produces cancer remains.

I thought, as we pulled into the harbour, that the sight of the skyline would have its effect upon me. After all, I was born here, right close to the river, and I grew up with this changing skyline. I had a right to expect some little thrill, some pull, some vestige of lost emotions. But no, I saw them just as I have always seen them in the past – with a sinking heart, with a feeling of foreboding. Everything seemed very familiar to me and very grim and very ugly – like coming out of a dream. *This*, I thought to myself, is the sensation people usually get when they talk about 'reality'. If going to Europe is a form of evasion, a running away from one's self, from *reality*, then I knew that I was back again and *that this was reality*. Or it should have been, and might have been, had I not tasted a deeper reality in my absence from my native land.

Suddenly I was back where I had started from – the same faces, the same voices, the same blatant stupidity. I remembered that that's how it always was, and that's why I ran away. Nothing had changed, fundamentally, except that what was was more so now. And it was worse because I myself had changed. Whereas before I knew nothing very different, and could therefore condone or ignore, now I *knew* and the only thing to do was to try to understand. The truth is, I had almost forgotten what my countrymen were like. This may sound incredible, since even in Paris there are Americans. But a stray American abroad, or even a flock of Americans abroad, is quite another matter from a solid population of Americans in America. It's one thing to drink with a fellow-American on the terrasse of a cafe, and it's another thing to walk among them on their own grounds, to see millions and millions of them and nothing but them all the time. Milling around in herds their true qualities assert themselves. You can't be mistaken about them when every man does the same thing, talks the same way, wears the same clothes, has the same ailments. You can't doubt *who* they are or *what* they are when between the cop on the beat and the director of a big corporation there is no difference except the uniform.

Every familiar spot I pass, every object I recognize gives me a fresh start, a stab of pain. At every corner comes the recollection of an old misery, of despair, starvation, failure, desperation. I see my old self walking these streets ten, fifteen, twenty years ago, always raging and cursing. I'm talking now of a time that antedates the crisis. What I see happening to men and women now I myself tasted long before the bubble had collapsed. I realize that had I never gone to Europe it would be the same for me now as it was then. I would be walking here unknown, unwanted, another piece of live junk for the scrap heap. Nothing here has value or durability, not even the skyscrapers. Sooner or later everything gets scrapped.

After the first shock of exposure to the American scene I am convinced that what I walked out on was, and still remains, a nightmare. Riding the subway it seems as if I were in the morgue; the bodies are labelled and ticketed, the destination clearly marked. Walking between the stiff, cold walls past the glitter of shops I see men and women walking, conversing, laughing sometimes or muttering to themselves, but they walk and talk and laugh and curse like ghosts. The day is full of activity, the night full of nightmares. On the surface things function smoothly – everything oiled and polished. But when it comes time to dream King Kong crashes through the windows; he pushes the skyscrapers down with one hand. 'Skyscraper souls!' That was the last message from America that I caught walking down the Champs Elysées the eve of my departure. Now I walk through the marvellous tunnels with the rest of the sewer rats and I read: '*It's good to change the laxative.*' Everything is better, cheaper, tastier, saner, healthier, lovelier than ever – if you believe in the advertisements. Everything has become more stupendous, more colossal, more this, more that. And yet everything is the same. It's marvellous. We've gotten beyond the superlative – we're in the higher mathematic now.

Walking through the waiting room of the Pennsylvania Station I get the feeling of unreality, of what it means to live between two worlds. Somewhere between the waiting room of the Pennsylvania Station and the phantom world of the advertising gentry lies reality. The train is standing on the siding, the freight is wheeling through the asteroids. The passengers sit in the vestibule waiting for the resurrection. They wait like the piano I saw this morning in the toilet room of a cafeteria. To invent something different from this situation would demand an act of creation – and this is impossible. We have left a few surprises, of a violent nature, but no creation. It is possible that the glittering pie which Celine cut into when he visited the Automat may metamorphose into a flaming flamingo. In fact, the whole city may rise up on wings and drown itself in the Dead Sea where, I understand, there are now beautiful casinos and gambling halls.

The City of New York is like an enormous citadel, a modern Carcassonne. Walking between the magnificent skyscrapers one feels the presence on the fringe of a howling, raging mob, a mob with empty bellies, a mob unshaven and in rags. The fighting goes on day and night, without let. The results are nil. The enemy is always at the gates, the bugles are always blowing. If one day a tiny little man should escape from the citadel, should get outside the gates and stand before the walls so that everybody could see him, if once everybody saw him plainly, saw that it was a man, a very little man, perhaps even a Jew, that little man, with just one breath of his lungs, could blow down the walls of the great citadel. Everything would crumble at a breath. Just the presence of a man outside the gates would kill off everything. Stop. *Full Stop.* The whole works would lie on the floor like the toys which a child drops when it falls asleep.

The faces I see! No anguish, no torment, no suffering registered in them. I feel as though I am walking through a lost world. What I saw years ago on the magazine covers I see now in actuality. The women's faces more particularly. That sweet, vapid, virginal look of the American woman! So putridly sweet and virginal! Even the whores have these vapid, virginal faces. They correspond exactly to the titles of the books and magazines for sale. It's a victory for the editors and publishers, for the cheap illustrators and the inventive advertising gentry. No more sales resistance. It's a push-over. Palm Olive, Father John, Ex-Lax, Peruna, Lydia Pinkham – *these* have conquered!

The face of the American woman is the index of the life of the American male. Sex either from the neck up or from the neck down. No American phallus ever reaches the vital centre. And so we get the gorgeous burlesque queen with the divinely beautiful body of a goddess and the mentality of an eight-year-old child, or less. On every burlesque stage a bevy of gorgeous nymphomaniacs, sexing and desexing at will; they writhe and squirm before an audience of mental masturbators. In all the world there are no bodies like these, nothing which for sheer physical beauty and perfection can compare with them. But if only they were decapitated! The addition of the head, of the sweet, virginal face, is heart-breaking. Their faces are like new coins which have never been put into circulation. Each day a fresh batch from the mint. They pile up, they choke the treasury vaults. While outside the treasury stands a hungry mob, an insatiable mob. The whole world has been ransacked, every available piece of gold melted down to make these gleaming new coins – but nobody knows how to put them into circulation. There she is, the American woman, buried in the treasury vaults. The men have created her in their image. She's worth her weight in gold – but nobody can get at her, lay a hand on her. She lies in the mint with gleaming face and her pure gold substance goes to waste.

I wander over to the cigar store to buy a cigarette which is not extensively advertised and which, therefore, I am reasonably sure must be more to my taste than the others. I see book racks stacked

284

with the world's best literature: volumes of Goethe, Rabelais, Ovid, Petronius, etc. One might imagine that Americans had suddenly developed an astounding taste for the classics, that overnight, as it were, they had become a cultured people. Yes, one might – if his ears were stopped or his eyes sealed. One *could* imagine that this flatulent array of imposing literature indicated an awakening. But one would have to be a dreamer and never go to a movie and never read a newspaper.

Of nothing are you allowed to get the real odour or the real savour. Everything is sterilized and wrapped in cellophane. The only odour which is recognized and admitted as an odour is halitosis, and of this all Americans live in mortal dread. Dandruff may be a myth, but halitosis is real. It is the genuine odour of spiritual decomposition. The American body, when dead, can be washed and fumigated; some corpses even achieve a distinct beauty. But the live American body in which the soul is rotting away smells bad and every American knows it and that is why he would rather be a hundred percent American, alone and gregarious at the same time, than live breast to breast with the tribe.

It's almost impossible to escape the radio, the telephone, the fat newspapers, the glass of ice water. In the hotel where I'm stopping I have no need of an alarm clock because at seven-thirty sharp every morning my breakfast is thrown on the floor with a bang. It comes like a letter through the post, only it makes a loud noise. A *'continental'* breakfast – with the coffee in a vacuum bottle, the butter wrapped in cardboard, the sugar in paper, the cream in a sealed bottle, the jam in a little jar and the rolls wrapped in cellophane. It's a continental breakfast such as was never seen on the Continent. There's one thing about it which distinguishes it from any breakfast served anywhere on the Continent – *it's inhuman!* And though I've lived in the lousiest hotels that Paris boasts, I've never eaten my breakfast from a shoe-box under electric light with the radio going full blast.

If I strike a match I read 'Ex-lax is non-habit forming', or some equally ridiculous piece of nonsense which provides hard-working imbeciles with a living wage. Walking down the hall a woman who resembles Carrie Nation says to the chamber maid: 'Put an extra roll of toilet paper in my bathroom, please.' Just like that. In a drug store the title of a book reads: 'Jews Without Money'. The elevator runners look smart, immaculate and intelligent – more intelligent, more immaculate than the manager of the hotel. To get a clean towel you just push a button and pull. If you want something, no matter what – a piano, a valise, a fireman – you have only to lift the receiver and ask for it. Nobody thinks of asking *why* you want this or that. All day long I walk the streets, but I see no place to sit down – no place, I mean, that looks inviting. On my wall is the photograph of a chair in the Tuileries Gardens, a chair photographed by my friend Brassai. To me it's a poem. I no longer see a wire chair with holes in the seat but an empty throne. If I had my way I would have this chair, this vacant seat, stamped on every silver dollar. We need to sit down somewhere, to rest, to contemplate, to know that we have a body – *and a soul*.

People who don't know how to eat or drink, people who live vicariously through the newspapers and the movies, people who walk around like ghosts and automatons, people who make work a fetish because they have no other way to occupy their minds, people who vote Republican or Democrat whether the dinner-pail is full or half-empty or rusty or full of holes, people who never sit down except to guzzle a little swill – well, what difference does it make what the new line-up is? The money-grubbers pretend to be worried about the impending revolution. As far as I can see, the revolution is already a fact. The stage is set, the machinery is in full operation, the mentality ripe for the coming Utopia. All that is required is to give it a name. The era of the collectivity is already inaugurated. America *is* communized, from top to bottom. She needs only a Lenin, or a Mussolini, or a Hitler.

I repeat, it doesn't matter what the new line-up is called. Once the corpse is dressed everything will be lovely. And if you want to know what it will be like when everybody is washed, starched, fumigated, sterilized, castrated and securely clapped in harness just read the great American novel – there's a new one every week. From the standpoint of Utopia it may seem like looking through the wrong end of the telescope, but all you need to do to correct this is to turn the telescope around.

Until this colossal, senseless machine which we have made of America is smashed and scrapped there can be no hope. The boss is a pimp, the worker is a whore. An economic revolution will accomplish nothing. A political revolution will accomplish nothing. Even if all the parts are replaced and a new model installed nothing of any value will happen. The malady is at the roots. The whole body of American life is affected.

If you are an artist you have one consolation which is denied the others: *you can play the role of undertaker*. It is an old and honourable profession and demands only a bare working knowledge of the human anatomy. It offers the satisfaction of walking and working with death in dignity while being very much alive and joyous oneself.

# From *The Air Conditioned Nightmare*

The most terrible thing about America is that there is no escape from the treadmill which we have created. There isn't one fearless champion of truth in the publishing world, not one film company devoted to art instead of profits. We have no theatre worth the name, and what we have of theatre is practically concentrated in one city; we have no music worth talking about except what the Negro has given us, and scarcely a handful of writers who might be called creative. We have murals decorating our public buildings which are about on a par with the aesthetic development of high school students, and sometimes below that level in conception and execution. We have art museums that are crammed with lifeless junk for the most part. We have war memorials in our public squares that must make the dead in whose name they were erected squirm in their graves. We have an architectural taste which is about as near the vanishing point as it is possible to achieve. In the ten thousand miles I have travelled thus far I have come across two cities which have each of them a little section worth a second look – I mean Charleston and New Orleans. As for the other cities, towns and villages through which I passed I hope never to see them again. Some of them have such marvellous names, too, which only makes the deception more cruel. Names like Chattanooga, Pensacola, Tallahassee, like Mantua, Phoebus, Bethlehem, Paoli, like Algiers, Mobile, Natchez, Savannah, like Baton Rouge, Saginaw, Poughkeepsie: names that revive glorious memories of the past or awaken dreams of the future. Visit them, I urge you. See for yourself. Try to think of Schubert or Shakespeare when you are in Phoebus, Virginia. Try to think of North Africa when you are in Algiers, Louisiana. Try to think of the life the Indians once led here when you are on a lake, a mountain or river bearing the names we borrowed from them. Try to think of the dreams of the Spaniards when you are motoring over the old Spanish Trail. Walk around in the old French Quarter of New Orleans and try to reconstruct the life that once this city knew. Less than a hundred years has elapsed since this jewel of America faded out. It seems more like a thousand. Everything that was of beauty, significance or promise has been destroyed and buried in the avalanche of false progress. In the thousand years of almost incessant war Europe has not lost what we have lost in a hundred years of 'peace and progress'. No foreign enemy ruined the South. No barbaric vandals devastated the great tracts of land which are as barren and hideous as the dead surface of the moon. We can't attribute to the Indians the transformation of a peaceful, slumbering island like Manhattan into the most hideous city in the world. Nor can we blame the collapse of our economic system on the hordes of peaceful, industrious immigrants whom we no longer want. No, the European nations may blame one another for their miseries, but we have no such excuse – we have only ourselves to blame.

Less than two hundred years ago a great social experiment was begun on this virgin continent. The Indians whom we dispossessed, decimated and reduced to the status of outcasts, just as the Aryans did with the Dravidians of India, had a reverent attitude towards the land. The forests were intact, the soil rich and fertile. They lived in communion with Nature on what we choose to call a low level of life. Though they possessed no written language they were poetic to the core and deeply religious. Our forefathers came along and, seeking refuge from their oppressors, began by poisoning the Indians with alcohol and venereal disease, by raping their women and murdering their children. The wisdom of life which the Indians possessed they scorned and denigrated. When they had finally completed their work of conquest and extermination they herded the miserable remnants of a great race into concentration camps and proceeded to break what spirit was left in them.

Not long ago I happened to pass through a tiny Indian reservation belonging to the Cherokees in the mountains of North Carolina. The contrast between this world and ours is almost unbelievable. The little Cherokee reservation is a virtual Paradise. A great peace and silence pervades the land, giving one the impression of being at last in the happy hunting grounds to which the brave Indian goes upon his death. In my journey thus far I have struck only one other community which had anything like this atmosphere, and that was in Lancaster County, Pennsylvania, among the Amish people. Here a small religious group, clinging stubbornly to the ways of their ancestors in comportment, dress, beliefs and customs, have converted the land into a veritable garden of peace and plenty. It is said of them that ever since they settled here they have never known a crop failure. They live a life in direct opposition to that of the majority of the American people – and the result is strikingly apparent. Only a few miles away are the hell-holes of America where, as if to prove to the world that no alien ideas, theories or isms will ever get a foothold here, the American flag is brazenly and tauntingly flown from roofs and smokestacks. And what sorry looking flags they are which the arrogant, bigoted owners of these plants display! You would think that such fervid patriotism would be inconsonant with the display of a torn, blackened, weatherbeaten emblem. You would think that out of the huge profits which they accumulate enough might be put aside to purchase a bright, new, gleaming emblem of liberty. But no, in the industrial world everything is soiled, degraded, vilified. It has become so today that when you see the flag boldly and proudly displayed you smell a rat somewhere. The flag has become a cloak to hide iniquity. We have two American flags always: one for the rich and one for the poor. When the rich fly it it means that things are under control; when the poor fly it it means danger, revolution, anarchy. In less than two hundred years the land of liberty, home of the free, refuge of the oppressed has so altered the meaning of the Stars and Stripes that today when a man or woman succeeds in escaping from the horrors of Europe, when he finally stands before the bar under our glorious national emblem, the first question put to him is: '*How much money have you?*' If you have no money but only a love of freedom, only a prayer for mercy on your lips, you are debarred, returned to the slaughter-house, shunned as a leper. This is the bitter caricature which the descendants of our liberty-loving forefathers have made of the national emblem.

Everything is caricatural here. I take a plane to see my father on his death-bed and up there in the clouds, in a raging storm, I overhear two men behind me discussing how to put over a big deal, the big deal involving paper boxes, no less. The stewardess, who has been trained to behave like a mother, a nurse, a mistress, a cook, a drudge, never to look untidy, never to lose her Marcel wave, never to show a sign of fatigue or disappointment or chagrin or loneliness, the stewardess puts her lily-white hand on the brow of one of the paper-box salesmen and in the voice of a ministering angel, says: 'Do you feel tired this evening? Have you a headache? Would you like a little aspirin?' We are up in the clouds and she is going through this performance like a trained seal. When the plane lurches suddenly she falls and reveals a tempting pair of thighs. The two salesmen are now talking about buttons, where to get them cheaply, how to sell them dearly. Another man, a weary banker, is reading the war news. There is a great strike going on somewhere – several of them, in fact. We are going to build a fleet of merchant vessels to help England – *next December*. The storm rages. The girl falls down again – she's full of black and blue marks. But she comes up smiling, dispensing coffee and chewing gum, putting her lily-white hand on someone else's forehead, inquiring if he is a little low, a little tired perhaps. I ask her if she likes her job. For answer she says, 'It's better than being a trained nurse.' The salesmen are going over her points; they talk about her like a commodity. They buy and sell, buy and sell. For that they have to have the best rooms in the best hotels; the fastest, smoothest planes, the thickest, warmest overcoats, the biggest, fattest purses. We need their paper boxes, their buttons, their synthetic furs, their rubber goods, their hosiery, their plastic this and that. We need the banker, his genius for taking our money and making himself rich. The insurance man, his policies, his talk of security, of dividends – we need him too. *Do we?* I don't see that we need any of these vultures. I don't see that we need any of these cities, these hell-holes I've been in. I don't think we need a two-ocean fleet either. I was in Detroit a few nights ago. I saw the Mannerheim Line in the movies. I saw how the Russians pulverized it. I learned the lesson. *Did you?* Tell me what it is that man can build, to protect himself, which other men cannot destroy? What are we trying to defend? Only what is old, useless, dead, indefensible. Every defence is a provocation to assault. Why not surrender? Why not give – give all? It's so damned practical, so thoroughly effective and disarming. Here we are, we the people of the United States: the greatest people on earth, so we think. We have everything – everything it takes to make people happy. We have land, water, sky and all that goes with it. We could become the great shining example of the world; we could radiate peace, joy, power, benevolence. But there are ghosts all about, ghosts whom we can't seem to lay hands on. We are not happy, not contented, not radiant, not fearless.

We bring miracles about and we sit in the sky taking aspirin and talking paper boxes. On the other side of the ocean they sit in the sky and deal out death and destruction indiscriminately. We're not doing that yet, *not yet*, but we are committed to furnishing the said instruments of destruction. Sometimes, in our greed, we furnish them to the wrong side. But that's nothing – everything will come out right in the end. Eventually we will have helped to wipe out or render prostrate a good part of the human race – not savage this time, but civilized 'barbarians'. Men like ourselves, in short, except that they have different views about the universe, different ideological principles, as

291

we say. Of course, if we don't destroy them they will destroy us. That's logic – nobody can question it. That's political logic, and that's what we live and die by. A flourishing state of affairs. Really exciting, don't you know. 'We live in such exciting times.' Aren't you happy about it? The world changing so rapidly and all that – isn't it marvellous? Think what it was a hundred years ago. Time marches on. . . .

A man of genius whom I know would like to be spared the ordeal of indiscriminate killing which they are preparing him for. He is not interested in putting the world to rights. He is interested in putting his thoughts down on paper. But then he has a good set of teeth, he is not flat-footed, his heart and lungs are sound, he has no nervous disorders. He is thoroughly healthy and a genius to boot. He never talks about paper boxes or buttons or new-fangled gadgets. He talks poetry, talks about God. But he doesn't belong to some God sect and therefore is disqualified as a conscientious objector. The answer is that he must get ready to be shipped to the front. He must defend our ideological principles. The banker is too old to be of service; the salesmen I was talking about are too clever; so the genius has to serve, though God knows, since we have so few of them, you would think we might be able to spare one now and then.

I hope that Walt Disney is exempted, because he's the man, though I doubt that he realizes it, to illustrate what I have to say. In fact, he's been doing it all along, unconsciously. He's the master of the nightmare. He's the Gustave Doré of the world of Henry Ford & Co., Inc. The Mannerheim Line is just a scratch on the surface. True, the temperature was abnormal – about forty degrees below zero on the average. (Amazing how men can be trained to kill in all kinds of weather. Almost as intelligent as horses.) But as I was saying, Disney has all kinds of temperature – a temperature to suit every fresh horror. He doesn't have to think: the newspapers are always on tap. Of course they're not real men and women. Oh no! They're more real than real men and women: they're dream creatures. They tell us what we look like beneath the covering of flesh. A fascinating world, what? Really, when you think about it, even more fascinating than Dali's cream puffs. Dali thinks too much. Besides, he has only two hands. Disney has a million. And besides hands he has voices – the voice of the hyena, the voice of the donkey, the voice of the dinosaur. The Soviet film, for example, is intimidating enough, but slow, ponderous, cumbersome, unwieldy. It takes time in real life to demolish all those concrete pill-boxes, cut all that barbed wire, kill all those soldiers, burn all those villages. Slow work. Disney works fast – like greased lightning. That's how we'll all operate soon. What we dream we become. We'll get the knack of it soon. We'll learn how to annihilate the whole planet in the wink of an eye – just wait and see.

The capital of the new planet – the one, I mean, which will kill itself off – is of course Detroit. I realized that the moment I arrived. At first I thought I'd go and see Henry Ford, give him my congratulations. But then I thought – what's the use? He wouldn't know what I was talking about. Neither would Mr Cameron most likely. That lovely Ford evening hour! Every time I hear it announced I think of Céline – Ferdinand, as he so affectionately calls himself. Yes, I think of Céline standing outside the factory gates (pp. 222-225, I think it is: *Journey to the End of the Night*). Will he get the job? Sure he will. He gets it. He goes through the baptism – the baptism of stultification through noise. He sings a wonderful song there for a few pages about the machine, the blessings that it showers upon mankind. Then he meets Molly. Molly is just a whore. You'll find another Molly in *Ulysses*, but Molly the whore of Detroit is much better. Molly has a soul. Molly is the milk of human kindness. Céline pays a tribute to her at the end of the chapter. It's remarkable because all the other characters are paid off in one way or another. Molly is whitewashed. Molly, believe it or not, looms up bigger and holier than Mr Ford's huge enterprise. Yes, that's the beautiful and surprising thing about Céline's chapter on Detroit – that he makes the body of a whore triumph over the soul of the machine. You wouldn't suspect that there was such a thing as a soul if you went to Detroit. Everything is too new, too slick, too bright, too ruthless. Souls don't grow in factories. Souls are killed in factories – even the niggardly ones. Detroit can do in a week for the white man what the South couldn't do in a hundred years to the Negro. That's why I like the Ford evening hour – it's so soothing, so inspiring.

Of course Detroit isn't the worst place – not by a long shot. That's what I said about Pittsburgh. That's what I'll say about other places too. None of them is the worst. There is no worst or worstest. The worst is in process of becoming. It's inside us now, only we haven't brought it forth. Disney dreams about it – and he gets paid for it, that's the curious thing. People bring their children to look and scream with laughter. (Ten years later it happens now and then that they fail to recognize the little monster who so joyfully clapped his hands and screamed with delight. It's always hard to believe that a Jack-the-Ripper could have sprung out of your own loins.) How-

293

ever. . . . It's cold in Detroit. A gale is blowing. Happily I am not one of those without work, without food, without shelter. I am stopping at the gay Detroiter, the Mecca of the futilitarian salesmen. There is a swanky haberdashery shop in the lobby. Salesmen love silk shirts. Sometimes they buy cute little panties too – for the ministering angels in the aeroplanes. They buy any and everything – just to keep money in circulation. The men of Detroit who are left out in the cold freeze to death in woollen underwear. The temperature in winter is distinctly sub-tropical. The buildings are straight and cruel. The wind is like a double-bladed knife. If you're lucky you can go inside where it's warm and see the Mannerheim Line. A cheering spectacle. See how ideological principles can triumph in spite of sub-normal temperatures. See men in white cloaks crawling through the snow on their bellies; they have scissors in their hands, big ones, and when they reach the barbed wire they cut, cut, cut. Now and then they get shot doing it – but then they become heroes – and besides there are always others to take their places, all armed with scissors. Very edifying, very instructive. Heartening, I should say. Outside, on the streets of Detroit, the wind is howling and people are running for shelter. But it's warm and cosy in the cinema. After the spectacle a nice warm cup of chocolate in the lobby of the hotel. Men talking buttons and chewing gum there. Not the same men as in the aeroplane – different ones. Always find them where it's warm and comfortable. Always buying and selling. And of course a pocketful of cigars. Things are picking up in Detroit. Defence orders, you know. The taxi driver told me he expected to get his job back soon. In the factory, I mean. What would happen if the war suddenly stopped I can't imagine. There would be a lot of broken hearts. Maybe another crisis. People wouldn't know what to do for themselves if peace were suddenly declared. Everybody would be laid off. The bread lines would start up. Strange, how we can manage to feed the world and not learn how to feed ourselves.

The Southland is a vast domain about which one could go on writing for ever. I have said scarcely anything about it and yet the South – and the Southwest, which is a totally different world – are the two sections of America which move me deeply. The old South is full of battlefields, that is one of the first things which impress you. The South has never recovered from the defeat which it suffered at the hands of the North. The defeat was only a military defeat – that one feels very strongly. The Southerner has a different rhythm, a different attitude towards life. Nothing will convince him that he was in the wrong; at bottom he has a supreme contempt for the man of the North. He has his own set of idols – warriors, statesmen, men of letters – whose fame and glory no defeat has ever dimmed. The South remains solidly against the North, in everything. It wages a hopeless fight, very much like that of the Irish against England.

If you are of the North this atmosphere affects you strangely. It would be impossible to live long in the South without being undermined. The climate, the landscape, the manners and customs, the soft speech exert a charm which it is difficult to resist. This world of the South corresponds more nearly to the dream life which the poet imagines than do other sections of the country. Little by little this dream world is being penetrated and poisoned by the spirit of the North. The South is crumbling under the heel of the conqueror. From Rome to Savannah, along the old wagon routes, one can still trace Sherman's march to the sea. It is the path of a vandal, the path of a soldier who said that war is hell and who demonstrated it by the use of fire and sword. The South will never forget Sherman, never forgive him.

At Gettysburg, at Bull Run, at Manassas, at Fredericksburg, at Spottsylvania Court House, at Missionary Ridge, at Vicksburg I tried to visualize the terrible death struggle in which this great republic was locked for four long years. I have stood on many battlefields in various parts of the world but when I stand beside the graves of the dead in our own South the horror of war assails me with desolating poignancy. I see no results of this great conflict which justify the tremendous sacrifice which we as a nation were called upon to make. I see only an enormous waste of life and property, the vindication of right by might, and the substitution of one form of injustice for another. The South is still an open, gaping wound. The new Atlanta, sprung from the ashes of the old, is a hideous nondescript city combining the evil, ugly traits of both North and South. The new Richmond is lifeless and characterless. New Orleans lives only in its tiny French quarter and even that is being rapidly demolished. Charleston is a beautiful memory, a corpse whose lower limbs have been resuscitated. Savannah is a living tomb about which there still clings a sensual aura as in old Corinth. Amidst these embers of the past the Southerner treads his defiant way. Compared to the man of the North, he is a charming, gracious, courteous, dignified, civilized being. He is sensitive and touchy also, capable of violent explosions which to a Northerner are most unpredictable. Some you find living in the pomp and splendour of Jefferson's time; some live like animals, in a condition comparable only to that of the primitive beings in Africa and other remote parts of the world where the benefits of civilization have been imposed by the white man; now and then you find a crumbling mansion occupied by a family of poverty-stricken, half-demented wretches surrounded by the faded relics of the past. There are beautiful regions, such as in the vicinity of Charlottesville, for example, where there seem to be nothing but millionaires. There are mill towns in the Carolinas, for instance, which, like the mining towns of Pennsylvania or West Virginia, fill one with terror and disgust. There are farming regions, in what was once the Old Dominion, where the land assumes a beauty and serenity unrivalled anywhere in the Old World. There are vistas, such as at Chattanooga, Harpers Ferry, Asheville, or along the crest of the Blue Ridge, or in the heart of the Great Smokies, to mention but a few, which instil in the human heart a deep, abiding peace. There are swamps, such as the Okefinokee and the Great Dismal Swamp of Virginia, which inspire an unspeakable dread and longing. There are trees, plants, shrubs, flowers such as are seen nowhere else, and which are not only extraordinarily beautiful but haunting and almost overwhelmingly nostalgic. At Biloxi, Mississippi, there is a row of live oaks planted a century ago by a Greek which are of such staggering loveliness and magnificence as to make one breathless. From the steps of Black Mountain College in North Carolina one has a view of mountains and forests which makes one dream of Asia. In Louisiana there are stretches of bayou country whose beauty is of a nature such as only the Chinese poets have captured. In New Iberia, La., to signal only one example, there is a house and garden belonging to Weeks Hall which constitute in essence and in fact the dream made real.

In Mississippi, near the banks of the great river itself, I came upon the ruins of Windsor. Nothing now remains of this great house but the high, vine-covered Grecian columns. There are so many elegant and mysterious ruins throughout the South, so much death and desolation, so much ghostliness. And always in the fairest spots, as if the invader aiming at the vital centres struck also at the pride and hope of his victim. One is inevitably induced to reflect on what might have been had this promising land been spared the ravages of war, for in our Southern States that culture known as the 'slave culture' had exhibited only its first blossoms. We know what the slave cultures of India, Egypt, Rome and Greece bequeathed the world. We are grateful for the legacy; we do not spurn the gift because it was born of injustice. Rare is the man who, looking upon the treasures of antiquity, thinks at what an iniquitous price they were fashioned. Who has the courage, confronted with these miracles of the past, to exclaim: 'Better these things had never been than that one single human being had been deprived of his rightful freedom!'

Who knows what splendours might have blossomed forth from such nuclei as Charleston, Savannah, New Orleans! The other day, picking up a travel book, I read with amazement and stupefaction of the dead city of Pagan, the old capital of Burma. 'Bleached as bones beneath the moon ahead of us lay the ruins of what had once been Burma's capital city, five thousand stupas, pagodas, temples dating from AD 108 and spread over a hundred square miles . . . It is said that in the days of Pagan's glory the pagodas and shrines and monasteries could be counted by the myriad; even now the remains of five thousand can still be traced. The ground is so thickly studded with them that you can scarcely move a foot without touching some sacred object made by the adroit hands of the Paganese.'*

It is doubtful if this continent will ever bequeath the world the deathless splendour of the holy cities of India. Only in the cliff dwellings of the Southwest, perhaps, does the work of man here in America arouse emotions remotely analogous to those which the ruins of other great peoples inspire in the traveller. On Avery Island, in Louisiana, I ran across a massive statue of Buddha, brought over from China, which was protected by a glass cage. It was startling to look upon in its bizarre setting. It dominated the landscape which was in itself a work of art in a way that is difficult to describe. Avery Island is an exotic piece of land in the heart of the Acadian country. It has a salt mine the interior of which is like the décor of some fabulous edifice out of the *Thousand and One Nights*. It has a bamboo forest the floor of which reflects a light that suggests the translucent glamour of *Pélleas and Mélisande*. It has a sanctuary for birds which makes one think of W. H. Hudson's purple pages. It is a haven and an ark for all that is exotic in flesh, form and substance. In the midst of a spacious jungle garden, resting immobile and impenetrable on the top of a gentle knoll, is the graven image of Buddha fashioned some eight or nine centuries ago in China. If one suddenly came upon a skyscraper twice the height of the Empire State building one could not be more astonished than by the sight of this silent, graven image which dominates the luxuriant, tangled landscape of Avery Island. An almost

* *Land of the Eye* by Hassoldt Davis.

oppressive poise and serenity is emanated by this massive figure of the Buddha. The landscape, for all the care that has been lavished upon it to make it seductive, seems in the presence of this transplanted idol to be almost as fragile as the glass which offers the Buddha a temporal and needless protection. The poise and serenity of the figure evoke the certainty of endless duration. The Louisiana earth seems more than ever restless, agitated, pregnant with life that must flourish and rot. Whatever the angle of the sun, the shadow of the Buddha falls with measure and precision, with gravity and dignity, as if defining with unerring exactitude the utmost limits of hope, desire, courage and belief.

There are thousands of dream places in the old South. You can sit on a bench in a tiny Confederate Park or fling yourself on the banks of a levee or stand on a bluff overlooking an Indian settlement, the air soft, still, fragrant, the world asleep seemingly, but the atmosphere is charged with magical names, epoch-making events, inventions, explorations, discoveries. Rice, tobacco, cotton – out of these three elements alone the South created a great symphonic pageant of human activity.

It is all over now. A new South is being born. The old South was ploughed under. But the ashes are still warm.

# Stand Still Like the Hummingbird

It was on the jet from New York to San Francisco, at an altitude of thirty to forty thousand feet and never so much as a tremor, that all unwittingly I moved a few centimetres into the future. We were making the flight in five and a half hours. It was a daytime flight and, despite the altitude, the earth below (and man's transformation of it) was clearly recognizable. What a geometer, man! Whole counties laid out in squares and rectangles: counties traversed in the wink of an eye. All very much like Walt Disney's graphic Pythagorean demonstrations in 'Mathemagic Land'.

It was the comfort, the motionless motion, the unaccustomed perspective which doubtless threw me. Together with the copies of *Life and Time*, now more than ever superannuated, which floated from hand to hand like the wreckage from some exploded planet. They belonged to such a distant past, it seemed. A past far more remote than that of Altamira or Lascaux. They belonged to the world of things, and we had left the world of things far behind. We were of the airs now, and they were filled with secret vibrations, with rays invisible and of power unimaginable. Yes, though only a few inches from the ground, so to speak, we were already verging on the *carrefours* of uncharted lanes of force, mysterious, magical force destined to alter not only our concepts of life but our very being. A little more effort, another push, and who knows? we might make it. Make it to Vega, Betelgeuse, farther even. Out of our limitless universe and into the blue – the blue of the poet and dreamer, the blue of the mystics. Perhaps into the 'upper partials' of some divine musical space.

Like a refrain I kept repeating to myself: 'Today five and a half hours; tomorrow two; the day after just a few minutes, perhaps. And then – for what's to stop us? – a speed which will render speed meaningless.

We speak so glibly of the speed of light. What reality has it for us, this speed of light? Man's struggle, ever since he ceased to grovel like the worm, has been to equate imagination with deed. For this the poets and the saviours were crucified. This was the nature of their

299

heresy, that they dared to reach out, touch fingertips with the Creator, complete the circle.

Nothing too startling will ever be accomplished by means of technic. The universe has no armature, no weight, no substance. No purpose even. Neither is it dream and illusion. *It is*. The highest thought can neither add to it nor subtract from it. It grows, changes, responds to every need, every demand. It can exist with God or without. It is like a Mind which asks and answers its own questions.

Our needs . . . What is it that we need? Certainly the more liberated one feels the less one needs. The sage demonstrates it daily, and the idiot too. Just to breathe, to know that you are alive, isn't it marvellous? Looking down from a height of forty thousand feet upon the activity of this geometer of an ant called man, one is struck by the utter senselessness of sweat and struggle, toil and bubble. For all that he has achieved – merely to sustain life, mind you – he has merely scratched the surface of the planet. Does all this effort constitute an advance? The birds wing their way above the din and hubbub, content to ride the wind. They leave no monuments in space, no writings in the sky. Every creature of the wild is a demonstration of faith and joy. Man alone, the Lord of Creation, suffers. Suffers not from want but from an unnamable deprivation.

The world of things is fast drawing to a close. It is inevitable. For the labour of man, his cunning and inventiveness, have been in vain. The mind of man is beginning to look not merely into space and the mysteries concealed therein but to some greater level of being. His thoughts already move in new dimensions. More and more he seeks to live imaginatively, daringly, in accord with his own divine nature. He is thoroughly sick of machines, of therapies which offer no balm, of religions and philosophies which have no rapport with the magical existence he is about to lead. He has come to perceive that life is everywhere, in all things, at the edges of the universe as well as the centre, and that nowhere is it absent, even in death. Why cling to it then with such stubbornness? What can be gained that is not already lost? Surrender! whispers the still small voice. Overboard with the baggage!

It seems impossible that in our present state of being we can hope to find out there anything vastly different than we already know, than we already have right here. We seek only that which we are ready and prepared to find. But it could happen that, struggling to perfect ways and means of assaulting the unknown, we may stumble on shattering verities which have ever been right under our nose. We may discover that in our own mysterious mind and heart there exists all that is necessary to satisfy our longings, our maddest dreams. It may prove not only dangerous and absurd to go on breaking down resistant nothingnesses, such as the atom, but futile as well. Are we not miraculous in our very being? Why not think miraculously, act miraculously, live miraculously? Fumbling with the lock – man's immemorial pastime! – the door may suddenly open of itself. The door to reality, I mean. Was it ever locked?

The greatest miracle is the discovery that all is miraculous. And the nature of the miraculous is – utter simplicity. Nothing has been gained by sweat and struggle, by taking thought, by devotion, prayer, perseverance, patience, fortitude – or by sloth, need it be added. Imagine the planets pausing to decide the direction of their orbits! Imagine them struggling to change their fiery courses! *Thinking* – what a vice! *Struggling* – what absurdity! To *know* is so easy, so painless. The ground for any kind of growth and cultivation is prepared by lying fallow.

How then is the break to be made? It is man himself who must break. Up to now he has only been splintered, like the glass he uses for his windshields. He has collided only with heavier bodies, never with a shattering, devastating idea. Craving a foolproof world, he refuses to submit himself to the slaughter which the mind can wreak. Even when he goes insane the thought machine still functions. No matter if the cogs be jammed – man is that peculiar breed of animal that can function in a world completely mad. It would still be *his* world.

And is it not an insane world which we have come to inhabit? What valid meaning is there to any of our acts, plans, thoughts? Whatever we create only adds to our distress and confusion, our eventual annihilation. Nothing our sick brains invent can add an ounce of joy to this thoroughly empty existence. The more we discover, the more we invent, the more crippled and frustrated we become. And this drunken mechanic, this push-button maniac, thinks to explore the outer universe. What a joke!

No, *Homo sapiens* will never make it. He is in the last stage of devolution. His world of things, thingamajig that it is, will vanish in the twinkle of an eye. The pity is that he could have come so close, and missed. Wherein did he fail? In refusing to recognize the wondrous nature of his own being. He asked for power instead of mastery, for efficiency rather than glory. In time to come it may be said of him that never did life spawn a more efficient misfit.

There may be such a thing as evolution, with all the incredible

301

tedium which the notion implies. But from seed to bud to flower is another thing. There is such a thing as growth – and there is endless transmogrification. One can rearrange the pieces ad infinitum, giving check and check again, but never mate. Or one can take the leap into the blue. For the visionary, the act is all. Nirvana, in the sense of awakening. The awakening being the fulfilment.

Is the future, like speed and motion, destined to become a meaningless term? Have not the men of the future been with us from the very beginning? What is the universe but a state of mind? Grappling with the problem of speed – or is it the riddle of light? – it becomes more and more evident that there is no such thing as motion, or gravity, or heat, or light. Any more than there are atoms, molecules, protons, electrons. Only gods and devils, birth and death, ignorance and bliss. Nothing out there can possibly be more mysterious, more enigmatic, than here within our own breasts. The corporeal is the phantasmal, the shadow realm. Mind *is* all, and its realm is reality. What is, defies knowing. With regard to the tiniest, the most insignificant morsel of this unsubstantial universe, thought wears itself out. The mind can only toy with what food or substance is presented to it; it can never know in any ultimate, absolute sense.

Without intention, though not without reason, we grow each day more metaphysical-minded. The dream of mastery over the forces of nature has finally led us to ask – what *is* mastery? At what point, for example, in the development of speed will it be possible to say that we have mastered the situation? When we are able to attain the speed of light? When we can transport ourselves instantaneously from any point in the universe to any other point? Is there any reason to attain such awesome speed? The only point in pursuing such miraculous ends, it seems to me, would be that in the doing we ourselves would become transformed. Perhaps only through the achievement of such freedom will we begin to question the nature and purpose of all our activity. If mind alone is capable of making these incredible leaps, why drag the body along? Or, if mind and body are one, as we tend more and more to believe now, would we not be there, in body, soul and spirit, wherever we wished whenever we wished?

From various quarters and from earliest times we have had testimony relating to superhuman feats on the part of certain beings. However sceptical we may be with regard to such statements, we are all nevertheless capable of being excited by the prospect of visits from other worlds. It has even been asserted that these visitors from outer space are at present walking about among us here on earth. Some indeed claim to have spoken with them. True or not, the point is that if they *are* here it did not take them a million years to make the journey. Nor, I venture to add, did it take them aeons to learn to speak our language, or any language used by earth men. And if they are capable of speaking in any tongue, what is to prevent us from assuming that they could speak to all men in all tongues simultaneously? Or, in Pentecostal fashion, give the illusion of doing so? Language at best is but a poor means of communication; it is the soul speaking to the soul, the spirit informing speech, which gives words meaning.

This is what I meant when I referred a moment ago to our growing metaphysical cast of mind. The problems which have plagued us for so many millennia tend to change face as we approach their seeming solution. What, for instance, will speed mean when one can travel faster than light, as some sober-minded men of science now predict is within the realm of possibility? What sense is there in developing radar or other techniques of communication when it has already been proved that men can communicate telepathically at any distance apart? (And would it be any more difficult, do you suppose, to communicate telepathically from one planet to another, one universe to another?) And if, as has also been demonstrated again and again over countless years, men have been healed (even brought back from death) by a word or a touch of the hand, sometimes by their own powers of suggestion, why go on turning out medicine men who make not the least effort to understand or investigate such phenomena?

At a certain point in his life Gautama the Buddha sat himself beneath a bo tree and resolved not to move from the spot until he had pierced the secret of human suffering. Jesus disappeared for seventeen years, to return to his native land steeped in a wisdom of life which sets at nought all our knowledge.

We are so accustomed to thinking in terms of death. Yet death promises nothing, solves nothing. Life does not begin in some remote, ideal world, some paradisiacal hereafter; it begins and ends here, wherever we are, in whatever circumstances. Three-dimensional beings that we are, we are nevertheless capable of living in multiple dimensions. That is the meaning of life, that it is infinitely variable, inexhaustible, inextinguishable.

The current desire to conquer space and time is premature, to say the least. It is only another, more spectacular, manifestation of our itch to free ourselves from the problems we have created for ourselves. Never has any real attention been paid to the words of the elect; in every domain, from jurisprudence to astrophysics, the quack still dominates. We make no effort to rid ourselves of our ills, our vices, our shortcomings; we beg for the impossible – to sin without paying the price. Refusing to admit that we ourselves are as mysterious and indestructible as the universe itself, we regard the outer universe as a kind of game reserve to be exploited for our televised entertainment and prolonged stultification. It is the familiar pattern of exploration, spoliation, exploitation, nullification.

What makes it all the more ironical is that our problems here on earth are as yet so ridiculously petty. Hardly have we begun to use our minds when we find ourselves dying. We grow old before we have matured. Worse, for the better part of our lives we are diseased, crippled, frustrated. In short, we are used up almost from the start.

There is one comforting truth which is inescapable. Each time we run away from ourselves we are driven home again with greater force. Every effort to break out only pushes us further back into ourselves. It *may* be possible for man to reach the outer edges of the universe, but the importance of it will lie not in the getting there but in knowing more about ourselves. If we could pick up a stone in the field and truly grasp its nature, its essence, its being, so to speak, we would understand and know and appreciate the whole outer universe. We would not need to fling our bodies around like comets gone wild. Being fully here and of the moment, we would also be there, anywhere, and of all moments.

Much too simple, doubtless. But such is the nature of the real. Why change the world? *Change worlds!* Quite a difference.

Thus I mused as we lumbered along at five hundred miles an hour. Tomorrow, a thousand an hour; the day after, five thousand. Multiply it by a zillion . . . what difference? Are we getting somewhere? *Where?* Is the body and mind of twentieth-century man geared to cope with all this abstract jazz? Ought we not first learn to fly backward too, or stand still in the air like a hummingbird? *And what about the honey?* Before we can get ahead of ourselves we must get behind ourselves. Licking space we lick time too. What time will it be then? And what vector would we then regard as ours?

Buddha gave us the eight-fold path. Jesus showed us the perfect life. Lao-tzu rode off on a water buffalo, having condensed his vast and joyous wisdom into a few imperishable words. What they tried to convey to us, these luminaries, was that there is no need for all these laws of ours, these codes and conventions, these books of learning, these armies and navies, these rockets and spaceships, these thousand

and one impedimenta which weigh us down, keep us apart, and bring us sickness and death. We need only to behave as brothers and sisters, follow our hearts not our minds, play not work, create and not add invention upon invention. Though we realize it not, they demolished the props which sustain our world of make-believe. True, the world still stands or spins, but the meaning has gone out of it. It is more dead, this illusory, everyday world, than if it had been shattered by a million atom bombs. We live as ghosts amid a world in ruins. All is senseless repetition. 'There am I, and there I always am,' as Rimbaud said. Neither Lao-tzu, nor the Enlightened One, nor the Prince of Peace made any excursions into outer space, unless in their astral bodies. They changed worlds, yes. They travelled far. But standing still. Let us not forget that the road inward towards the source stretches as far and as deep as the road outward.

Among other bizarre thoughts which invaded me as we hummed along up there a few inches above the skin of the earth was this one about Milarepa, the Tibetan saint. According to his biographers, he had ascended to heaven not in the dead of night but in broad daylight, and in full view of his beloved followers. He had left his raiment behind, in a little pile, and even as he was ascending heavenward he warned his disciples not to quarrel about his belongings, few that they were. But lo and behold, his feet had hardly left the earth when they fell to, snatched the beloved's garments from one another's hands, and in their greed to possess tore them to shreds. This drama so familiar, so oft repeated, served to remind me that the disciple is ever the betrayer, the believer ever the murderer.

From this I fell to thinking of a book which had greatly intrigued me, *Star of the Unborn*.* It concerns a Utopia which comes about some five hundred thousand years hence. A monumental reach of the imagination, this work. How did it come about, the great change in man's outlook? How did it happen that from the senseless savage such as man now is he became a man of peace, a space traveller, an immortal, if he chose to be? By pure happenstance. By the fact of the stars moving in a little closer, overwhelming men by their radiance. Preposterous as the device may seem, it should not be overlooked that for all our skilful reading of the movements of the celestial bodies, no one can say with certainty that tomorrow or the next day new planets, new stars, even more resplendent worlds may not heave into view, travelling from some corner of the universe (or multiverse) we have

---

* By Franz Werfel, Viking Press, New York.

overlooked, travelling at a speed greater than any we have been able to imagine, much less calculate.

That things may simply *happen* – let us reckon with that always. Marvellous geometers that we are, drunken mathematicians that we are, nevertheless we are always a few light years behind in our reckoning. We deal only with what is given, not with what is about to be or may be. No, we have yet to come face to face with the supreme Mathematician, the faceless mind of Mind itself. Plot, plan, calculate or postulate as we may, there will always be surprises in store for us. Count on it!

'Up, Josephine, in our flying machine . . . and away we go!' Up we have been going, for fifty years or more now. Yet we do not know, can not say, which way is up or down, backward or forward, outward or inward. One thing is certain: if parallel lines can meet in infinity then machines can run without fuel and men fly without machines and thought travel faster than light and neither bend nor refract.

The machine is only the substance of a thought. Think harder, think faster, my lads! These awesome rockets are just so many fire-crackers and pinwheels. Bounce your radar signals back and forth from galaxy to galaxy – it's fun. But why play badminton when there are beings out there, lesser or greater than ourselves, who knows? waiting for us men of earth to really say something? Are you working on the message you will send when you finally make contact with our celestial neighbours? Will you be able to describe in code the array of new-found lethal weapons we have created? And if they are bored, will you bully them into listening?

If at only forty thousand feet above sea level such queries sound ridiculous, how must they sound twelve million light years distant on some unspotted planet to minds which no longer think as primates, bipeds and quadrupeds?

(A suggestion: don't fail to inquire as early as possible whether there are Communists out there in space or not. You might also ask the titles of their favourite banned books. And if they use flush toilets or simply plain 'loos.)

If evolution is a fact, and why not, since there are slow facts and fast facts, just as there are cold wars and hot wars, then it is safe to predict that in less than a light year we shall be able to do all the fool things we now dream of, perhaps more. If in a slow-moving jet at an altitude of only forty thousand feet one can still hear the music of a departed Beethoven, the lullabies of a Crosby, the sugared messages of an Eisenhower or the ravings of a Khrushchev, what's to hinder our listening eventually to that music of the spheres which, according to the men of old, is forever going on, without scores, conductors or instruments? Perhaps in Einsteinian fashion that modest saint Milarepa, seated on a comet's horn, holds converse even now with that delicious rogue Lao-tzu, as they make their merry way from planet to planet, universe to universe. Perhaps they have long ceased to discuss the impossibility of transmitting from one level to another, unless asymptotically, the elixir of wisdom, the truth of love, the bliss of perfect understanding.

Ah yes, musing thus I sometimes wonder if one of the great surprises in store for our bold space explorers may not be the collision with murdered saints and saviours, their bodies fully restored and glowing with health as they move along in the etheric currents, sportive as dolphins, free as the birds, cured of all such follies as doing good, healing the sick, raising the dead, instructing the ignorant.

We are only, alas, what we imagine ourselves to be. But in that 'only' vast universes of being are capable of taking form and shape. If only we knew that we can be all that we imagine! That we already are what we wish to be.

Even a peek into the future can give the illusion that the hideous clamour has ceased. Is it because the necessity, or compulsion, to make and destroy is done for? I could not help thinking what this continent of ours was like before the white man took it over. It seemed to me that silence was a great factor in the world of the Indian, that he made no unnecessary stir, that he took the long way about rather than the short cut. Perhaps his mind was at rest. Certainly he had no need of stock exchanges, iron foundries, sheet and roller mills, Krupp works, laboratories, newspapers, mints, ammunition dumps. He had need of nothing, it would seem, which to us is so indispensable. Not that his world was a Paradise. But it was never a senseless world. It had beauty, depth, great interludes of silence, and it vibrated with feeling.

From the clouds all that appeared to be left of this ancient world was the great barren stretch which begins with the Far West. The most beautiful, the most exciting part of the five-hour spectacle. Deserted though it was, an air of peace pervaded it. The remainder of the continent appeared to be criss-crossed by the tracks of a maniac, a monster of a chess master who had forgotten the rules of the game.

So transitory, the maniacal labour of the geometer! Above, all was smooth, co-ordinated, effortless; below, babel and confusion, struggle and ineptitude. For a brief moment I had the impression that

I was riding out of it, leaving it all behind, permanently. But the voices coming over the air belied the thought. They were the voices of earth men, and whether they crooned or rocked and rolled, whether they threatened imminent war or babbled of lasting peace, they had the ring of dolts, blunderers, misfits. No escaping them, even up there in the blue. The machine was theirs and would come home to roost. It would engender more machines, more intricate machines, more amazing machines, more machine-like machines, until the world and all its man-made parts became one vast interlocking machine of a machine.

# Part V

# The Last Years

# The Waters Reglitterized

In this room where I lie I am surrounded with paintings – Nancy's wild Ionian horses, Reichel's ethnological study of wigwams, which is a masterpiece in its genre, his Rosicrucian abstract on glass, the 'failed' tapestry which I rescued from the waste basket, the girl in the red hat which is the cover design for the child's book I gave you – and several of my own recent attempts. One of these, in which I used some Chinese white, is an astounding advance on my other 'self-portraits'. I say self-portraits, because, as Anaïs aptly remarked one day, it is always the same face, whether it be a Chinese sage, an African Negro, a war victim or a madman. This one has the real colour of flesh in the face, of which I am rather proud. For me, to acquire the slightest technique is always a long but joyous process. My watercolours are always voyages of adventure and, whether 'successful' or unsuccessful, they give me real satisfaction. I can swim in their presence just as gratefully as if they were Picassos or Rembrandts. I am never totally disappointed in them, no matter how bad the attempt.

But all this is preliminary to the thought I had in mind when I began. That was a sudden recollection of the night I stood with Joe O'Reagan in front of a department store window – on Livingston Street, Brooklyn, I believe – and took in with all my senses the Turners hanging there. Of course I had begun before, if I remember rightly. I had begun with a box of child's paints and a very bad brush, and a piece of wrapping paper from the butcher shop. I did a copy of George Grosz's self-portrait as *Number One*. That, I vividly remember because of the delight I had in discovering that I could really do something which faintly resembled the original. (Later I had a similar shock, when I did likenesses of my mother and sister from life – in black and white. They thought me a little cracked at the time to be so earnest about such a matter, especially when I was without a job and penniless.)

Everything, however, dates back to your studio on 50th Street, where I got the original impulse, watching you at work and listening to your very sage explanations of the reason for this and that. I remember another period, when I was installed with June at Remsen Street, reading Walter Pater's *Renaissance* and pumping you about not only Botticelli but the Italian Primitives. I can almost hear you again as you discoursed most eloquently on Cimabue and Giotto. And then one day it was Uccello!

Well, during my visit to London recently I saw a Uccello at the National Gallery. You probably know which one I mean – a battle scene, with a marvellous rising background. I studied it for a long while, feeling finally that it was as much of a mystery as ever. (Anything I profoundly like, I notice, always remains a *mystery* to me! It is as true of writing as of music or painting. For example, in literature, no matter how much I know and recognize of 'technique', books like Hamsun's *Mysteries*, Dostoievski's *Eternal Husband* and Nijinsky's *Diary* will always be *MYSTERY*. And if you will not think me vain to say so, now and then, in rereading passages of my own work, I feel the same thing. It makes me feel grand – and awed and subdued, at the same time.)

But to come back to that Uccello in the National Gallery – it was only this time that I suddenly realized how *modern* the picture is. How modern Uccello is! Cézanne is an intellectual boy by comparison. And Van Gogh! Why Van Gogh is just a tortured neurasthenic! Uccello taught me a great deal. And how, I ask myself, could his followers have failed to learn? How could we have had such terrible gaps in the real tradition of painting? What monstrosities of learning and bad taste lie between him and Picasso, let us say. Uccello revealed a grandeur and simplicity of soul. He was eloquent in *deed*, not in mere conception or technique. He went straight from vision to the canvas. He did not merely depict a battle-scene. He depicted the state of his, Uccello's, soul at the moment. The canvas is full of soul, full of noble *feeling*. With this soul feeling one can paint or dance or sing or build pyramids. Feeling, feeling. Van Gogh asserts it in a *maladif* way. But Uccello is healthy feeling, strong, contained emotion, a balanced universe – the equilibrium established from within, from his relationship with God, and not from a knowledge of the Golden Rule.

I have noticed, to speak of little things, the great difference in results, when sitting down calmly and undisturbed to do a watercolour, as against those feverish rushes in between times, when the idea of 'doing something' seems paramount.

The remarkable thing to observe, in children's work (as you will see from the book I sent) is that the child gives the impression of having done it with his whole being. They surrender themselves completely to what is in hand. Whereas even the biggest artist has to wage a constant fight against distraction. He is conscious not only of the future opinions of the critics, the price it will fetch (or *not* fetch!), the value of his tubes, the nicety of his choice of colour or line, but also the temperature of the room, the stains on the floor, the bath he forgot to take, and so on.

For one like myself, who is not *obliged* to do watercolours for a living, how wonderful that feeling, as happens sometimes, when coming home about midnight, the place extremely quiet, the light giving just the right glow about my work table, my senses keenly alive, yet not so sharp as to push me on to further writing, (a sort of sifting-of-the-ashes feeling, the fire warm but dying), I sit down before the little pad, determined to do just *one* watercolour in peace and harmony. To paint in this way is like communing with oneself – and with all the world too. I seem to carry on a perpetual conversation. The colours talk to me. I cajole them, I implore them. And, in the right mood, I will take infinite pains, for some unknown reason, to mix a little splotch of colour which will fill about an eighth of an inch on the paper.

But one of the moments I like best, after having done what I imagine to be my utmost, is the realization that it won't do at all. I decide to convert the quiet, static picture in front of me into a live, careless, free and easy thing. I strike out boldly with whatever comes to hand – pencil, crayon, brush, charcoal, ink – anything which will demolish the studied effect obtained and give me fresh ground for experiment. I used to think that the striking results obtained in this fashion were due to accident, but I no longer am of this mind. Not only do I know today that it is the method employed by some very famous painters (Rouault immediately comes to mind), but, I recognize that it is often the same method which I employ in writing. I don't go *over* my canvas, in writing, like the meticulous Fraenkel does with his drafts, but I keep breaking new ground until I reach the level of exact expression, leaving all the trials and gropings there, but raising them in a sort of spiral circumnavigation, until they make a solid under-body or under-pinning, whichever the case may be. And this, I notice, is precisely the ritual of life which is practised by the man who evolves. He doesn't go back, figuratively, to correct his errors and defects: he transposes and converts them into virtues. He makes wings of his larval cerements.

That last 'self-portrait' on the wall, which has the appearance of a medieval alchemist, contains a discovery connected with 'ears' which pleases me no end. Ears are a bugaboo for me – just as fingers and necks. I had used up all my knowledge of ears – and still they looked like cauliflowers or kohlrabies. Gradually, in working in towards the face from the outside, with more and more transparency, more and more magic, I finally eliminated the ears altogether. And then, as by a stroke of genius (sic!), I slashed a few stigmata on the cheeks, thus giving myself the unconsciously desired aspect of one who had endured many trials, who had perhaps sacrificed his ears for a higher purpose, but who was nonetheless 'all there' *avec ou sans oreilles*. The judicious use of a little Chinese white heightens the mystery and gives luminosity to the intent regard of the visionary who perhaps in a dream had seen the philosopher's stone.

If one day this particular effort should be displayed in the window of the Gotham Book Mart, where I am sending it shortly, it would give me intense pleasure to have you stop and examine it. Still greater pleasure, I might add, if you would go inside and inquire who did it. And the most extreme pleasure, need I say, if after inquiring the price of this masterpiece, you would say, 'Wrap it up, please, I'll take it with me.' To make sure you will recognize it (!) I shall inscribe on the back of it *'The Philosopher's Stone*, in memory of my friend Emil Schnellock who initiated me into the mysteries of Chinese white.' You will find the stone just at the base of the neck. It is a little patch of under-painting which I left untouched. For *you* Emil, at $1.98.

And now, as I am filled with chills and fever, I will lay the pen aside and dream of the Uccellos we used to talk about – I then in the height of ignorance and you patient and instructive . . .


An additional thought while eating lunch at my worktable and looking at my watercolour through the reflection in the mirror. For the first time in my experience I suddenly see that the bluish white rays I ran down the man's chest are really vaporous streaks of luminosity and not just paths of blue colour mixed with a little white. When I am in the metro, waiting for a train, I instinctively study the posters – and that has to do with tricks of shadow, flashes of stuff, differentiation of texture through line, colour or shape. I never get anywhere because I simply cannot hold the remembrance of the technique I have studied and the efficacy of which I perceive. I see only what the artist intended me to perceive – that is, a crease in the trousers, not a thin black line with an edge of parallel white. In my own work I only see the 'causes' – never the effects. Only now and then, when a visitor comes and begins telling me what he sees in the painting do I begin to see these things myself. I see only my efforts and abortions – never the desired result. I remember once Reichel coming and criticizing a watercolour I had just finished, and which I was rather unusually proud of because I thought I had been more than usually successful. It was a memory picture of the Parc Montsouris – the lake with the swans, etc. Reichel said, 'I don't like so much childish paintings.' Implying that I had *tried* to paint like a child! I was flattered as well as dumbfounded. But I wasn't at all trying to imitate a child. I was doing my utmost. That he had made a distinction between this picture and others I had shown him baffled me. Where was his sense of criticism? Couldn't he see that they were all fundamentally 'childish'? Another time, looking at a hasty, freakish portrait of Fred which I had just finished, he remarked – 'What a cruel conception of an *ami!*' But I hadn't the slightest tinge of cruelty in me when doing it. If I had given Fred an idiotic expression it was because the brush had failed me. I was looking at him intently, while doing it, and the result was what apparently horrified Reichel. He was crediting me with a power and control which I have never possessed.

Now, in writing, if someone had made that remark about a piece of portraiture, I would have accepted it silently as a just criticism, even if, as sometimes happens, I had had no malice in the forefront of my brain. But in writing, you see, I know I am responsible. I know every trick – where to use a semi-colon instead of a dash, when to give a short stabbing thrust, and when to wax loquacious or even circumlocutious – *even when to stammer!* But I know, too, that beyond a certain point I am no longer responsible. At a certain point the man in me gets the better of the artist. The artist does, can, and will lie – for effect. But not the man! In the realm of watercolour I am neither of these two creatures: I am simply the blind instrument of chance. I work according to the 'Principle of Least Action'. What I do not know counts more than what I do know. I should not really sign my name to these things – I am an anonymous creature, a neophyte, a stutterer and stammerer in form and colour. You follow me?

The greatest joy, and the greatest triumph, in art, comes at the moment when, realizing to the fullest your grip over the medium, you deliberately sacrifice it in the hope of discovering a vital hidden truth within you. It comes like a reward for patience – this freedom of mastery which is born of the hardest discipline. *Then*, no matter what you do or say, you are absolutely right and nobody dare criticize you. I sense this very often in looking at Picasso's work. The great freedom and spontaneity he reveals is born, one feels, because of the impact, the pressure, the support of the whole being which, for an endless period, has been subservient to the discipline of the spirit. The most careless gesture is as right, as true, as valid, as the most carefully planned strokes. *This I know*, and nobody could convince me to the contrary. Picasso here is only demonstrating a wisdom of life which the sage practises on another, higher level.

This morning, awake at five o'clock, the room almost dark still, I lay awake quietly meditating about the essay I would get up to write, and at the same time  as though playing a duet, watching the gradual change of colours in my paintings beside the bed, as the light slowly increased. I had the strange sensation then of imagining what might happen to those colours should the light continue to increase in strength *beyond full daylight*. And from thinking about the unknown colour gamut to the forms themselves and then to their significance – what a world of conjecture I explored! In that moment I was able, so to speak, to place myself in a future which may one day be realized. I saw not only what I might one day be able to do, but also I saw this – that the anticipation of the event was an augury of the deed itself. Suddenly I realized how it had been with the struggle to express myself in writing. I saw back to the period when I had the most intense, exalted visions of words written and spoken, but in fact could only mutter brokenly. Today I see that my steadfast *desire* was alone responsible for whatever progress or mastery I have made. The reality is always there, and it is preceded by vision. And if one keeps looking steadily the vision crystallizes into fact or deed. There is no escaping it. It doesn't matter what route one travels – every route brings you eventually to the goal. 'All roads lead to Heaven,' is the Chinese proverb. If one accepted that fully, one would get there so much more quickly. One should not be worrying about the degree of 'success' obtained by each and every effort, but only concentrate on maintaining the vision, keeping it pure and steady. The rest is sleight-of-hand work in the dark, a genuine automatic process, no less somnambulistic because accompanied by pains and aches.

Since 11.30 pm this evening I've been carried away by the discovery of yellow *ochre*! Marvellous colour! I put it in the sky and get dawn, put it in the grass and I get a golden light. Since twilight I've been shuffling back and forth between two watercolours – the same theme, different treatment. In each there is a tree (always the same tree, like the one I did in front of St Augustin's), a body of water – tarn, creek, lake, river?? – and hills, green as the hills of Ireland. I used sap green hoping to get a faint gold, but got Irish green instead. A little Prussian blue near the tops of the hills and they glow with all the metallic ores deposited there and guarded by the seven dwarves. Trying to throw the reflection of the hills into the water I had to go over the water so often that there is every kind of blue and green in it. Before going out to the cinema, to see the beloved *Raimu* (the only *human* figure in the movies), I gave the smaller picture a bath. Astonishing effect – and I'm sorry now I went over it again. Everything took on a supernal hue, as at dawn. Where the colours washed out completely it was not just white paper but a windswept space in which the vanished colours still spoke faintly. You could see that the hand of man had passed here – like the breath of God moving over the face of the waters. The tree had been smitten by cold blasts. It was wonderful, but like a chump I thought to myself that everybody could see it had been washed – and not made that way by sleight of hand. And finally I got a boat – right shape and right glint fore and aft as she turns with the sun and tide. In the little picture I manage to convey the illusion of two females without (for the first time in my life) putting in hair, eyes, and nose. You can successfully imagine their faces this time. You know they *have* faces! A triumph of the first order! But best of all is the ground – inlaid with yellow ochre so that it gleams in a heavenly way, suggesting not so much 'earth' as *the earth* – the earth in some fabled time before the machine was invented. (In the Greek heroic legends, when you think of the battles and the *pourparlers* between the demigods, you conjure up a quite different earth and soil than you get, for example, in a Utrillo or a Cézanne. The earth *was* more golden then, no doubt about it. When a man fell wounded to the earth he felt a kinship with it. There were no shell-holes and gas-eaten grass to sink into. He died in strong sunlight, in a riot of yellow ochre, grass green, chrome yellow, and raw umbers. Or else under a full moon, really *argent* and really swollen to frightening proportions. He saw the trunks of the trees coal black and flecked with silver. He saw in the thick foliage above him a vernal stain in which there were still traces of russet and orange.) Sometimes, in reading a book, you see all these colours again. Sometimes I see it in the movies, leaping out of the black and white film. Tonight, when Raimu was in a rage, his back to the open French window giving out on the Riviera, I saw the most wonderful greens and yellows and wisp-blown foliage and jagged cork-lined trees. And I saw the armchair and the sofa with the Matisse wallpaper, the human figures moving in another dimension from the *décor*, and though violent and tragic in their gestures, still not as convincing as the armchair, the half-open French window, the serrated and granulated hills, the sword-fish palm leaves, the shrub-stunted olive trees, the quiet heaving bay.

And now I'll tell you a funnier thing still. When I was two-thirds through with my pictures I went back to the studio to have a look at the child's picture I had cut out from that book. And I saw at a glance that 'she' knew more about painting than I will ever know. Even when she made the shadow of a swan's long neck in the wrong direction it did not disturb the general air of veracity. What she put down with her brush was absolutely true to her vision. *I* often forget to put in the shadow – until I go to the art gallery and happen to notice that most things cast a shadow. The child is very keenly aware of the aura which surrounds men and things. Grown-up children like myself, who are often only addlepated adolescents, forget all about the aura, just as the scientist forgets about the dwarves which inhabit the metals, as Fred says. When I write I am aware of all these things, but when I take up the brush I am so prepossessed with the idea of making something resemble something that I lose track of all reality. My creations, if I can call them that, swim or float or gasp in a vacuum of the senses. Tonight I came closer to this reality than ever before. And I managed it with the *little* brush, which I am usually too impatient to use. I *thought* long about each detail – about the feel of water and the look of hills and how and where the bow of a boat curves. And when the wind sweeps the earth I remembered how it pulls the heavy foliage of the tree, almost as though it would uproot it. I think I conveyed a little of all this in my two long-winded attempts. (Still, when I hang them beside the child's work they are not nearly so good, so honest, so true. The child did not give her picture baths – of that I am certain. And when she made a path in the greensward it *became a path*. Mine are calcimined into the ground.)

But just the same, I praise God for his savin' and keepin' power. I came closer than ever, and I can go to bed with a clear conscience.

But don't forget to see Raimu in *Noix de Coco, drôle de titre! Quand il se met à pleurer, c'est magnifique! C'est un homme, quoi!!!*

Before falling off to sleep last night I ordered my subconscious mind to remember, on waking, the last thought in my head – and it worked. It was to tell you of my impressions on seeing a tiny reproduction in Paris-Soir of a painting by some female artist (perhaps Suzanne Valadon). Looking at the head she had made I was struck by an oft-recurring thought I have when observing heads. It was a head such as only the painters give us; you could not find its counterpart in literature, or even in sculpture. It was – or *is*, because it's an eternal phenomenon in painting – a face dictated by the logic of the brush. From top to bottom the face is foreshortened, and of course correspondingly widened from side to side. You see it most typically, I should say, in Braque's figures. The heads are definitely moulded by the paint to suit the exigencies of the rest of the canvas. The head flows in a sculpturesque way, creating another kind of grace and beauty than that which we are familiar with in life. There is usually a quality of stone-crushed rudeness to the features. When I saw this head in the *rubrique*, '*A travers les galéries*', I felt a great joy – partly in recognition of a principle, partly in the discovery of an element which is usually absent from my portraits. If one were to attempt this visage in water-colour one would have to do it on moist paper, I imagine. I intend, by way of beginning, to try it with powdered crayon, using the fingers for the explosive quality of bone structure, socket and frontal convolutions. It is somewhere around the jaw that I feel the keenest pleasure – hard to describe it, but it is as if the jaw were set deep back in a widening mound of flesh. It is the carnal voracity of the mouth and not its verbal facility, or its 'kissability', which gets me. Reichel did one in oil once, of a medieval German type, in dark olive green with tawny earth-laden flesh, which haunts me. He gave such a spread to the face as almost to make it batrachian. It is, however, a face 'for all time', as you said once of Shakespeare's horses. And there is another thing about these heads – what I should call the 'post-medieval' head. When set against a landscape or fragment of a landscape (an effect terrifyingly enhancing, I always think – as though to say *Man dominating Nature*) – the face intuitively reflects the curves and rhythms of nature. The stark lone head of modern times is frightening because of the unrelatedness. It is the symbol of the brain functioning in a void. This alone is sufficient reason to justify your continued admiration of that French painter whose name I forget – the one who finally painted with the stump of an arm! (*Renoir*) All his women have the quality I speak of. When we come to Picasso's women we have the flowers of the machine age, even though they are classified as belonging to his 'classic' period. His massive madonnas are vultures of the great void. Now he is giving them profiles with a double eye. I don't know the plastic or aesthetic reasons for these strange apparitions, but I think I detect a metaphysical reason – and that is, that his women, *our* women, have no 'etheric' body, so to speak. Being entirely physical, they become atomic syntheses, immaterial conglomerations of electrons, having no real dimensions. Hewed out by the axe, as it were, they are nevertheless impalpable and unsubstantial. The planes which Cézanne discovered fade in to Einsteinian abstractions of flesh. They have neither front nor back, and of course no sides. Dali always sees through to the plumbing apparatus. Picasso, being more *Scorpionic*, searches for a more solid substratum, but however frantically he swings the axe his figures are composed on one plane only – and that is cardboard. We have become so accustomed to this cardboard verity that we see nothing unnatural in it. But when we step back a few paces, and look with the eyes of a Renoir, we can discern a tremendous difference.

This is all I have to say, for the moment, about the 'broadened' face. I am now going to take a walk through the Parc Montsouris to study the lake, the swans, and the greensward. . .

Walking along the Boulevard St Michel tonight studying the reproductions in the windows. Studying eye sockets and lips mostly. Came upon a clump of Renoir women. Discovered all over again the smiling upcurved mouth which enhances the roundness of all his women's faces. A mouth almost like a vagina, if placed Chinese fashion. Decidedly *Renoir* mouths! From this to ancient faces – of every school and age. Examining the modelling employed by various moderns. Cézanne's self-portrait – that slightly bald knob with a sheaf of dandruffy hair falling over his greasy black coat – a hideous portrait, from every standpoint. Absolutely no sense in making self-portraits in such garb and with such uninteresting character. However, the eye sockets interested me. Such a simple technique – yet I miss it constantly. Only this time I saw a little more, saw that he had carried the revolving planes of light and shade into the eyeball itself, or at any rate into the socket. Going home in the metro, got so interested in that bit of flesh above the eyeball, in the spaciousness and voluptuousness of it, that I rode past my station. . . . There are several other spots in the human face which are sensually and mysteriously fascinating – the indenture below the nose, the under part of the nose itself, the lobe of the ear, for example. If you begin to concentrate on these you get lost in introspection. The piece of flesh over the eye in a woman can be bewitching. What a big place the eye consumes! I have only recently caught on to that: I am going to increase the prominence of the socket from now on. Noticed too, in my microscopic examinations, that the less the ear is tinkered with the better. So much of the colour of life in the face goes dead in the 'oriferations' of the ear that unless you use your colours sparingly the ear becomes monstrous. The real tinge of blood, an ebb tinge, as it were, seems to concentrate in the lobe. Right?

Banal deduction, but better late than never. However, thinking of the endless varieties of depicting the face, I got to wondering if you ever thought of lecturing on the various features of the physiognomy, comparing one man's vision or technique with another's. Da Vinci's mouths, as against Rubens', Renoir's, Cézanne's, Picasso's, etc. Botticelli's eyes, as against Cimabue's or Giotto's or Van Gogh's. Perhaps a lot could be said this way – I mean, by the dissection and concentration on single items of the face, rather than the 'expression', which is a soul quality and ultimately unanalysable. I am so thoroughly aware, with writers, of how each one goes about the trick of gesture, conversation, reverie, exclamation, and so on. Herr Peeperkorn's stammer, for example – what a monumental piece of labour! The stammer raised to its ultimate significance. As though Thomas Mann, in sculpturing the human figure, had concentrated all his attention on this one detail, and thereby given us the secret of the man's character.

Yes, I would like to hear you lecture about the face! I ask myself if other men before me have been engrossed by eyeballs or ear lobes. Doubtless they were. Balzac says somewhere, to George Sand, I think it was, how he wrote so and so many bad books, this one to learn French, this one to learn the art of description, this one to learn the knack of conversation, etc. Undoubtedly, anatomists such as Rembrandt, Raphael and Rubens, must also have taken the human figure apart many times and for periods on end seen only this or that which perplexed and intrigued them. Once you begin to concentrate this way, it's amazing what you discover. For, as you well know, you can look at things all your life and not see them really. This 'seeing' is, in a way, a 'not seeing', if you follow me. It is more of a search for something, in which, being blindfolded, you develop the tactile, the olfactory, the auditory senses – and thus *see* for the first time. One day, odd as it sounds, you suddenly see what makes a wagon for example. You see the wagon in the wagon – and not the cliché image which you were taught to recognize as 'wagon' and accept for the rest of your life as a time-saving convenience. The development of this faculty, for an artist in any realm, is what stops the clock and permits him to live fully and freely. He gets out of rhythm with the crowd and in so doing he 'creates time' to see what surrounds him. If he were moving (*living*?) like the others he would remain deaf and blind with them. It is the voluntary arrest that really sets him in heavenly motion and permits him to see, feel, hear, think. Eh what?

When I was busy writing *Capricorn* I went dead as regards all these things I now tell you about. It is only now, when my purely critical faculties alone are involved (for my study of Balzac) that the sensuous elements of my being come to life. Now, while I meditate on the phases of Balzac's life, I see with extraordinary relish all the trifling items which go to make up the colour and movement of life. Standing before the shop window earlier this evening, I became so engrossed in the shape of a man's lips – the man beside me – that suddenly he became aware of my stare and frowned at me, which woke me up. But looking at those lips I certainly never thought for a moment of the owner of them. They were just lips to me, item no. 946572, in the museum catalogue of Henry Miller lips. They belong more to the shop window than to *Monsieur Tel et Tel*. And more to Giotto, Botticelli, da Vinci, than to the shop window. Finally, pursuing the trend still further, I actually got to imagining the formation of lips in the womb – the whole genetics of lips. And if I had struggled a little more, perhaps I'd have seen the hand of the Creator as he moved over the inchoate flesh and pronounced them to be lips!

And this reminds me that where I so often fail in the water-colour is in not using the 'little' brush, as I remarked before. I should acquire the patience to build up the flesh bit by bit, *feeling* my way along, as I think or sense the meaning of each item in the physiognomy. In oil painting this business of item by item, inch by inch, seems so much more evident. Sometimes I see the whole job as a fine piece of mosaic work, which it is, of course. *Lead and glass*, I often think to myself. No different than a stained glass cathedral window. In Rouault it is pronounced. But with him, the mosaic is so grand and architectural that this pattern-like ant work is lost sight of. I seem to see him pouring the molten glass over the slowly cooling lead. He doesn't wait to get a little slab or globule, but empties the bucket over the face or body or road. He's able to do that, because unlike his *confrères*, he really knows all about stained glass. He's at home with his molten hues and his sombre leads and his iron framework. (I did several heads which people told me later reminded them of Rouault. Small wonder! I remember the moods in which I did these. I remember the bursts of savage freedom.)

In my big Scrap Book, where I occasionally vomit these epileptic

fits, I have one especially that I think remarkable. It was unrecogniz-
able for a while, until I got hold of the axe (the 'axe' being the crayons)
and swung into it with all my muscle and will. The result is a terrifying
piece of insanity, regarded exteriorly. In its essence, however, it is a
very tender piece of portraiture. It violates all the canons save one –
sincerity. It is so earnest and sincere, that if you study it patiently it
will make you weep. Because a line, too, if followed back to the
original impulse, can reveal all the emotions of the heart. Even when
the effect is 'cruel', the beat and rhythm of the line reveal the truth of
the moment in which it was born. (I am always astonished when
people pass ethical judgement on a work. I remember a Frenchman
saying to me, when I was making him a gift of one of my best jobs –
'Very fine work, yes indeed, but isn't it a bit terrifying?' That query
suddenly woke me up to the *external* aspect of the picture, its obvious
meaning. I had forgotten all about the subject. I was thinking only of
how 'successful' it was.)

In Neuilly the other day, attracted by a tiny water-colour in the
window of a bookshop. A man in overalls, with fedora and spectacles,
wearing huge boots, is standing before the water-colour muttering and
mumbling to himself. I love to listen in on soliloquies, especially
*critical* soliloquies. I edged up close to him and watched him intently.
He was saying that it was not bad, the *aquarelle*, but very amateurish,
unfinished. It was the haste with which it was done that seemed to
irritate him. Still looking at the picture, and without putting the
question directly to me, he asks, as though still talking to himself (still
reflecting on it), whether the 'tree' is not too sketchy. (The picture, I
must say, was a little scene of the Seine – a scow, a bridge, a tree, a
rope – very simple and very adroitly done.) I said aloud, without
looking at him, but regarding the picture steadily, 'The tree is perfect.
The man has said all he wanted to say. It's a tree, and that's enough.'
Thereupon began a lively discussion about *aquarelles*. The man was a
*dealer in pigs* and an amateur collector of *aquarelles*. He bought only
what pleased him. But apparently he demanded something more than
a five minute sketch. He wanted a tree to have leaves, etc. I repeated
that the tree was very obviously a tree, leaves or no leaves. And
thereupon I added that I was a painter myself (sic!) and that watercolours were my speciality. This provoked a renewed interest on his
part. He apologized for being too critical and said what could one
expect of a man who is obliged to spend the whole day with pigs. I told
him I was delighted to hear this, and that I valued *his* opinion more

than that of the critics. That started things. Suddenly, as if by magic, we were talking animatedly, like old friends, about Cézanne, Rouault, Braque, Utrillo, Dostoievski, Hamsun, Francis Carco, Blaise Cendrars, etc. Amazing the things we touched on. Finally he told me how, some twenty years or so ago, he was up in Montmartre one day, and in an art shop he saw some paintings of a man called Utrillo. This man, unknown to him then, had left the paintings to be framed, but not having the money for the frames, was obliged to leave them with the art dealer. He confessed that he was not very much impressed with the paintings, but that a friend who happened to be with him bought the Utrillos and *he* bought some others 'which pleased him'. The friend, of course, later sold the Utrillos for a good sum. I asked him if he had changed his opinion of Utrillo since, whereupon he said very truthfully and humbly – 'No! there is something *sordid* about his pictures which I don't like. I know he is famous now, but that doesn't matter to me.' I liked his answer immensely. I told him so. And then, without transition, I launched into a eulogy of Carco's book on Utrillo. I talked about Utrillo as if I knew him intimately. I spoke so convincingly, even in my poor French, that I brought tears to the eyes of this dealer! But what got me was this – the word '*souffrance*' had stirred something in him. He couldn't get over it. '*Souffrance*' explained everything. '*Ecoutez, monsieur,*' he said, '*moi je ne suis qu'un ignorant, un sacré marchand de cochons, mais j'ai vécu . . . j'ai mes experiences de la vie . . . j'ai souffert. La vie d'un artiste, surtout la vie d'un peintre, n'est qu'un Calvaire. Ce que vous dites, monsieur, me touche profondémente. Je m'excuse d'avoir fait la critique d'une oeuvre qui est probablement au-dessus de ma compréhension. Moi, je ne suis qu'un amateur. J'aime les aquarelles. Je les garde chez moi pour le simple plaisir de les contempler. C'est curieux, mais c'est la vérité. Si vous avez du temps, monsieur, je vous invite à m'accompagner pour que je puisse vous montrer ma petite collection . . .* ' And so I went with him and I saw his collection. And I had a couple of cognacs with him and we wept together, the pork dealer and I, over the crucifixion of the artist. A wonderful day! All due to a *Monsieur Asselin, peintre, que je ne connais pas. Vive Monsieur Asselin! Vive l'aquarelle! Vive les marchands de cochons! Par un beau jour, l'aquarelle, même celle d'un inconnu, peut ouvrir les portes du Paradis. Vive la Seine, et la chalande qui passe sous les ponts! Vive l'arbre, sans ou avec feuilles! Vive le soleil! Vive Asselin!*

The opposite of this is an experience with a fat female clerk at the Post Office. Curious about a roll of water-colours I was dispatching for my show in Washington, and it being just around Xmas, I impulsively offered to do a water-colour for her while in London. I felt sorry for her, sitting behind the bars all day, gluing stamps to other people's letters. *Eh bien*, I gave her one on my return from London. She was absent that day, so I left it for her with the *chef du bureau*. A few days later I arrived and greeted her. She barely greeted me. I waited until she had stamped my things, waited while she made change, waited, waited . . . and not a word out of her regarding the *aquarelle*. Finally I thought to myself – perhaps the *chef* forgot to give it to her. 'Did you get the aquarelle I left the other day?' I asked as I was making ready to go. She looked at me coldly, dropped her eyes, and said in an irritated manner: '*L'aquarelle! Oui, oui, on me l'a donnée. Oui!' Et c'était tout!* I turned on my heel and walked away. I walked around the block three times, debating whether to go back and ask her what the hell she meant by such insolence *or* give me back my aquarelle! I was furious. Finally I closed the matter in my mind by calling her a '*vieux con, une salope, un chou, une branleuse, une grosse légume, une abrutie* . . .'

The *aquarelle* was a bit mysterious, I'll admit. You couldn't tell whether it was two birds fighting in the dark or a waterfall in sunlight. For me it was very clear: it was 'light and dark,' the confluence of all the juxtapositions of colour. The *carrefour* of twilight, or – just a 'glassy wet fart', if you like. But how explain such subtleties to an ignoramus? And in bad French! I gave it up. Spent the rest of the day conjugating French verbs, making genders, choosing elegant, cynical, sinister subjunctives. My water colourist's heart was wounded to the core. It was a royal setback. *Mieux vaut un marchand de cochons! Si je ne suis pas un Asselin je suis tout de même un Henri Miller. J'ai du coeur, quoi! Je suis un sensible. C'est une sacrée vie, cette vie sacrée d'un peintre* . . .

Sunday, March 12, 1939
2:00 am.

Emil, I must get this down before going to bed or I never will. An evening with my friend, 'the Aztec', as I call him. Here in the studio. At dinner he begins talking, as he often does, about the period just after the war. 'L'époque bohème.' I can't give it to you in an orderly fashion. Suffice it to indicate the highlights. It's a good note to close this little book on, because it's extremely human and perhaps not a little sad.

As I've told you before, this friend of mine was intimately associated with the poets and painters of the period. He was himself a painter, a bad one, I gather. He came out of the war in a trance-like state, too deeply shocked by all he had experienced to recapture the gaiety of youth. He counted as his friends such figures as Blaise Cendrars, Max Jacob, Kisling, Leger, André Salmon. He was a *copain* of Modigliani, Apollinaire, Vlaminck, Picasso, Derain, Braque, Juan Gris, Diego Rivera and others.

What started the conversation this evening was a remark which he let drop about Picasso and the origin of Cubism. He practically gave me the day and hour of its birth. The sudden transition from the Blue period to the African. The curious coincidence between Picasso's intellectual *floraison* and the treatments he was receiving for some mysterious ailment. A vivid picture in my brain of Picasso seated at the old Rotonde with the others – neither jovial not glum, but a bit detached. Drinking only Vittel.

To proceed more rapidly, because I can give you only the highlights . . . Vlaminck is then a bicycle rider, a man of the country, 'a tender one', always talking about painting with his guts. Derain is already fat, extremely well read, a terrific drinker, charming, and all that. Apollinaire is the *metteur-en-scène*. Max Jacob, always the buffoon and the wit, is also the kind-hearted Jew who takes Picasso's work and, harnessing himself to a push-cart, makes the rounds of Paris trying to sell Picasso's canvases.

There are reunions in the rue Ravignan where Picasso then worked and slept – just above the Place des Abbesses, Montmartre. You probably remember the spot. Juan Gris is there – handsome, intellectual, rather *sec*. Diego Rivera also, who is soon to do the most wonderful imitations of Picasso's cubistic paintings. He has an Arabian beard, an air of Toledo. (A little later, at the beach at Arcachon, he will give milk – when the moon is full.)

Then Bougival . . . the outdoor banquets by the Seine, the discussions about Negro sculpture, the primitives, mythology and so on. Derain perhaps the most sensitive of all. Braque applying himself to the theories in intellectual fashion. Vlaminck pounding his chest and bellowing like an ox. Everything is in the bag. It needs only a touch of genius to explode the magazine. And of course Picasso does it!

To me it was all like a description of worlds in process of birth. (Does not everything happen in flashes, in moments of inspiration?)

Soutine also enters the picture. The boon companion of Modigliani who, up until his third or fourth apéritif, is brilliant and entertaining – after that a madman, *un exalté*. (Soutine is now quietly living below me, with his new red-haired model, a 'Soutine' in every respect. He seems tame now, as if trying to recover from the wild life of other days. Hesitates to salute you in the open street, for fear you will get too close to him. When he opens his trap it's to say how warm or how cold it is – and does the neighbour's radio bother you as it does him?)

Anyway, the period in question is still one of real camaraderie, of reunions, of feasting and drinking. When it is too cold to work one digs up a few bottles of *vin rouge*, locks the door, and goes to bed with the model. For months after the war my friend continued to wear the uniform which was too small for him – no money for civilian clothes. Now and then there was a sensational duel, over some trifle, followed by a lively banquet and a boost in the price of paintings (for those involved). Some grew wealthy overnight, and of course quickly forgot about their more unfortunate comrades. Max Jacob seeks a retreat in a monastery where he will continue to paint and write. And this reminds me of a line I stumbled on recently, from Chesterton's book on St Francis of Assisi: 'It was in fact his (St Francis') whole function to tell men to *start afresh* and, in that sense, to tell them to forget.'

All of them, from Cendrars on down, had a terrible baptism in the war. Cendrars, the eternal adventurer, has to learn how to do things all over again – with his left hand. Their whole world is smashed. Their best friends are dead, their ambitions nipped in the bud. Yet, as I listen to all this, I realize that for most of them the catastrophe served to augment their human qualities. They sound 'tender' compared with the generation of today. Now they are dispersed, each one famous in his way, each one working alone, indifferent perhaps to the fate of the others.

In his long monologue this evening my friend brought them all to life for me – and the epoch and the climate. Speaking of Paris, the changing Paris he has known, speaking of the 'greys' which make Paris, he says: 'It requires a long education to appreciate the nuances of grey . . . *c'est toute une histoire.*' How true! From Paris to Istanbul, Morocco, Toledo, and always the 'values' of each clime, each scene. Then back to Paris, to that sombre hue which at first seems sordid – until one begins to recognize here and there, little by little, the nuances of grey. From the 'greys' he goes into a eulogy of Léon Paul-Fargue's poetry. 'The master of greys,' he calls him. 'The magician of nuances.' I know what he means. I know what a magician Paul-Fargue is. To read him makes me tongue-tied.

From the magician to the 'mage' – *Balzac*! The esoteric doctrine. The religion of the magi. In his vest pocket my friend always carries the little fetish containing those same precious gifts which the Three

Wise Men from the East once brought with them. He burns a tiny bit of myrrh for me, to give me an idea of what is meant by 'the odour of sanctity'. With it a discourse on the doctrine of Unity, as revealed by Claude Saint-Martin, *'le philosophe inconnu'*. *En passant* a 'profile' of Jolas looking towards the source of the Rhine, undecided whether he is a Field-Marshal or a reincarnation of Wotan. Between times making cryptic references to Paracelsus' thaumaturgy and the real meaning of the philosopher's stone. Asking me abruptly to find out for him all I can about the mystery of Mesa Verde. (Balzac too was mad about the Indians!) Would I care to see some Mayan alphabets? Showing me thereupon the lost continents – on my map in the studio. Explaining why he believes there was a green or a blue race of men as well as red, brown, yellow, black and white.

And me saying – *'Pourquoi pas?'* Which is exactly what started us off earlier in the evening. It was this expression of Picasso's which had set me going. *Pourquoi pas?* to everything!

Who is the man who triumphs? The one who *believes*. Let the 'intelligent' ones doubt, criticize, categorize and define. The man of heart believes. And the world belongs to him who believes most. Nothing is too silly, too trivial, too far-fetched or too stupendous for man to believe. Learning crushes the spirit; belief opens one up, delivers one. When I listen to my friend I sometimes wonder what people would say if they could hear what passes between us. He has never said anything, let me tell you, too fantastic for me to swallow. From poetry and painting to mythology or alchemy, from the mundane to the sublime hierarchies, it all makes one to me, and sense too. Profound sense.

It is getting late and I am weary. But I thought you would relish getting a whiff of this talk-fest. Often during the evening I thought of Reichel whose glass mystery hangs just behind me. He too belongs to this world of magic and mystery. He comes no more, Reichel, but his spirit is here – and his pictures talk incessantly. I think of him on his weekly visits to Notre Dame, entering by the Porte Astrologique and mounting to the tower *'to feel the chimères'*, as he says. Then descending to leave by the Porte Chimique. But always hoping that one day they will open the Porte Magique for him. Reichel, incidentally, has a mortal fear of decomposing into 'a chemical fluid' when he dies. Does not want to be corked up in a bottle. Has a dread of being 'misused'. But all of this more another time . . .

'It makes fun,' as Reichel used to say. But it's getting late. Tonight I will sleep with the stars, the symbols, the fluids and the dreams of another epoch. *Je me griserai avec les paroles des poètes maudits. Vive la magie! Vive le magisme! Bonne nuit!*

# Postscriptum

After eating a bit of ginger from Hong Kong, after preparing the glass slab with colours, after buying a palette knife, I settle down to my first *gouache*. From now on I'm going to paint for myself – decorate my own walls.

But first a coda to the Picasso business. It was while taking the injections that Picasso, who had now begun to paint in earnest, gave himself up to night work. In the morning his friends would find the paintings lying on the floor.

That's all! *The Night Life!*

# On Turning Eighty

If at eighty you're not a cripple or an invalid, if you have your health, if you still enjoy a good walk, a good meal (with all the trimmings), if you can sleep without first taking a pill, if birds and flowers, mountains and sea still inspire you, you are a most fortunate individual and you should get down on your knees morning and night and thank the good Lord for his savin' and keepin' power. If you are young in years but already weary in spirit, already on the way to becoming an automaton, it may do you good to say to your boss – under your breath, of course – 'Fuck you, Jack! you don't own me.' If you can whistle up your ass, if you can be turned on by a fetching bottom or a lovely pair of teats, if you can fall in love again and again, if you can forgive your parents for the crime of bringing you into the world, if you are content to get nowhere, just take each day as it comes, if you can forgive as well as forget, if you can keep from growing sour, surly, bitter and cynical, man you've got it half licked.

It's the little things that matter, not fame, success, wealth. At the top there's very little room, whereas at the bottom there's plenty like you, no crowding and nobody to egg you on. Don't think for a moment that the life of a genius is a happy one. Far from it. Be thankful that you are a nobody.

If you have had a successful career, as presumably I have had, the late years may not be the happiest time of your life. (Unless you've learned to swallow your own shit.) Success, from the worldly standpoint, is like the plague for a writer who still has something to say. Now, when he should be enjoying a little leisure, he finds himself more occupied than ever. Now he is the victim of his fans and well wishers, of all those who desire to exploit his name. Now it is a different kind of struggle that one has to wage. The problem now is how to keep free, how to do only what one wants to do.

Despite the knowledge of the world which comes from wide experience, despite the acquisition of a viable everyday philosophy, one can't help but realize that the fools have become even more foolish and the bores more boring. One by one death claims your friends or the great ones you revered. The older you grow the faster they die off. Finally you stand alone. You observe your children, or your children's children, making the same absurd mistakes, heart-rending mistakes often, which you made at their age. And there is nothing you can say or do to prevent it. It's by observing the young, indeed, that you eventually understand the sort of idiot you yourself were once upon a time – and perhaps still are.

One thing seems more and more evident to me now – people's basic character does not change over the years. With rare exceptions people do not develop or evolve: the oak remains an oak, the pig a pig, and the dunce a dunce. Far from improving them, success usually accentuates their faults or shortcomings. The brilliant guys at school often turn out to be not so brilliant once they are out in the world. If you disliked or despised certain lads in your class you will dislike them even more when they become financiers, statesmen or five star generals. Life forces us to learn a few lessons, but not necessarily to grow. Off-hand I can think of only a dozen or so individuals who learned the lesson of life; the great majority would not recognize their names if I were to give them.

As for the world in general, it not only does not look any better to me than when I was a boy of eight, it looks a thousand times worse. A famous writer once summed it up thus: 'The past seems horrible to me, the present grey and desolate, and the future utterly appalling.'* Fortunately, I do not share this bleak point of view. For one thing, I do not concern myself with the future. As for the past, whether good or bad, I have made the most of it. What future remains for me was made by my past. The future of the *world* is something for philosophers and visionaries to ponder on. All we ever really have is the present, but very few of us ever live it. I am neither a pessimist nor an optimist. To me the world is neither this nor that, but all things at once, and to each according to his vision.

At eighty I believe I am a far more cheerful person than I was at twenty or thirty. I most definitely would not want to be a teenager again. Youth may be glorious, but it is also painful to endure. Moreover, what is called youth is not youth, in my opinion; it is rather something like premature old age.

I was cursed or blessed with a prolonged adolescence; I arrived at some seeming maturity when I was past thirty. It was only in my forties that I really began to feel young. By then I was ready for it.

* Joris Karl Huysmans, author of *Against the Grain.*

(Picasso once said: '*One starts to get young at the age of sixty, and then it's too late.*') By this time I had lost many illusions, but fortunately not my enthusiasm, nor the joy of living, nor my unquenchable curiosity. Perhaps it was this curiosity – about anything and everything – that made me the writer I am. It has never left me. Even the worst bore can elicit my interest, if I am in the mood to listen.

With this attribute goes another which I prize above everything else, and that is the sense of wonder. No matter how restricted my world may become I cannot imagine it leaving me void of wonder. In a sense I suppose it might be called my religion. I do not ask how it came about, this creation in which we swim, but only to enjoy and appreciate it. Much as I may rail about the condition of life in which we find ourselves I have ceased to believe that I can remedy it. I may be able to alter my own situation somewhat but not that of others. Nor do I see that anyone past or present, however great, has been able to truly alter '*la condition humaine*'.

What most people fear when they think of old age is the inability to make new friends. If one ever had the faculty of making friends one never loses it however old one grows. Next to love friendship, in my opinion, is the most valuable thing life has to offer. I have never had any trouble making friends; in fact, it has sometimes been a hindrance, this facility for making friends. There is an adage which says that one may judge a man by the company he keeps. I often wonder about the truth of this. All my life I have been friends with individuals belonging to vastly different worlds. I have had, and still have, friends who are nobodies, and I must confess they are among my best friends. I have been friends with criminals and with the despised rich. It is my friends who have kept me alive, who have given me the courage to continue, *and* who have also often bored me to tears. The one thing I have insisted on with all my friends, regardless of class or station in life, is to be able to speak truthfully. If I cannot be open and frank with a friend, or he with me, I drop him.

The ability to be friends with a woman, particularly the woman you love, is to me the greatest achievement. Love and friendship seldom go together. It is far easier to be friends with a man than with a woman, especially if the latter is attractive. In all my life I have known only a few couples who were friends as well as lovers.

Perhaps the most comforting thing about growing old gracefully is the increasing ability not to take things too seriously. One of the big differences between a genuine sage and a preacher is gaiety. When the sage laughs it is a belly laugh; when the preacher laughs, which is all too seldom, it is on the wrong side of the face. The truly wise man –

even the saint! – is not concerned with morals. He is above and beyond such considerations. He is a free spirit.

With advancing age my ideals, which I usually deny possessing, have definitely altered. My ideal is to be free of ideals, free of principles, free of isms and ideologies. I want to take to the ocean of life like a fish takes to the sea. As a young man I was greatly concerned about the state of the world; today, though I still rant and rave, I am content simply to deplore the state of affairs. It may sound smug to speak thus but in reality it means that I have become more humble, more aware of my limitations and those of my fellow man. I no longer try to convert people to my view of things, nor to heal them. Neither do I feel superior because they appear to be lacking in intelligence. One can fight evil but against stupidity one is helpless. I believe that the ideal condition for humanity would be to live in a state of peace, in brotherly love, but I must confess I know no way to bring such a condition about. I have accepted the fact, hard as it may be, that human beings are inclined to behave in a way that would make animals blush. The ironic, the tragic thing is that we often behave in ignoble fashion from what we consider the highest motives. The animal makes no excuse for killing his prey; the human animal, on the other hand, can invoke God's blessing when massacring his fellow men. He forgets that God is not *on* his side but *at* his side.

Though I am still quite a reader I have come more and more to eschew books. Whereas in the early days I looked to books for instruction and guidance, today I read primarily for enjoyment. I can no longer take books, or authors, as seriously as I once did. Especially not books by 'thinkers'. I find such reading deadly now. If I do tackle a so-called piece of serious writing it is more to seek corroboration than enlightenment. Art may be therapeutic, as Nietzsche said, but only indirectly. We all need stimulation and inspiration, but they can be had in many different ways, and often in ways which would shock the moralists. Whichever path one takes it is like walking the tightrope.

I have very few friends or acquaintances my own age or near it. Though I am usually ill at ease in the company of elderly people I have the greatest respect and admiration for two very old men who seem to remain eternally young and creative. I mean Pablo Casals and Pablo Picasso, both over ninety now. Such youthful nonagenarians put the young to shame. Those who are truly decrepit, living corpses, so to speak, are the middle-aged, middleclass men and women who are stuck in their comfortable grooves and imagine that the *status quo* will last for ever or else are so frightened it won't that they have retreated into their mental bomb shelters to wait it out.

I have never belonged to any organization, religious, political, or otherwise. Nor have I ever voted in my life. I have been a philosophical anarchist since my teens. I am a voluntary exile who is at home everywhere except at home. As a boy I had a number of idols, and today at eighty I still have my idols. The ability to revere others, not necessarily to follow in their footsteps, seems most important to me. To have a master is even more important. The question is how and where to find one. Usually he is right in our midst, but we fail to recognize him. On the other hand I have discovered that one can learn more from a child very often than from an accredited teacher.

I think the teacher (with a capital T) ranks with the sage and the seer. It is our misfortune not to be able to breed such animals. What is called education is to me utter nonsense and detrimental to growth. Despite all the social and political upheavals we have been through the authorized educational methods throughout the civilized world remain, in my mind at least, archaic and stultifying. They help to perpetuate the ills which cripple us. William Blake said: *'The tigers of wrath are wiser than the horses of instruction.'* I learned nothing of value at school. I don't believe I could pass a grammar school test on any subject even today. I learned more from idiots and nobodies than from professors of this and that. Life is the teacher, not the Board of Education. Droll as it may sound, I am inclined to agree with that miserable Nazi specimen who said: *'When I hear the word* Kultur *I reach for my revolver.'*

I have never been interested in organized sports. I don't give a damn who breaks what records. The heroes of baseball, football, basketball are virtually unknown to me. I dislike competitive games. I think one should play not to win but to enjoy the game, whatever it be. I prefer to get my exercise through play rather than through doing calisthenics. I prefer solo performance to team work. To swim, to ride a bike, to take a walk in the woods, or to play a game of ping pong satisfies all my need of exercise. I don't believe in push ups, weight lifting or body building. I don't believe in creating muscles unless they are to be used for some vital purpose. I think the arts of self-defence should be taught from an early age and used for that purpose only. (And, if war is to be the order of the day for the next few generations, then we should stop sending our kids to Sunday School and teach them instead to become expert killers.)

I don't believe in health foods and diets either. I have probably been eating all the wrong things all my life – and have thrived on it. I eat to enjoy my food. Whatever I do I do first for enjoyment. I don't believe in regular check-ups. If there is something wrong with me I'd rather not know about it, because then I would only worry about it and aggravate the condition. Nature often remedies our ills better than the doctor can. I don't believe there is any prescription for long life. Besides, who wants to live to be a hundred? What's the point of it? A short life and a merry one is far better than a long life sustained by fear, caution and perpetual medical surveillance. With all the progress medicine has made over the years we still have a pantheon of incurable diseases. The germs and microbes seem to have the last word always. When all else fails the surgeon steps in, cuts us to pieces, and cleans us out of our last penny. And that's progress for you.

What is so woefully missing in our world of today are grandeur, beauty, love, compassion – and freedom. Gone the days of great individuals, great leaders, great thinkers. In their place we are breeding a spawn of monsters, assassins, terrorists: violence, cruelty, hypocrisy seem to be inbred. In summoning the names of illustrious figures of the past, names like Pericles, Socrates, Dante, Abelard, Leonardo da Vinci, Shakespeare, William Blake, or even the mad Ludwig of Bavaria, one forgets that even in the most glorious times there was unbelievable poverty, tyranny, crimes unmentionable, the horrors of war, malevolence and treachery. Always good and evil, ugliness and beauty, the noble and the ignoble, hope and despair. It seems impossible for these extreme opposites not to co-exist in what is called a civilized world.

If we cannot better the conditions under which we live we can at least offer an immediate and painless way out. There is escape through euthanasia. Why is it not offered the hopeless, miserable millions for whom there is no possible chance of enjoying even a dog's life? We were not asked to be born; why should we be refused the privilege of making our exit when things become unbearable? Must we wait for the atom bomb to finish us off all together?

I don't like to end on a sour note. As my readers well know, my motto has always been: 'Always merry and bright.' Perhaps that is why I never tire of quoting Rabelais: '*For all your ills I give you laughter.*' As I look back on my life, which has been full of tragic moments, I see it more as a comedy than a tragedy. One of those comedies in which while laughing your guts out you feel your heart breaking. What better comedy could there be? The man who takes himself seriously is doomed.

The tragedy which the vast majority of human beings is living is another matter. Therein I see no comic element of relief. When I speak of a painless way out for the suffering millions I am not speaking cynically or as one who sees no hope for mankind. There is nothing wrong with life itself. It is the ocean in which we swim and we either adapt to it or sink to the bottom. But it is in our power as human beings not to pollute the waters of life, not to destroy the spirit which animates us.

The most difficult thing for a creative individual is to refrain from the effort to make the world to his liking and to accept his fellow man for what he is, whether good, bad or indifferent. One does his best, but it is never good enough.

*Finis*